SCIENCE

in general education

BROWN

GENERAL EDUCATION SERIES

EARL J. McGRATH, *General Editor, Institute of Higher Education, Teachers College, Columbia University*

CARPENTER: *The Larger Learning*

CARLIN: *Curriculum Building in General Education*

FISHER: *Humanities in General Education*

HAUN: *Science in General Education*

MAYHEW: *Social Science in General Education*

MORSE-DRESSEL: *General Education for Personal Maturity*

SHOEMAKER-FORSDALE: *Communication in General Education*

SCIENCE

in general education

ROBERT RAY HAUN
Editor
Drake University

Wm. C. Brown Company Publishers, *Dubuque, Iowa*

Manufactured by WM. C. BROWN CO. INC., Dubuque, Iowa

Printed in U. S. A.

table of contents

foreword

Twelve years ago when programs of general education were multiplying rapidly in the colleges and universities of this country, the editor of this series of volumes on the general education in major branches of learning conceived the idea that an interchange of experience among institutions would be advantageous to all. Hence, he asked a group of teachers of general education courses to contribute an article on their own programs to be brought together under one cover with other similar institutional statements in the natural sciences, social sciences, humanities, and communications. The four volumes which resulted, were widely used not only among institutions which had already inaugurated a program of general studies, but also among those attempting to design such a program suitable to the needs of their own students.

The William C. Brown Company of Dubuque, Iowa, the publishers of the original volumes, has long felt that they should be brought up to date. Several have been out of print for a period of years. In the time since the books originally appeared, many new programs have come into existence, some in the colleges and universities represented in the earlier volumes, and some in institutions which have launched a general education program in the past decade. In the main the present volume, therefore, represents a review of the changes that have occurred in a number of the original programs. These statements have been supplemented by others from institutions in which promising new programs are in operation.

In contrast to the earlier works, each of these new volumes has been prepared by a person who is, or has recently been, teaching a general education course in one of the major fields of knowledge. This volume has been prepared by Dr. R. Ray Haun of Drake University who has for some years been thoroughly familiar with the developments in general education in the natural sciences. He has brought together an excellent collection of critical essays in this field. He has also prepared a chapter summarizing the trends in the natural sciences over the past decade. Anyone who wishes to gain an overview of the philosophy and the practice of general education in the sciences will find this volume especially useful. Persons working in the other divisions of knowledge will be interested in the companion volumes also issued by the William C. Brown Company. They are *Humanities in General Education*, the *Social Sciences in General Education, Communications in General Education, Curriculum Building in General Education, General Education for Personal Maturity,* and *The Larger Learning.*

The one outstanding generalization gained from a reading of these compendiums is that many faculty members in colleges and universities are convinced that a broader education in the various disciplines is essential if American youth are to understand the complex world in which they live. The recognition of this fact has caused many faculties to launch comprehensive programs of instruction as described in this and the companion volumes. There would be many more such efforts if broadly educated teachers and suitable teaching materials were available. And these preconditions of a suitable general education would exist if the graduate schools would produce teachers prepared for and dedicated to the important work of providing that general education without which the fruits of specialized learning cannot be effectively used in the improvement of American society. These volumes suggest the type of advanced education college teachers must have if this significant mission is to be accomplished. They also stand as eloquent testimony that there is in higher education a sizable group of men and women who have caught the vision of America's most pressing educational need, and are daily devoting a portion of their lives to better education of this generation of students for their broad responsibilities as citizens in a democratic society.

Earl J. McGrath
Executive Officer
Institute of Higher Education

chapter 1

CHANGES WITHIN THE DECADE

*R. R. Haun**

Man's insatiable desire to investigate, to search, to find the answer, and *to know* has resulted in an accumulation of knowledge about the natural world which is so prodigious that even its storage and utilization produces problems. To put it in books and to make the books available in libraries is but part of the answer. To have it in books is of no value unless it gets from the books into the minds of men other than the ones who wrote them. To transfer the accumulated knowledge of the past to the next generation, and to help younger men and women learn how to use it, and subsequently to expand it, is the vocation of a great host of teachers; many of whom have an impelling desire to teach effectively, which is as strong as the insatiable desire to discover the truth itself.

The effective transferring of this accumulated knowledge to the next generation is complicated by several factors. One of these is that the accumulations are too great for one mind to contain. Therefore, division and fragmentation of the knowledge has resulted, and specialists in these fragments have developed. Specialization seems absolutely necessary, but the natural world does not operate in compartments, fragments or specializations, and the more specialized a particular individual becomes, the more certain it is that his knowledge will be too limited to understand all the factors operating in a particular situation. More than that, the accumulations are growing at such a pace that in succeeding generations an

---

*The author is Professor of Physical Science, Drake University.

1

individual must become more specialized and as time goes on any particular specialist will acquire still smaller fractions of the total findings, and will have even less opportunity to acquire other areas of knowledge, and to comprehend the interrelationships. The same situation exists with our knowledge and understandings in the social world and in the humanities. The accumulations are likewise vast, and the consequent specializations numerous, so that the possibilities of comprehending the interrelationships within any realm of knowledge, and the interrelationships between realms of knowledge, become increasingly difficult.

The second complicating factor in education, is that man himself cannot live effectively within a compartment of knowledge. He needs to comprehend the whole in order to master the compartment, and he needs to have some understandings of the specializations of other people to live effectively with them. With increasingly clarity, we are learning that to master a limited field of knowledge is not enough. There must be more, and the question we now face is how much more. What are the minimums in areas of knowledge, other than the specialization, that an individual must have to be effective in his vocation and in his personal and social living.

The term minimums is used because of a further complicating factor in the educational process, and that is a present philosophy toward education, which leads to minimums. Currently, our society is saying that educational systems should prepare youth for vocations, that it should prepare them by ages 21 to 25, and that the formal and intellectual part of their education should be completed by that time. It must be admitted that the teaching profession has given leadership to the development of this philosophy, and that no one can be blamed more than ourselves for it, particularly for the inability of our graduates to effectively continue their education after graduation.

We are thus in a situation which demands that we assist youth to obtain minimums about all areas of knowledge and a maximum about one, with a great tendency to stress the maximum about one. The current development of, and emphasis upon, general education is a consequence of the realization that every youth should obtain some minimums about all realms of knowledge. General education is frequently defined as that education which is non-special, or which is not an immediate part of the specialization. The question being faced is: What shall be the nature of these general education minimums in the program of the college? This book is devoted to the answers to this question, which are now being given by a number of colleges and universities concerning the minimums in the realm of science. The writers are men and women who are trying to give all students the science part of their general education. They do not feel that they have the complete and final answers, as is evidenced by the continual revisions and changes in their courses, but they face the problem with great vigor and enthusiasm; and as one author writes, "the result is exciting."

The contributors are to a large extent the same contributors who wrote for the original volume twelve years ago, or their successors at the institutions which were represented previously. However, some of the original group have changed positions, or are not now teaching general education courses, and in some cases individuals have retired or are deceased, so that replacements have been found and there are some new contributors to this volume. The contributors are from all sections of the country. The kinds of institutions show distribution in size and in type with representations from both large and small colleges, private and public, and with many patterns of organization from the junior college to the large university. One contributor also discusses the developments of science general education courses in the high schools on the basis of his own experience, as he visited many of them during the past two years. It is hoped, therefore, that the volume will give a rather representative picture of science in general education throughout the country at the present time, although it is frankly admitted that there are many institutions which are giving general education courses now and there may be innovations or special developments in some of them which did not get into this book, and would have contributed equally well to its story.

The contributors were asked to tell if there had been changes in the courses during the past twelve years, and without exception changes have been indicated. These changes have been based largely upon the re-examination of the purposes and objectives of general education in the respective institutions, and also in part upon the changing attitude of the faculty and administration towards them, often paralleled with and influenced by changing philosophy concerning the whole program of higher education at the college or university. Very frequently, therefore, the contributors have discussed the total general education situation at their institutions as a background for the science courses which they explain; and the book as a whole reveals a picture of general education throughout the country at the present time. Part of this picture will be indicated as the science courses are further described, and some additional comments about its growth and modification will be made at a later point in this article.

A summary and comparison of the objectives of the present courses with those of a decade ago show that in many ways they are the same, but on the other hand, definite changes have taken place, and some new trends are indicated. One notices, for example, that there is now an established recognition for the need of two kinds of courses. These may be distinguished by saying that some courses are designed for students specializing in science, and others for non-science or general students. The questions that have been raised concerning the most valuable kind of science experiences for the non-major has also produced a re-examination of the science objectives for the major. A quick one sentence summary, needing further explanation and substantiation, is that the traditional courses for the major are taking on more breadth, and the general courses more depth.

This leads to the next most obvious change that has taken place in science for general education during the past decade. The survey course has been black-listed. Even the term, survey course, is taboo. The writer, who was enthralled by one of the first survey courses ever given, often decrys the extent to which the pendulum has swung, since he feels that there is merit in the non-science student becoming acquainted with the major findings in as many sciences as possible. However, there is no doubt that his own, as well as many other courses, have attempted in the past to cover too much within the time allowed. Everyone now realizes that it is impossible to cover all of the sciences, even all of the physical sciences within one physical science course. As a consequence there have developed a number of modifications of the old objective to survey the physical sciences. One of the modifications has been the so-called block-and-gap course, which was discussed in the previous volume of *Science In General Education*.

This term implies that certain topics are to be discussed and others are to be omitted. Many people, feeling that there is an undesirable implication in the term gap, have avoided the usage of the term "block-and-gap" and simply say that certain topics will be selected for the course. However, there is, no agreement among the various people offering such courses as to which topics shall be selected. Apparently different people place different weight and different values to many topics that may be selected for the general course.

There is another area in which science courses in general education have made marked changes. This can be best summarized under the term, methods of science, although the term is a dangerous one. The term, "The Scientific Method" has likewise become taboo although the "teaching of the scientific method" has been the major objective argued for including a science course in the liberal arts requirements ever since group requirements came into liberal arts curricula. However, there is now a correct emphasis upon the fact that there is no single, simple method, procedure or formula by which the scientist grinds out his conclusions. There are many approaches to a problem, many paths which may lead to the end and many facets which reflect and refract the conclusion, principle, law, or construct when it is obtained. The denial of a single, simple scientific method is reflected in the current objectives of science courses which have substituted for "to teach the scientific method" some expression which is more extensive or else emphasizes an aspect which is an essential part of the scientist's procedures. Illustrative of these modifications are such expressions as: the methods of science, the tactics and strategy of science, to demonstrate (and develop in the student) the methods of observation and inferences required to reach conclusions in science, to convey some understanding of the scientific enterprise as a means of getting knowledge and solving problems, to develop critical thinking and logical reasoning, to develop the intellectual tools for investigation, to develop a scientific attitude, to understand the scientists point of view and what he does, to analyze scientific data summarized in maps, tables, charts and graphs, to become acquainted with sources of scientific information and to give a few glimpses into the evolution of ideas in science.

There is another older objective in the teaching of science that has suffered an extensive metamorphosis. It was said that the student should get an understanding of the scientific applications around him, the pump, the fire extinguisher, the purification of water, the automobile and the aeroplane. If man now knows too much pure science to teach in one course, it is obvious that any coverage of the practical applications is hopelessly impossible. Many applications are still discussed but as illustrations of principles rather than as an attempt to give explanation to all the gadgetry around us. There is a new emphasis in science general education courses that might well be regarded as a metamorphosis from teaching about all the applications in modern engineering. This is a trend to discuss more extensively the impact of scientific developments upon society and upon the life of the individual. This trend is substantiated by such statements as the following which are found in the objectives listed by contributors to this volume: to point out personal and social implications of the scientific endeavor; to cultivate those illusive and priceless faculties of reasonableness and thoughtfulness; to understand the role, importance and limitations of science; to face facts, revise judgment and change behavior in light of appropriate evidence; to develop an understanding of the contributions of science to the solution of contemporary problems.

Associated with the changes in objectives one also finds changes in the approaches which are being used in the science general education courses, and these will now be considered. One of these approaches would still be the survey approach. The term may be taboo but the fact remains that many of the courses and most of the books which are written for them approach the course more from a survey view than from any other perspective. These courses were designed to give some comprehension of the natural world to students who otherwise would not get it and with this kind of philosophy the course must have a survey approach. Those opposing the development of the survey courses said the courses could not have depth and, while one might raise the question as to what is meant by depth, a consequence of this accusation has been the development of the block and gap or simply of the selected topics approach, which was mentioned previously. In both of these approaches a fundamental problem arises about a way to tie together the selected topics and the materials from the several disciplines. Within the disciplines accepted continuities have developed although it is interesting to note that even these continuities are now being challenged. But in the general education courses no accepted continuities have been established. To the writer, one of the most interesting discoveries has been that there are sound continuity reasons for all of the many course organization outlines that different people use in physical science courses. This is now being interpreted as another indication that the natural world does not operate in compartments or by disciplines. A search for understanding and explanation at any point in the natural world soon involves one or more of our conventional disciplines and if questions continue farther and farther the search will undoubtedly lead to everything known in all the disciplines.

It is at this point that the integration and interdisciplinary approach appears. By disregarding departmental lines it is easier to treat more comprehensively and possibly with greater depth a few basic and fundamental topics, principles or constructs. A number of general education programs stress this aspect by naming their programs and curricula "interdisciplinary studies." Thus, by the use of this term, there is obtained not only a reaction against the fractionation and specialization referred to in the introduction of this article but also an emphasis upon the interrelatedness of the disciplines and possibly by implication upon the desirability for greater unity of knowledge. Integration can be done nowhere as well as in general education courses. It is regarded as a prime function of the courses described in this volume not only by those institutions which use the term, "interdisciplinary studies" but by others as well. This is indicated in many of the stated objectives and by the very fact that the content material is always taken from more than one discipline. In fact it is in this selection of content which requires integration and shows interrelatedness, that the present course contents differ from that of the older "survey courses." Very popular now for this approach is the topic of structure of matter, frequently limited to the structure of the atom. Similar topics for this approach are the conservation principles, the nature of energy and photosynthesis.

There is another approach to these kinds of topics which is being used with increasing frequency and enthusiasm. This is the historical approach. However, a different objective is generally stressed with this approach. The historical approach is regarded by many as a superior way to show the methods of science. By the use of case histories the student can read about the classical experiments as they were originally performed and consider the kind of reasoning that leads to their interpretations, both the interpretations that were tentative and frequently wrong because related ideas were wrong or had not been discovered, as well as final conclusions on the basis of further information. Sometimes the classical experiments are repeated by the instructor or by the students in order to place the student in the position of the original discoverer and to better understand his interpretation. However, emphasis here is not upon the experimental procedure, but upon logical reasoning and critical thinking. To express it another way, the historical approach is used to help students appreciate the way scientific concepts develop. Some of the case histories that have been used are: Copernicus and the Heliocentric system, Robert Boyle and The Spring of the Air, Lavosier's work on combustion, Pasteur's and Tyndall's study of spontaneous generation, Harvey and the circulation of the blood.

There is another approach, called the problems approach, which is used primarily to carry out the methods of science objective. In this approach, no attempt is made to emphasize the history. Emphasis is upon problem solution and the problems to be solved may be either historical or current. Some typical problems are: how did the solar system originate? what was the origin of the "Carolina bays"? how are the motions of the celestial bodies explained? why does the body have useless parts? how is the circulation of the blood controlled? and how does life depend upon light? In this approach, it is likewise possible to analyze the problem step by step, to bring in various kinds of data and information and then to show how logical conclusions can be drawn to find answers to problems. Here, too, some experimentation may be introduced and library reference work required to obtain student participation of an inquiring and reflective nature.

Finally the discussion of approaches should not be completed without pointing out that laboratory work has always been regarded as an important, generally the most important, approach to an understanding of the methods of science and the work of the scientist. While it is undoubtedly true that too much student laboratory work has been performed under cook-book instructions with more and more elaborate equipment for greater precision of measuements in order to obtain conclusions already established thouands of times, nevertheless it is a new experience for the student and it not only supplements his reading and listening for learning that well established conclusion but it does also give him some comprehension and understanding of the procedures, experimental and reflective, that the scientist uses in his work.

There is a very important development, growing with increasing rate during the past decade, which is adding more value to the laboratory work for the general education student. This new, or revitalized old, approach is to make the laboratory work more investigative in nature and to throw the student more on his own resources. This is being done in three different ways. One is to simply give less instruction with the conventional experiments, that is to give less cooking instructions. The purpose or objective is made clear, the materials are made available under supervision and the students, generally working together, are expected to devise their own procedure and conduct the experiment to a conclusion. A second type of investigative experiment involves the use of problems, generally very simple and restricted, for which answers cannot be found in the books and other literature, and, therefore, the student must make his own investigations. For example a student is given a set of liquids or of solutions, metals, solids of various kinds. He is given the problem of finding sufficient characteristics about each one that when given an unknown sample of one of them he could determine which one of the original set it is like. Like unknowns in qualitative analysis these kinds of problems generally intrigue students and with proper selection of materials the instructor can make the problem very challenging for any level of student. A third type, being frequently referred to as "open end" experiments specify no particular problem to be solved but simply that a particular situation be investigated as far as possible within the limits of the student's time, interest, and ability, emphasis being placed only upon obtaining good results. In all of these types of experiments emphasis is upon the student conducting his own experiment, collecting his data and making his own interpretation. Difficulties arise in finding the problems or situations to be investigated which are challenging to the student and at the same time simple enough for him to investigate with his limited background and experience. Also the time consumption on the part of the instructor as well as the student is exorbitant.

The discussion of the laboratory approach just given leads to the question of the overall status of laboratory work in general education science courses. Since the inception of science courses for the non-major in science the question has been continuously raised about the necessity, importance or even desirability of individual laboratory work in such courses. It has been argued that the time, space and instructional costs may not be justified in terms of the values obtained. Experiments have been attempted in an effort to compare groups who have laboratory work with those who do not have the laboratory experiences but the results are generally inconclusive as is reported in one of the articles in this volume. When studies by some people report favorable conclusions for the non-laboratory course there are always others who look over the report and argue that the evaluation instruments used do not measure the kinds of values to be obtained from laboratory experience. So far as the contributors to this volume are concerned, they are overwhelmingly in favor of laboratory experience as a part of their courses. Most of the courses now have laboratory work of some kind and generally those contributors who do not have, imply that they would do so if it were possible in their local situations.

At the close of the previous volume of *Science in General Education* the problem of securing staff for these courses was discussed. It was pointed out that in the physical science courses especially it was almost impossible to secure teachers who had been prepared in all the physical sciences because of the intense specialization required in the graduate schools for advanced degrees. Fortunately there is some improvement in this situation although there is still great need for teachers for these courses as there is also for all science courses. For one thing some graduate schools are now announcing special programs of study for the preparation of teachers in general education and in the second place many teachers, who have a sufficiently thorough training in one discipline to see the relationships of other disciplines to theirs are finding that they can teach the general courses if they want to do so. A recognition of the importance of such courses and the desire to teach them seems to be more important than formal training in the various disciplines.

Certainly a well-trained Ph.D. in any one of the sciences can, with some intensive study, quickly master much more in the other sciences than the time and scope of the general course requires for teaching freshmen and sophomores. Many people now teaching the general courses began teaching a segment of the course with a team representing the other disciplines and subsequently found that they could handle the course individually. It should be pointed out in this connection that one of the discoveries of the past decade is that students make better achievement under one instructor than under a group of specialists each discussing his own specialization. In fact courses have almost always failed when they have been set up on a compartmentalized plan of having representatives from various departments teach certain parts of the course. Even the plan of having all lecturers for the course attend all class sessions to learn exactly what the others have given, has not generally proved as successful as that of having each instructor carry his own section clear through the course.

Another point is very strongly emphasized by one of the contributors in this volume. If the general education course is to achieve its maximum success in any situation it must have the favor and approval of the other members of the science faculty. In some places this may be very difficult since much depends upon the background situation and the personalities involved. The general education course must be a strong science course and not an easy, shallow substitute for the courses which the students might otherwise take in the departmental offerings. On the other hand the faculty members of the regular departments must recognize the needs of the general student and the desirability of the course being offered for them. They must also recognize that the removal of the general student from their classes enables them to design their courses for the science majors and related professional students and thus develop stronger courses for that group. Unfortunately in some situations competition for students has arisen and proliferation of courses for the major and for the non-major has grown within the several departments. While many of the departmental courses are undoubtedly excellent for general education purposes and, as frequently pointed out, all education may be considered general education, the more commonly accepted viewpoint is that a well designed broadly integrated course is better for the general student. Sometimes the faculty differences in a local situation are settled by administrative fiat but obviously it is better to have agreement, understanding and cooperation on the part of all groups concerned.

This leads us finally to the relation of administration to the development of science in general education and to the entire program of general education. Several patterns for administering the general education program are in operation. In one pattern, to be found in some universities, general education is centered in an independent college with its own dean, separate staff and freeedom to establish its educational policy and to develop courses accordingly. At the other extremes, not entirely limited to the small college, the general education courses are given by another college, generally liberal arts, as a part of its total program. Each plan has both its advantages and its difficulties. During the past decade several of our larger institutions have shifted from one to the other and new colleges are being established under both patterns. Some of the problems and issues involved can be quickly stated here.

From the standpoint of the student it is being increasingly recognized that general education is needed by all students at least in their non-major areas, so that courses should be easily available for all students in all colleges on a campus. These courses can usually be established and administered better with an independent general education college, open to all students on the campus. On the other hand, under the American philosophy of education, only an occasional student will take nothing but general education. He must specialize and that specialization must start as soon as possible in order to build customary sequences. Also the specialization courses assist in maintaining motivation by emphasizing the vocational objectives. Therefore, the present trend is to require general education courses of all students but to also allow them to start vocationally oriented courses early in the college program, and this may be done a little easier when both types of courses are given by the same college. Although some schools are requiring the general education courses to be completed first and some are requiring all students to take all general education courses regardless of their eventual major, the trend is to develop programs which combine these two types of courses and to allow the student majoring in an area to omit the general education course in that area. This automatically means that the class taking the area general educ-tion course will not contain majors, and that there is no problem of integrating the general course with succeeding courses in the major field.

The problems involved with the faculty under these two patterns of organization are harder to handle than those of the student. Very few faculty members, at least at the present, are content to teach nothing but general education courses. They like to also teach some advanced courses and have opportunities for research. This is not easily possible within the framework of a college limited to general education. So the faculty member would like the freedom of a general college to develop his course for the general student but wants to be tied to the liberal arts or professional college program for advanced courses and research. Also in an independent general education college the teacher is more easily rewarded with salary increments and advancement in ranks. In a program affiliated with liberal arts or some other college the general education courses are most frequently assigned to lower level instructors and the faculty member must get out of them to secure recognition.

It would seem superfluous to use any time and space to discuss the relation of college administrations to science in general education were it not for the fact that a number of contributors to this volume have implied that their superiors are the main problems in the development of successful science courses at their institutions. No one who follows the American scene in higher education can fail to see the development of specialization in college administration and the shifting of leadership in educational philosophy and policy from the old faculty organization or faculty senate to the deans, vice-presidents and presidents. There is no note of sarcasm to be read between the lines. This is in accord with our developing society which has found that maximum progress is obtained by specialization and it is to be expected in the college operation to somewhat the same degree that it operates in business and industry. Again it is a specialization which can not operate within a compartment. There must be understood interrelationships, and without doubt there are situations in which they are not clearly understood. A science course in general education will develop to its maximum value only in a situation where it has the full support of the dean, and any other administrative superiors, in giving it plant space, financial assistance, curricular place, and administrative favor and status. The course must also have adequately trained and enthusiastic teachers.

Only slight modifications of the introductory part of this article need to be made to use it for closing. General education has developed to the point that it is becoming a specialization. But general education cannot be compartmentalized because it is composed of the other areas of knowledge and the interrelations are very intimate. The problem in the general education course in science, and in all general courses, is to discover how to give the student who is not specializing in science, the best comprehension of scientific endeavor possible within the time alloted for that purpose. A comparison of the volume on *Science in General Education* issued a decade ago with this one reveals changes in the courses offered which can well be interpreted as progress. To expect further progress as time marches on is in accord with the history of scientific endeavor.

In Summary

There now exists a well established recognition of the need for science courses specifically designed for the non-specialist in science. There is, as yet, no complete agreement about the nature of these courses although certain trends are indicated.

Survey courses which make any attempt to cover large areas of knowledge have been blacklisted and the term "survey course" has become taboo.

However, comments, course outlines, and texts being used indicate that some coverage of the various sciences is regarded as highly desirable; but for this purpose departmental lines are dissolved and broad integrating topics, principles, and laws or conceptual schemes are used, with the interrelationships stressed in many cases.

More emphasis is being placed upon the student acquiring an understanding of scientific endeavor and the scientific enterprise. This is shown in the objectives and in the approaches to the course by such indicated emphases as: methods of science, logical reasoning and critical thinking, tactics and strategy of science, the development of scientific concepts, the historical approach, the case history approach, and the problems approach.

The desirability of laboratory work is accepted by practically everyone teaching general education courses, but there is a strong shift away from cook-book experiments to those which give greater emphasis to an understanding of scientific endeavor, either by repeating the historically classical experiments or by developing problems approach and open-end experiments for students in this level course.

The staff situation has shown some improvement during the past decade and the promise for the future looks better but there is still great need for teachers with broader backgrounds for these courses. Greater understanding of the philosophy and importance of general education courses in the educational program is needed not only by the persons teaching the courses but also by the regular departmental science teachers and by the administration.

chapter 2

THE PHYSICAL SCIENCES IN GENERAL EDUCATION AT ANTIOCH COLLEGE

*Oliver S. Loud**

A chapter with this same title and by the same author appeared more than ten years ago in the volume, "Science in General Education," edited by Dr. Earl J. McGrath. The program described was in rapid evolution at the time and each succeeding year has brought significant changes. In fact, the Antioch Faculty is just now approaching a goal self-assigned some five years ago: a thorough reexamination and, wherever indicated, a revision of the College program. It is an appropriate time to describe once again the place of the physical sciences in general education at Antioch College.

Antioch College

Antioch College is a private, non-sectarian, coeducational, liberal arts college in south-western Ohio. It offers the A.B. and B.S. degrees under the cooperative program of alternating study and work periods. One year of the five-year program may be spent in study and work abroad. About one quarter of the 150 graduates in any recent Commencement have completed the requirements for the degree in four years — because they showed that they had come to Antioch with superior achievement in general education during their pre-college years.

---

*The Author is Professor of Physical Sciences, Antioch College, Yellow Springs, Ohio.

The Antioch design for a liberal education continues to comprise three distinguishable yet interacting components: (i) academic study, almost entirely in residence, (ii) off-campus work and residence experience and (iii) participation in Antioch's experiment with its self-governing community. Perhaps the two most significant developments since 1948 have been the extensive redesign of the general education part of the academic program and the establishment of Antioch centers abroad so that students can study and work in another culture.

In the Antioch calculus, 160 academic credits and 90 work credits are required for either degree. The typical student will spend nine 12-week quarters and one 8-week quarter in academic residence; he will spend a total of 90 weeks or more in a succession of carefully selected jobs.

The typical Antioch course is weighted at 5 credits. It may be either a *terminal* course, completed within an academic quarter at an intensity of 15 hours of effort each week, including time spent in class meetings, or a *split* course, interrupted by a work period, extending through two academic quarters, and taken at half intensity. An important function of the terminal course in this program is to reduce the number of courses carried concurrently by the student. The split course — as indeed the terminal course *if* it is one course in a departmental sequence — has the "longer arch of time" and opens up the possibility of the deliberate integration of academic and work experiences.

Antioch students are an academically able sampling of young people. On almost any measure of academic aptitude or achievement, their distribution lies almost wholly above the national median.

General Education at Antioch College

One consequence of these recent years of program revision has been the production of a "Syllabus for Students' Programs of General Education at Antioch College" — currently in its second edition of 53 mimeographed pages, dated July 21, 1958. It is divided into two parts: one on "General Objectives and Requirements," which explains the design of the general education program as it involves each of the three components of the larger program

— academic, off-campus work and residence, and community living; the other, "Objectives and Requirements of Specific Areas and Groups of Disciplines," defines in detail the academic component.

"General education, as Antioch uses the term, includes study of the liberal arts and experience as a worker and citizen. . . [It is] not just incidental intelligence that anyone can pick up at leisure. . . [The student is encouraged] to keep up a constant interplay between general education and field courses, between both of these and . . . work experiences, and between all of these and campus and off-campus experience of our and other cultures . . . [He is] expected to plan a program in which he works to capacity . . . learning increasingly to choose and to reach his own educational objectives, with the faculty serving as resources rather than as taskmasters. . . . .

"Among the most significant features of the program are . . . [these, that] it is —

  (i)   differentiated from strictly professional training or specialized scholarship, but involves frequent overlapping of specialized interests with those of general education;

  (ii)   oriented to the acquisition of the knowledge, skills, habits and value commitments needed in avocations, as a citizen, as a member of a family, and as an individual;

  (iii) geared to individual differences (capacities, interests, and the like), hence flexible enough to allow for significant choices on the part of the student;

  (iv)   extended as widely as possible over the whole scope of important human knowledge and yet avoiding superficiality by examination of some fields in depth;

  (v)   constructed in such a way that 'the tail does not wag the dog' — in other words, that the means (choosing courses, taking examinations, gaining credits, and the like) do not encumber the *ends* (achieving desirable and understood goals, meeting individual and community needs, and the like)."[1]

---

[1]"General Education Syllabus," 1958 edition. pp 2-5.

The general education part of the academic program adds up to 70-75 credits of the 160 credits required for either degree — 70 if the student elects to count 5 of the general education credits as part of his field of concentration. In addition to courses, there is an array of examinations to be passed. Both courses and examinations are arranged on three levels, insuring that general education extends *in parallel* with field concentration and with electives *across the college years*. This is one of the most distinctive features of the Antioch program.

Level I General Education (38 academic credits and 8 examinations)

Level I courses and examinations are intended for the first two college years and may not be deferred beoynd the third year. At this level, for purposes of insuring distribution, the curriculum is subdivided into six groups of disciplines:

Humanities —
    Group A: history, philosophy
    Group B: design, drama, languages, literature, music

Social Sciences —
    Group A: education, psychology, sociology, anthropology
    Group B: business administration, economics, government

Physical Sciences —
    Group A: chemistry, engineering, mathematics, physics
    Group B: biology, earth science

For *each* of these six groups, the requirements are: (i) passing a 5-credit course (*or* passing the Level I achievement examination for that group with a grade of "H" *and* passing the first Level II course in the area with a grade of "B") and (ii) passing the achievement examination. (Up to 30 academic credits can be earned in this part of the program "by examination and by subsequent Level II course performance" — in this way making possible the 4-year accelerated program for some students.)

In addition, 2 academic credits are earned in the first-year orientation program; 6 credits are earned, at the rate of one each quarter, in physical education; and two skills examinations (English and mathematics) must be passed.

This Level I program is controlled within the following time schedule: 14 credits must be earned by course or by examination and course in the first year (orientation 2, physical education 2, distribution courses 10); by the end of the second year, the two skills examinations and four of the six achievement examinations must be passed; no more than 12 credits (physical education 2, distribution courses 10) and two achievement examinations may be left for the third year; no part of the Level I program may extend beyond this third year.

A simple calculation shows that, during the first and each succeeding year, the student is expected to choose not only general education courses but electives and field courses as well.

Level II General Education (30 academic credits and 1 examination)

Level II courses and the Level II examination are intended for the middle years of the program. For purposes of integration and depth, the curriculum is collected into the three areas: *Humanities, Social Sciences,* and *Physical Sciences.* In each of these three areas, 10 academic credits must be earned by taking courses; the credits can be earned in no other way. In addition, a writing skills check is administered and the Level II examination must be passed.

The quality of the Level II course is controlled through the careful definition of prerequisites for admission to them. Each teacher is given the responsibility of defining particular prerequisites necessary to his course. In addition, there are these three alternative sets of generalized prerequisites: (i) the passing of *two* Level I courses (one in *each* of the two groups in the area) *and* the passing of *either* of the two achievement examinations in the area; (ii) a grade of "H" in *both* of the two achievement examinations in the area; or (iii) the passing of *one* of the Level I courses in the area *and* a grade of "H" in *either* of the two achievement examinations. While a Freshman might directly enter one or more Level II courses, a Senior must leave no more than one Level II course for his final year.

The Level II achievement examination can be taken only after the first year and only when all of the Level I program as well as one Level II course in each of three areas have been completed. It consists at present of the General Education part of the Graduate Record Examination, together with a test of the skills of critical and creative thinking.

Level III General Education (7 academic credits)

The Level III program is wholly confined to the Senior year — two academic quarters running consecutively, January to June. The Senior chooses a 5-credit general education seminar and writes a (2-credit) "terminal integrating essay" on some assigned topic. The Faculty's directive to those teachers who administer the seminar and the essay is two-fold: that both *integrative* effort and a deliberate attention to *values* be exacted from the participants. For, as set forth in the General Education Syllabus —

> ". . . . It is part of the philosophy of Antioch College that the process of acquiring knowledge and un-derstanding of self and universe is not separable, actually or ideally, from the process of developing some set of value-commitments and preferences . . . The student is expected to make the examined *life* (and not merely the examined *ideas*) his concern, drawing upon all of the arts and sciences, experiences on and off campus, and the resources of teachers, advisers ,and fellow students to assist him in the achievement of the most meaningful and worthy way of life of which he is capable. . .
>
> "To any minimum demands are, of course, added greater hopes: intellectual curiosity, intellectual integrity, the treasuring of well-authenticated knowledge, persistence in the quest for such knowledge, active interest in under-standing accurately the convictions and grounds of convic-tions of others, determining to accept or reject ideas only after scrupulously fair weighing of their merits; indus-triousness, thoroughness and good craftsmanship in work, and a habit of satisfaction in good workmanship; inde-pendence of judgment and courage in acting upon one's judgment; appreciation for one's limitations, his indebted-ness to others, and his continued need for enrichment through them; constructiveness as a critic; responsibility in the discharge of obligations; a sense of aesthetic satis-faction and enjoyment from many experiences, including some involving the grasp of order in conceptual schemes for organizing human experiences; and determination to increase these enjoyments both for oneself and for others. . . .
>
> "By virtue of the amicable interplay of the diversity of views and manners of life represented in the student body and faculty, the College has its own distinctive philosophy and way of life. It seeks to influence its

members to follow and further improve this way, but by its very commitment, as part of this way of life, to individual freedom of thought, expression, and action, it does not make any test of agreement with its ethic a criterion for graduation. It does hope to cultivate a common faith and ethic, an enterprise that is one of common quest rather than of indoctrination and yet one whose methods are imposed by the 'rules of the game' accepted by those who join either faculty or student body."[2]

The three-level general education program, then, accounts for 70-75 of the 160 academic credits required for either Antioch degree. For A.B. candidates, at least 60 more will be chosen in the field of concentration; the rest will be electives. For B.S. candidates, at least 40 more will be chosen in the field of concentration *in addition to* 50 credits in the "basic science" sequences. These are: in *chemistry* 15 credits (5 waivable without credit by placement examination), in *physics* 15 credits, and in *mathematics* 20 credits (5 waivable without credit by placement examination). In order to enrich the electives opportunity for the B.S. candidate, 15 of these 40-50 "basic science" credits — 5 on Level I and 10 on Level II — are allowed to count also as general education credits.

To assist the B.S. candidate to realize some of the general education objectives defined for the physical sciences — since he is likely to by-pass the general education courses themselves — we rely upon the following: (i) independent study guided by the General Education Syllabus, (ii) the increasingly integrative character of Level II and Level III courses in which the sciences will be involved as relevant, and (iii) the reflexive consequence in field courses of the teacher's experience with the general education course or courses that he is also teaching.

One other consequence of these recent years of revision is, then, the availability to student and to faculty adviser of the previously cited "Syllabus for Students' Programs of General Education at Antioch College." Especially in Part II of this Syllabus, the student can find a guide to his *independent study,* beyond or instead of courses available in the Antioch curriculum. In this way, the teacher of a Level I general education course is freed from the terrible objective of preparing students for the hurdle of an achievement examination. In this way, the student who encounters

---

[2]General Education Syllabus, 1958 edition, pp 12-13.

difficulty in a particular group of disciplines can choose between committing some of his elective credits to additional Level I courses and a program of independent study, when preparing to pass an achievement examination. So too the accomplished student who has by-passed the Level I course requirement can recognize and by independent study repair a "gap" in his achievement.

The Physical Sciences in General Education

The common objectives for the broad area of the physical sciences as part of general education are described as follows, beginning on page 26 of the General Education Syllabus:

> "It is all too tempting to set down objectives so ambitiously that no undergraduate — scientist-to-be or layman-in-science — is likely to achieve them. For it is generally acknowledged that men, facing the problems of our time and seeking their own fullest development, need an effective understanding of science and mathematics, which includes an appreciation of their prospects, their limitations, their consequences, and their requirements. Clearly these are not be "learned once;" they are issues for continuing inquiry. (Just as clearly, they require indispensable contributions from the social sciences and the humanities.) And when, as above, we propose "understanding" and "appreciation" we mean open-ended processes that can never be considered completed while life and opportunities for learning remain. None the less, we must try to define the levels of achievement in the physical sciences and mathematics expected of everyone who earns the Antioch degree.
>
> "The courses and other experiences in the physical sciences and mathematics provided in the Antioch general education program can be expected to *initiate* a sequence of learnings that, for scientist and layman alike, are at the same time a responsibility of citizenship today and an invitation to share in the cultural heritage. (For the scientist, they are an important component in his professionalization — beyond the immediate objectives of technical courses and cooperative jobs.)
>
> "A generally educated man will be continually *interested* in the physical sciences and mathematics and in learning more about them. He will have acquired some sampling of the vast body of organized knowledge won through scientific work. He will have much of the vocabulary needed for scientific discourse. He will be

ready to learn the science relevant to some problem that proves to concern him. He will be disposed to take advantage of occasions where science is presented to the layman. He will be acquainted with the best of the available literature whenever he resumes his learning.

"Beyond these achievements, he will have become familiar with many of the major ideas through which scientists understand physical and biological events and processes and upon which technology develops. He will know something of the methods used by scientists at work and will appreciate the attitudes and commitments that seem essential to a vigorous scientific enterprise. So too he will understand the principal mathematical concepts that are basic not only to mathematics and to the physical sciences, but to the social sciences and other human endeavors as well. He will have, in short, some feeling for the 'strategy and tactics' of these disciplines. He will have some sophistication in distinguishing between processes and events of the physical, biological, and technological worlds and the signs, symbols, and models devised to investigate and to communicate concerning them — in relating verifiable 'data' to predictions deduced from the integrative principles of science. Thus, he will be concerned with the nature of scientific theory and of its revisions. He will begin to appreciate the cumulative character of science and technology.

"Beyond science and mathematics as organized into conventional texts, then, the educated man considers their history, their philosophy, and their social relations. Case studies — in the controversies through which scientists clarified their hunches ,their doubts, their convictions — would seem instructive. If broadly enough documented, they would illustrate the interrelatedness of science, mathematics, and other cultural developments: the impact of social, economic, political, philosophical, and spiritual conditions in society upon developments in science and mathematics; the interactions of scientific and technological changes; and the impact of both scientific and technological changes upon the other elements of culture.

"The educated man will have discovered that not even ethics or aesthetics can be considered irrelevant to the study of science and mathematics. Inquiry has its exacting canons; the consequences of inquiry for human technics — powerful though they usually are for either good or evil — change the form in which questions of right or wrong present themselves to governments, to organizations and to individuals. There is an aesthetic aspect to the ordering and interrelating of phenomena; and there is a creative process in science or mathematics, as in literature, music, or art, when the disciplined imagination ventures the 'inspired flight.'

"Fateful issues of public policy are emerging in our time as men seek appropriate ways to interelate institutionally the scientific, educative, productive, resource-conservation, public health, and defense establishments of our nation and of the United Nations.

"In all of this, one objective of general education that cuts perhaps most clearly across many disciplinary boundaries is that of 'understanding the nature of scientific inquiry.' If we reject the sterile extremes that 'there are as many methods as there are problems' and that 'the scientific method' can be schematically described, a more useful level of abstraction can be proposed. Then scientific inquiry can be recognized as involving the establishment of 'facts' by accurate observation; verification according to the criterion of reproducibility by independent investigators; analysis and correlation of 'data' (by induction) to establish general relationships ('laws'); development of correlative principles ('hypotheses') to 'explain' the the relationships with a minimum of assumptions (often concerning an economically designed 'model'); testing such hypotheses by deducing predictions of new 'data' and designing experiments to produce or not to produce such 'data'; development of still more broadly correlative principles ('theories'); and so on."[3]

Limitations of space prevent further selections from the General Education Syllabus. On page 28 "Sources of Information" for the Physical Sciences Area are provided. On pages 29-30 the mathematics program is set forth, again with "Sources of Information". This pattern continues, with "Chemistry, Physics, and Engineering" — program and "Sources of Information" — on pages 30-34; "Biology" similarly on pages 34-36, and "The Earth Sciences: Geology, Geography, and Astronomy" on page 36.

Limitations of space also preclude the publication here of typical examinations — mathematics skills, physical sciences group A achievement, physical sciences group B achievement, Level II critical and creative thinking skills, or Level III terminal integrating

---

[3]General Education Syllabus, 1958 edition, pp 26-27.

essay. The committees responsible for the frequent revision of these examinations are guided by the General Education Syllabus in their work.

Ten Level I Physical Science Courses (8 PSA; 2 PSB)

At present, a student can select a Level I course to meet the Physical Sciences Group A requirement from an array of eight offerings, six of them designed as general education courses and two of them from the "basic science" sequences required of the B.S. candidate. This rich elective opportunity reflects the Antioch preference for small classes and respect for varied teaching styles. Presumably a course has greater vitality if in design and conduct it is the creation of the individual teacher. Very few Antioch teachers confine their teaching responsibilities to field courses; no Antioch teacher confines his responsibilities to general education courses.

Concise characterizations[4] of the eight level I Physical Sciences Group A courses follow: There is one course in mathematics which can be divided into sections, each taught in his own way by any member of the department:

M 101-2   *Fundamental Concepts of Mathematics.* Staff member(s). Lectures, discussions, laboratory. Designed to develop an appreciation of basic mathematical philosophy and methods. It is *not* remedial in nature, nor designed to prepare the student for any specific examination.

There are three "integrated" courses, not distinguishing chemistry from physics unnecessarily. Each of these courses is uniquely the creation of the teacher who offers it and is available only when that particular teacher is in residence.

PS 101-2   *Physical Science World-Picture.* Mr. Loud. Lectures, discussions, laboratory. Selected concepts from chemistry and physics with philosophical implications, such as the fine structure of matter, material and energy transformations, particle, wave, and field. The procedures used by physical

---

[4]For each of the courses concisely described in the article, the Antioch teacher prepares a mimeographed syllabus setting forth in detail the objectives, content, procedures, and resources of the course.

scientists. This course should contribute toward more intelligent participation in philosophical discussion.

PS 104T *Physical Science for the Consumer.* Mr. Loud. Lectures, discussions, laboratory. This course is organized around practical problems such as maintaining a car and using the electrical circuit in the modern house, with emphasis upon understanding the physics and chemistry involved.

PS 106T *The Development of Atomic Concepts and Theories.* Mr. Owen. Lectures, discussions. The methods of experimental science and growth of the scientific enterprise are illustrated by the development of atomic concepts and theories from Lucretius through the 17th century revolution in science, and from Dalton's atomic theory to modern concepts and theories, including nuclear transmutations and energy.

Mr. Owen administered the celebrated Natural Science 4 course at Harvard for President Conant during the academic year 1948-49 and returned to Antioch to develop his particular adaptation of the case study approach. The most evident modification is the selection of a unifying theme for the selection of case studies that culminate in contemporary science.

There are two courses that are more conventional than these "integrated" courses in the limits within which they develop:

PS 108T *General Education Physics.* Staff member. Lectures, discussions, laboratory. General physics for A.B. students who prefer a physics course to an integrated course in physics and chemistry.

PS 110T *General Education Chemistry.* Staff member Lectures, discussions. General chemistry for A.B. students who prefer a chemistry course to an integrated course in chemistry and physics.

Then there are two courses usually but not necessarily chosen by B.S. students to serve *both* as "basic science" *and* general education courses. Of these, the chemistry course can be waived as a "basic science" requirement depending upon a student's score in a chemistry placement examination.

C 110T   *General Education Chemistry.* Staff member. discussions, laboratory. Designed especially for students who have not had high-school chemistry or whose preparation in chemistry has been inadequate.

P 102T   *Technical Physics I.* Staff member. Prerequisites: high-school algebra and trigonometry. Lectures, recitations, laboratory. Mechanics and heat.

In Physical Sciences Group B, the student has two alternatives:

B 101-2   *General Biology.* Staff member. Prerequisite: high-school chemistry passed or PS 110T.

G 101-2   *Introduction to the Earth Sciences.* Mr. Lounsbury and Mr. White. Lectures, discussions, laboratory and field work. Basic concepts dealing with the development and structure of the surface of the earth and the atmosphere.

These courses serve *both* as general education courses *and* as courses introductory to field concentration. They are likely to have large student enrollments, requiring the subdivision of the class into several sections.

Fourteen Level II Physical Science Courses

If the student has passed a Level I achievement examination with a grade of "H" or when he has moved through the Level I requirements, he finds at present an array of fourteen Level II physical sciences courses — three of them from the "basic science" sequences required of B.S. candidates — from which he selects two in order to meet the general education requirement for the degree. It is on this level that the student is more likely to find deliberate integration attempted across disciplines — in some instances involving the collaboration of two or more teachers in designing and conducting a course. Of special interest here are the specific prerequisites designed to insure the intermediate level of the learning.

The three courses from the "basic science" sequences are:

M 210T   Calculus *I.* Staff member. Prerequisite: M 172T (College Algebra and Trigonometry) *or* a high placement score on the placement examination in mathematics. Organized around the historical development of analytical geometry and calculus. The early part emphasizes technique and problem-solving. The direction is toward ever more careful formulation and proof.

C 212T   *General Chemistry II.* Staff member. Prerequisite: C110T *or* a high placement score on the placement examination in chemistry. Primarily for B.S. candidates and for others who have an adequate background in chemistry.

P 204T   *Technical Physics II.* Staff member. Prerequisite: P 102T. Lectures, recitations, laboratory. Introductory consideration of basic principles of electricity, electro-magnetism, and geometrical optics.

The other eleven courses, all specifically designed as general education courses, will be grouped as nearly as possible according to the disciplines that they represent. There are two offered by the mathematics department:

M 216T   *What Is Mathematics?* Mr. Blau. Prerequisite: a grade of "B" in M 101-2 *or* its waiver, *or* M 210T. Lectures, discussions. A survey of topics that display the beauty, power, and scope of mathematics, from the classical theory of numbers and a critique of Greek geometry to modern topology.

M 240T   *Introduction to Mathematical Logic.* Mr. MacDowell. Prerequisite: a grade of "A" on the mathematical skills examination *or* permission of the instructor. Lectures, discussions. Logic studied by mathematical methods. The nature of mathematical and scientific theories in general. Such topics as object and meta language; axioms for the theory of "if," "and," "or," "not," "some," and "all"; critique of the axioms; Gödel's theorem on the incompleteness of mathematical languages.

There are three other courses that derive wholly or primarily out of the disciplines of Physical Sciences Group A:

PS 206T   *Engineering for Civilization.* Mr. Myatt. Prerequisites: passing both skills examinations *and* completing the Level I requirements for PS Group

A. Lectures, laboratory. The role of engineering science in modern civilization. Dependence of the growth of society upon technology, the scientific bases and limits of technological decisions, and the social and economic bases and limits of technological decisions are investigated through study of the utilization and conversion of power and the utilization of controls and automation in manufacture.

PS 207-8   *Physical Science of the Industrial Revolution.* Mr. Loud. Prerequisites: passing both skills examinations and completing the Level I requirements for *both* PS Groups A and B *and* passing one course in history, economics, government, sociology, or anthropology; *or* permission of the instructor. Lectures, discussions, laboratory demonstrations, field observation of contemporary techniques. The relationship of science to the continuing industrial revolution — from 1000 AD to the present and into the future, from the nations of the North Atlantic community to the one world. We focus on such problems as ferrous metallurgy, energy resources, water supply, and river valley development.

PS 212T   *The Development of Physical Ideas.* Mr. Stewart. Prerequisite: PS 101-2 *or* PS 106T *or* PS 108T; *or* permission of the instructor. Lectures, discussions. The development of the theories of relativity and quantum physics. The role of experiment, induction, and analogy in the formulation of these theories.

There are two courses that are offered by the Biology Department:

PS 230T   *The Oceans.* Mr. Bieri. Prerequisites: B 101-2, C 212T, P 102T, *and* G 101-2; *or* permission of the instructor. Lectures, discussions. The interactions of physics, chemistry, geology, and life of the seas, including a survey of the history and methods of man's study of the marine realm.

This course represents perhaps the broadest integration of the physical sciences and is distinguished by its array of prerequisites, which include two "basic science" courses!

B 233-4   *Biogeography.*   Mr. Crenshaw.   Prerequisite:
           B 101-2 *or* permission of the instructor. Lectures,
           discussion. Factors involved in changes in the dis-
           tribution and abundance of living organisms; the
           role of man in effecting some of these changes.

Three courses are offered by the earth sciences department.
One of these represents the collaboration of three teachers — one
from geography, one from government, and one from sociology —
in the design and conduct of the course; this course is also found
in the Level II Social Sciences array.

G 204T   *Earth History and Present Patterns.*   Mr. White.
           Prerequisites: G 101-2 *or* permission of the in-
           structor. Lectures, discussions, laboratory and
           field work. Evolution of the physical world and
           of life. Origin and age of the earth. Principles
           of historical geology. Recent patterns and their
           implications.

G 240T   *Human Geography.*   Mr. Lounsbury.   Lectures,
           discussions. A regional study of man's activities
           in relation to the distribution of the world's re-
           sources. Environmental factors influencing man's
           economic, social, historical, and political activities.

SS 206T   *Basic World Trends:*   Mr. Lounsbury, Mr. Hol-
           lister, Mr. Gordon. Prerequisites: completion of
           either Social Sciences Group A *or* Group B *and*
           of PS Group B on Level I. Lectures, discussions.
           Facts and theories from human geography, polit-
           ical science, and sociology are integrated to show
           the relationship of basic world trends such as
           population growth, nationalism, urbanization,
           uneven economic development, and communica-
           tion to the integration and disintegration of the
           world community.

Finally, it is possible for a student in residence at the Antioch
center in Guanajuato, Mexico to earn 5 credits toward the Level
II Physical Sciences requirement *if* the project undertaken in an
intensive 10-credit course emphasizes geology or geography. The
components of this course are concisely defined below:

Mx248T   *Mexican Civilization.*   Antioch coordinator and
           staff members of the University of Guanajuato.

A. History of Mexico (5 hours weekly): Mexico's 400 years, from the pre-Columbian civilization of the Aztecs, Toltecs, and Mayas through the Conquest, Colonial Period, War of Independence, Reform, Revolution, and Reconstruction Periods.

B. Problems of Understanding Mexico (3 hours weekly): the Antioch coordinator supplements and interprets the lectures by the University professors and evaluates the community experiences and problems encountered by the Antioch students.

C. Arts of Mexico (3 hours weekly): for Humanities credit.

D. Social and Economic Development of Mexico (3 hours weekly); for Social Science *or* Physical Sciences credit. Plans and problems in developing Mexican industry, education, agriculture, and commerce; the interplay of many geographical, political, economic, technological, and cultural factors.

It is clear that the revised general education program at Antioch College has provided: for *distribution* — on Level I with the 6 groups of disciplines and the corresponding achievement examinations; on Level II with the 3 broad areas; for *acceleration* by the students of superior background — through the provisions for waiving Level I courses with credit, by examination and subsequent Level II course performance; for *individualized program design* — primarily through the generous array of courses available for election, but also through independent study facilitated by the General Education Syllabus; for *successive levels* — primarily by the definition of prerequisites for Level II courses; for *depth* and *integration* —again through sequences of courses, one the prerequisite for the next, and through courses that cut across conventional disciplines. To accomplish these good ends Antioch has for the most part rejected the kind of course that is usually designated as a "survey" course and is all too frequently characterized by superficiality. So too we have abandoned the illusory objective of "completing" a student's general education by the time of his commencement exercises; rather a "gap and block" design has been conceded. Except for the control exercised by the achievement examinations and the prerequisites for Level II courses, a student can "avoid" a discipline as he moves from Level to Level through the revised curriculum. However, we can now claim that no student is "backed into" any particular course because there exist no alternative courses for meeting a degree requirement. The students assembled in any Antioch course have *chosen* to participate in that particular course, with that particular instructor. This was less frequently true ten years ago and the gain in morale, for student and for teacher, has been very much as we expected.

Limitations of space preclude any attempt to convey the unique character of each of the courses in the array of choices before the student on the three levels of the general education program. In the Antioch community — with its intimacy, freedom, vitality, and seriousness — this is peculiarly a function of the particular teacher's personality; what the student experiences is at the same time dependent upon the composition of the group enrolled for the course and upon his own investment in the work of the course. Really to judge these things, the interested person would need to visit the campus and to participate in the program he finds in progress.

Methods of Instruction

THE USE OF THE LABORATORY

In the invitation to write this description of the Antioch program, the following topics were specified: "the amount of credit, the methods of instruction, the laboratory work — if any, the types of students, and the curricula in which the course is given." Much of this assignment has been covered. The attempt has been made to present the rich array of 25 courses available in the program, with as yet no special consideration of those courses known best to the author because of his teaching responsibility for them.

Twelve of the courses make use of the laboratory. Clearly there is no fetish made of this particular means of learning. Of the twelve, four are courses in the "basic science" sequences where the decision against laboratory work is least conceivable; two more serve both as introductions to field concentration and as general education courses. Of special interest, then, are four integrated physical science courses, designed for general education purposes and "stubbornly" retaining laboratory work as an indispensable component in the student's experience: PS 101-2 *Physical Science*

World-Picture, PS 104T *Physical Science for the Consumer*, PS 108T *General Education Physics*, and PS 206T *Engineering for Civilization*. Since the first two of these are the author's and since he takes his turn at teaching the third, perhaps his rationale for making use of the laboratory should be set forth.

Before taking a closer look at one of these courses, PS 101-2 *Physical Science World-Picture*, the others can be passed in quick review. The *General Education Physics* course involves more of a need for agreement among department members, any of whom might be called upon to teach it, and, then too, it departs less from the "basic science" physics courses than do the integrated courses, in the purposes of the enrolling students and so in its content and conduct. The *Consumer* course uses laboratory work for a very special purpose: inducting verbally facile Antioch students over the inhibition that keeps them from educating their eyes and their fingers, while relating the unusual manipulative skills of relatively fewer Antioch students to the relevant theoretical concepts. (No other science teacher known to the author on a college level condescends to teach such a course, a course that *could be* so recently observed humanities programs in other universities find non-intellectual! But his respect for the objectives and achievements of students who invest seriously in this course has strengthened over the years. The hiatus that often separates the powerful abstractions of physical science from the intelligent solving of practical problems in modern living *can* be bridged without sacrificing intellectual challenge.) The author's third general education course of his own devising, PS 207-8 *Physical Science and the Industrial Revolution*, substitutes for laboratory work by students laboratory demonstrations and audio-visual aids in preparation for time-consuming visits to observe current production techniques.

PS 101-2, *Physical Science World Picture*, then, is a science course with the humanities aspect of science deliberately revealed. The autumn quarter is built around the theme of man's investigation of the fine structure of matter and uses the modern classic, Hecht's and Rabinowitch's "Explaining the Atom," as a "syllabus!" The spring quarter deals with the rise and decline of the mechanical world-picture and uses another modern classic, Einstein's and Infeld's "The Evolution of Physics," as the "syllabus!"

Three kinds of laboratory experience are required of the student; other laboratory experiences are available at his option. First, the lectures include as rich a selection of demonstrations as possible. The student is required to follow up certain lecture-demonstrations with supervised individual observations not easily visible in the lecture room — for instance, Brownian movement viewed through an ultramicroscope. He is invited to visit the shifting "museum display" of recently presented lecture-demonstrations, set up in the adjoining laboratory for closer inspection and in some instances for repeated operation.

Second, the student is required to perform a very few "standard experiments" such as those used in the chemistry and physics laboratories for the "basic science" sequence courses. In these experiments, full discussion of the theory and procedure is available to him. He usually has a choice among several recommended experiments, as well as the option to work with one or more fellow students in a team. He can elect to do more experiments than the minimum requirement.

Two of the "standard experiments" — one each quarter — are used in a very special way. They are performed by the instructor and assistant "for" the entire laboratory section. The data are taken; their graphical interpretation and calculations from them are completed publicly, step by step, the students imitating, in an informal and leisurely atmosphere of question and demonstration. Particular emphasis is laid upon a systematic analysis of sources of error encountered or conceivable. These two experiments serve as "model" investigations.

Third, the student is required to perform at least two "original" experiments — one each quarter — working strictly independently except for conference with the instructor. He is expected to devise his own procedure, to complete a run, to analyze his sources of error, to devise an improved procedure, to complete a second run, again to analyze the sources of error, . . . Here he is allowed to interrupt the spiral of scientific inquiry! Beyond these two "originals" he is invited to undertake others, either from an available list or preferably from a point of particular concern to him.

The "models" and the "originals" built into the course have been selected, after years of experience, by the teacher. They are:

in the autumn quarter, a "model" investigation of the percentage composition of water and of the number of coulombs per gram-equivalent of element liberated in electrolysis — followed by the "original" determination of the solubility of a salt; in the spring quarter, a "model" determination of the local free-fall acceleration — followed by the "original" determination of the mathematical interrelations of the measurable factors affecting the period of a pendulum.

An "arch of time" of several weeks is provided for an "original" experiment. For greater privacy, the student reserves laboratory space, when he is ready, much as he reserves a tennis court or a library volume. The evaluated consequences of such laboratory work as this seem to warrant the "stubborn" decision to include it in this general education course.

AN INDEPENDENT STUDY EXPERIMENT

This account of the physical sciences in general education at Antioch College would be incomplete if mention were not made of a program of experimental teaching that has been proceeding, with foundation support, for three years already, in a representative array of Antioch courses — including todate four[5] of the courses previously cited in this article.

The author's syllabus for his *Physical Science World Picture* course in the academic years 1957-58 explained the experiment to the student considering enrolling in the course as follows:

> "In one sense, PS 101-2 has always been taught experimentally — for two very good reasons: (i) the teacher enjoys 'never teaching the same course twice' and (ii) although Antioch College pioneered thirty five years ago in the design of science courses for those not specializing in science, neither here nor anywhere else will *the way* be found to interest non-scientists significantly in science . . . With the help of constructive criticism from many Antioch students, PS 101-2 has always been experimental — changing by 'cut and try' . . .
>
> "This year foundation support has made possible an unusual and most welcome opportunity for a carefully designed experiment involving several courses at Antioch,

---

[5]These have been: Mr. Lounsbury's G 101-2 and G240 T and Mr. Loud's PS 101-2 and PS 207-8; next year, the "basic science" physics courses and their teachers will participate.

Carleton, and Oberlin Colleges — and the faithful participation of several hundred students. The most immediate advantage has been the collaboration of the several teachers responsible for the experimental courses. The larger concern is how best to use the teacher's limited time, especially in the years upon us when, across the nation, expanding student populations will be served by much more slowly increasing faculties. None of the three participating colleges intends to grow away from the tradition of small classes and intimate teacher-student relations. But all of us acknowledge a responsibility to serve the larger community and this experiment is one of several ways to meet this obligation.

"And even for Antioch College, with its small informal classes, the central problem of all education needs systematic investigation in addition to the 'cut and try' of conscientious teachers and students. This problem is how to assist young people toward really independent study, toward full learning resourcefulness — not for the college years only but for all the years thereafter. And we should like to know how to accomplish this better through the best possible use of the teacher's and the student's time . . . Carefully respecting the purposes and the style of each teacher, the experiment sets certain limits within which each teacher has agreed to operate, designing his own best version of the common plan: to evaluate comparatively the consequences of three different procedures for helping students reach the stated objectives of the course. . . .

"If registration is sufficient, PS 101-2 will be divided into three sections: Section I which will meet regularly according to the official weekly schedule with the teacher, Section II which will be subdivided into *teams* specially trained to function effectively — more often than not, meeting without the teacher's attending, and Section III which will be subdivided all the way to autonomous study by individuals. Yet every student, no matter what his section assignment, will deal with the same course material, be held to the same course requirements, have the same schedule of assignments, and take the same tests. And every student will have the same opportunity to seek individual conference with the teacher as needed."[6]

---

[6]Syllabus for PS 101-2, *Physical Science World-Picture*, 1957-58, pp 2-3.

Very briefly, the findings during the academic year 1957-58 were consistent across the array of experimental courses: (i) there are *no* significant measurable differences in student achievement when the three teaching procedures are compared, and (ii) there *are* significant differences in student satisfactions. While each procedure was preferred by some students — as experienced or as judged "from outside, looking enviously in" — the majority of students viewed the more conventional procedure of teacher-dominated class meetings as most desirable, as the expectation they had purchased with their tuition!

In the academic year 1958-59, the experimental design was relaxed and PS 101-2 and G 240T were the physical science courses used. Each teacher was thus freed to make whatever use he chose of the experiences of the previous year, improvising without any restriction other than that of reducing drastically the usual number of hours spent in teacher-dominated class meeting. The objective shifted to that of making as much progress as possible in the development and refinement of teaching aids and of procedures for assisting either small teams or lone individuals to function effectively though autonomously. A prediction easily made was clearly verified: student satisfactions were generally greater when they were taught — not by one of three methods in parallel — but by one method, all in the same relationship to the teacher, whatever that might be!

In both of these latest years of the experiment, each teacher has kept a close accounting for every half-hour he invests in the course. This investment has understandably been excessive. But during the coming year and in the years that follow, perhaps increasingly, the return on this excessive investment should be realized. Hopefully, the teacher will be teaching more effectively with a decreased expenditure of time and energy per student taught. Hopefully too, the student will learn more powerfully, recording greater gain without an increased expenditure of time and energy.

Looking ahead, then, to the academic year 1959-60, the teachers have considerable confidence in what they are trying to do. They have an accumulating array of teaching aids and procedures, adapted from one another's work and tested in previous years. The time investment will return significantly toward the normal load of earlier years. Above all, they can hope to witness increasing numbers of their students progressing toward independence in their learning.

Conclusion

Although the Antioch Faculty is emerging from a massive revision of the College program and, in particular, a restructuring of its general education academic component, so that the place of the physical sciences in general education at Antioch College has been redefined, further development can be expected to continue. The freedom and the vitality of the Antioch campus guarantee that courses will come and courses will go and that courses, between their coming and their going, will evolve!

chapter 3

SCIENCE PROGRAM AT BOSTON UNIVERSITY
COLLEGE OF GENERAL EDUCATION

Wesley N. Tiffney and Ernest H. Blaustein*

In 1946, the College of General Education was founded (as the General College) to offer students a program of education in which the relationships within and among the principal fields of knowledge would be stressed. The subject matter of this program has undergone repeated study and change in the intervening years but the philosophy, general objectives, and values maintained by the College for the integrated program of study have remained constant. This can best be illustrated by the following excerpt taken from the current College Bulletin[1]:

"The distinctive characteristic of this program is its integrative nature. It is a directed program of study which provides a common background for all students. Taught without reference to the lines of demarcation which normally set off one subject from another, the two-year curriculum includes material from five broad areas of human interest: Human Relations (psychology, sociology, and anthropology), Political Economy (history, government, and economics), Guidance (personal and occupational psychology), English and Humanities (composition, literature, music and art), and Science (biology, geology, physics, chemistry, and astronomy). In the field of Science, for instance, topics are selected and presented in such a fashion as to give an integrated picture

---

*Wesley N. Tiffney is Professor of Biology and Chairman of the Science Department and Ernest H. Blaustein, Professor of Biology, College of General Education, Boston University.

of the organic and inorganic worlds. A similar broad approach is made in the other general fields.

"Interdependence is an inherent characteristic of the social order. For example, the separation of such subjects as economics, sociology, and government into separate disciplines, while a necessity for convenience in advanced study and research, has not destroyed the essential interdependence of this knowledge. Social science cannot be treated adequately in isolation from relevant data found in science. By bringing these subjects into their logical relationships, a true perspective is established early in the students' thinking.

"This concept of relationship and the method of close coordination among the divisions of the College have proved beneficial to the instructors and the students. Above all, this method of correlation is effective in enriching the curriculum and in broadening knowledge and understanding. . . ."

In July, 1959, the College of General Education and the College of Liberal Arts were united under a plan by which the College of General Education retains its administrative and academic identity with the attendant privileges of control of its curriculum structure and promotion and tenure of its staff. This merger was the result of deliberations which extended over a two year period of a joint committee representing the faculties of the two Colleges. Students satisfying the admissions standards for the liberal arts program and admitted to the freshman class may take either one of two programs to satisfy their distribution requirements in liberal education. One of these programs is the Integrated Studies in General Education offered by the College of General Education, the other is a program in Distribution Groups offered by the College of Liberal Arts. These are described in the College Bulletin[1] as follows:

THE INTEGRATED STUDIES APPROACH

This course of study is designed to offer an organized sequence of related courses which reinforce one another by utilizing an integrated approach. Its purpose is to provide a breadth of knowledge in the freshman and sophomore years by integrating materials drawn from the social sciences, the natural sciences, and the humanities. In addition to the basic program of integrated studies, the student has opportunity to take elective courses.

English and Humanities _____ 18 hours
Natural Sciences _____ 14 hours
Human Relations _____ 9 hours
Political Economy _____ 9 hours
Guidance _____ 2 hours
Elective Courses _____ 12 hours

THE DISTRIBUTION GROUPS APPROACH

Both for self-development and social usefulness every student requires a measure of understanding in three great fields of knowledge. Within each of the following three distribution groups he must choose courses from at least two departments of instruction.

1. Literature and the Arts (12 hours)
2. The Natural Sciences and Mathematics (12 hours)
3. The Social Studies (15 hours)

The Integrated Studies Approach represents a two-year unit of general education courses supplemented by electives of sufficient scope to permit a student to prepare for a specialized area of concentration without the penalty of unduly prolonged undergraduate study. It not only fulfills the distribution requirements for the liberal arts undergraduate, but also presents the material in a carefully prepared integrated sequence. The Distribution Groups Approach presents a student with a wide selection of courses from each of the three major groups mentioned above. Thus a student is required to select a broad base of subject matter consistent with a liberal education. In the Natural Sciences group, six of the required twelve hours must involve laboratory work. For a more detailed description of this plan the reader is referred to the Bulletin of the College of Liberal Arts.[2]

The science program at the College of General Education is a laboratory course extending throughout the freshman and sophomore years. It represents a considerable change from the first course of study offered at the General College during the academic year 1946-47.[3] The rigid pattern of the original program of 62 credit hours (18 hours in Science, 18 hours in Social Science, 18 hours in English and Literature, and 8 hours in Western Civilization) permitted no electives, consequently students in certain areas of specialization were required to spend an additional semester or more fulfilling the requirements for graduation in a major field. Certain science majors were precluded from taking the program while others were urged to transfer at the completion of the first year. Now a student may begin his specialized program in the freshman year with appropriate electives and at the completion of two academically successful years at the College of General Education may continue his liberal arts training or transfer to such undergraduate Schools or Colleges as the School of Public Relations and Communications, the College of Business Administration, the School of Education or others.

Freshman Science Curriculum

This course is biological in nature and meets for three hours of lecture, one hour of discussion and two hours of laboratory each week. It carries eight credit hours for the year and is taught in cooperation with the Biology Department of the College of Liberal Arts. Although designed as an introductory biology program for freshman without previous science training, the course is taken by prospective non-science and science majors alike. We feel that such a course, designed to illustrate the basic principles of a scientific discipline, should be a necessary part of the educational background of students with varied academic interests. The professional aspects of a particular science (in this case Biology) can and should be taught in the subsequent upper-level courses offered by a science department to its majors. The enrollment includes all students of the College of General Education, those taking biology at the College of Liberal Arts and Sargent College and also some students from the School of Education, the Junior College, the Summer School and the Evening Division.

The approach to General Biology is physiological since from this point of view we can observe the interdependence of the fields of biology, physics, chemistry, and mathematics[4]. Fundamental biological concepts are taught without regard to the conventional lines of demarcation which traditionally separate the botanical from the zoological. In addition, the research experiences of various staff members, where applicable, have been introduced directly into the laboratory to bring something of the excitement and satisfaction of original research into a phase of the course often dulled by time-consuming drawings and tedious descriptions. A brief outline of the freshman science program is given here to indicate the scope of the course. A more detailed outline is mimeographed and distributed to the students as a study guide.

1. INTRODUCTION
   Historical background
   Philosophy and methods of science
   Scope of the science of Biology
2. NATURE OF LIFE
   Cell structure and function
   Diversity of living forms
   Relation of matter and energy to life
3. PROCESSES OF LIFE
   Origin and manufacture of foods
   Digestion and assimilation of foods
   Transportation and distribution of materials in a living system
   Respiration and excretion
   Integration and coordination
   Reproduction and heredity
4. ECOLOGY
   Relation of the environment to living organisms
   Relation of living organisms to one another
5. EVOLUTION
   Development of the concept
   Evidences
   Mechanisms

This outline may vary in detail from year to year as we find more effective techniques of illustration, or as different phases of the subject become more prominent in the research activities of the staff.

The fusion of the freshman science program of the College of General Education with that of the Biology Department of the College of Liberal Arts has been in operation for two years with considerable success as evidenced by a growing number of students majoring in Biology and an increasing interest on the part of students in science generally.

Sophomore Science Curriculum

The science program in the second year is physical in nature. It is offered only to the College of General Education students and, unlike the freshman program, is restricted to non-majors. The course meets for one hour of lecture, one hour of discussion, and two hours of laboratory work a week. It carries six hours of credit a year. There is more supplementary assigned reading in this program than in the freshman year allowing the student to develop a mastery of the subject matter on his own initiative. As in the freshman program, the related sciences of chemistry, physics, astronomy, and mathematics are welded together by a careful selection of topics to indicate certain fundamental concepts of the physical sciences and to show the dependence of one area of science on another. The physical science course attempts to achieve a balance between the historical and philosophical development of ideas and their quantitative interpretation and application as considered in the laboratory.

A brief outline of the sophomore science program is given here to indicate the scope of the course. A more detailed outline is mimeographed and distributed to the students as a study guide.

1. NATURE AND SIGNIFICANCE OF PHYSICAL SCIENCE
   Basic premises
   Physical science, literature, and the arts
   Early Greek science
2. MOTION, FORCE, ENERGY
   Concepts and terminology
   Aristotelian views and the work of Gallileo
   Newtonian laws
3. HEAT, TEMPERATURE, THERMODYNAMICS
   The caloric theory
   Kinetic-molecular theory
   Rumford, Joule and the mechanical equivalent of heat
   Heat engines
4. ELECTRICITY, MAGNETISM
   Historical development — static and current electricity
   Electromagnetic induction and electromagnetic effects
   Circuits
   Electricity and matter
5. ATOMIC STRUCTURE OF MATTER
   Development of atomic theory
   Atoms and the periodic table
   X-ray, charge and mass of the electron, and radioactivity
   Significance of nuclear concepts

Language of nuclear particles
Nuclear reactions and apparatus

This area of science lends itself admirably to integration with history, government, and economics, and illustrates the anatomy of thought and development of scientific ideas through the ages.

Course Presentation

The lectures in each course are given to the students in one large group in lecture halls designed for that purpose. A public address system is used and the lectures are simultaneously recorded for the future use of the instructional staff and for the Hospital and Tutorial program, a course of study sponsored by the College of General Education for students hospitalized in the Greater Boston area. Visual aids in the form of lantern slides, moving pictures, film strips, and models are used extensively. In the larger freshman lectures, the blackboard viewing problem is eliminated by the use of an overhead projector (Tecnifax, manufactured by the Tecnifax Corporation, Holyoke, Mass.) which permits the lecturer to write or draw on a twelve inch square transparent surface and enlarges the impression on a large screen in the fully lighted auditorium. The lectures are the responsibility of several staff members, each covering subjects related to his own special interest. Continuity of the material is maintained by the attendance of lecturing personnel at all lectures and by weekly conferences. The program is under the direction of a single course coordinator (the Science Department chairman at the College of General Education) who is also responsible for the mechanical and physical well-being of the program.

The discussion sections of each course meet for one hour a week and provide a further means of coordinating the lectures and the laboratory work. In the discussion sections, students meet in groups of twenty-five or thirty under the direction of a full-time staff member assigned to the particular group for the school year. Here active student participation permits two-way questioning, comparison of ideas and an opportunity to carry the subject matter beyond the scope of the assigned reading and the lectures. Students benefit from the opportunity afforded to whet mind on mind in the informal exchange that occurs. Moreover, the small sizes of both discussion and laboratory sections permit a personal relationship between student and teacher eliminating the chief objection to the large lecture groups.

The laboratory sections for each course consist of groups of approximately twenty-five students and meet for two consecutive hours a week. A laboratory outline has been developed to amplify and illustrate the major concepts presented in lecture and is coordinated so that lecture and laboratory follow the same sequence. New laboratory manuals, containing experiments specifically designed for both freshman and sophomore courses, have been prepared and repeatedly revised by the staff.

The writers wish to acknowledge the debt owed to the many people who have participated in the program throughout the development of this course. The administration has provided the College with quarters tailored to its needs and situated on the main campus. Here students and faculty have benefited from the improved facilities for study and contact with other University scholars. The dedication of an energetic staff through the years has been responsible for the success of the program at the College of General Education.

Bibliography

[1]Boston University Bulletin, College of General Education, 1959-1960, 855 Commonwealth Avenue, Boston, 15, Mass.

[2]Boston University Bulletin, College of Liberal Arts, 1959-1960, 725 Commonwealth Avenue, Boston 15, Mass.

[3]Tiffney, W. N. The Science Program in the Boston University General College. Science in General Education. Edited by Earl J. McGrath, 170-184, Dubuque, Iowa, W. Brown Company, 1948.

[4]Fulton, G. P. and W. N. Tiffney, The New Look in General Biology at Boston University: An Intercollegiate Approach. Boston University Graduate Journal, 6: 77-82, 96, 1958.

chapter 4

THE BIOLOGICAL SCIENCES IN GENERAL EDUCATION AT THE UNIVERSITY OF CHICAGO

*Benson E. Ginsburg**

The present general education curriculum in biology at the College of the University of Chicago is the result of the confluence of three points of view in two stages, each of which represented a departure from previous local tradition.

The first stage occurred in the forties, when the College, concerned about the incommensurability of the potential of the abler American high school student and the educational opportunities offered him, set out to develop a superior program combining the last two years of high school with the first two years of college. Such a program would, it was felt, afford the student an opportunity to learn much more than could ordinarily be encompassed in the corresponding four years in a conventional system, and could appropriately be crowned with a diploma signifying the completion of a formal general education. The necessity for spending an additional two years in order to acquire a liberal arts baccalaureate degree for the mere sake of gentility and intellectual respectability could thus be obviated, and a new pattern established that would boost the student to the next step on the ladder of life two years earlier with better preparation than before. At the time that the program was instituted, this next step would normally have

---

*The Author is Professor of Biology, Head Biology Section in the College, The University of Chicago.

been military service for a significant proportion of the undergraduate male population.

Such a departure was geared to the social and intellectual problems of the forties, and served to help underscore some of the inadequacies of our traditional educational system. It provided a much needed impetus for reevaluation and experimentation, and foreshadowed the greater dissatisfactions soon to be highlighted by the post-Sputnik aspects of the cold war. In a way, it was fortunate that it did not achieve the seeming success of changing the American pattern of secondary education. If it had, it would have resulted in a more limited operation from a narrower base than subsequently occurred. Instead, the dominant national concern has been with an upgrading of the high school programs and acceleration by earned advanced standing in colleges. The effects are similar, but the base is broader and the goal more advanced — the diploma being conferred after a reasonable amount of special study in a chosen area, rather than at the earlier point of completion of a general studies program.

The second stage in the development of the present curriculum was capped only very recently (1958) by the administrative reorganization of the College faculty in order to convert it from a faculty having jurisdiction and domain solely over the "general education" courses which had, since 1954, become only a component of the baccalaureate program, to one exercising dominion over the entire undergraduate course ot study.

Prior to the reorganization of the forties (the first stage), the foundation of the general education program consisted of four so-called survey courses (the first point of view), each of one year's duration, including one in the biological sciences. This course has been described by the late M. C. Coulter in the earlier edition of the present volume. Its format was lecture-discussion, and its backbone was a synoptic, authoritative presentation of the major conclusions in a selected sampling of the mainline areas of biology through the use of textbooks and lectures given, for the most part, by eminent biologists. Laboratory demonstrations were used illustratively, and exercises involving reasoning from evidence to conclusions were also used, to help develop an understanding of scientific methodology. Students were evaluated by means of a six-hour long comprehensive examination administered after all three quarters of the course had been taken. The anonymity of each student on the examination was preserved until after the grades had been assigned. Tests administered during the regular instructional time formed the basis for an advisory grade, only. Students who wished to major in biology went on to take laboratory courses in botany, zoology and physiology, after which they were qualified to enter conventional departmental courses.

The reorganization of the forties ushered in the second point of view (also described in the previous edition of *Science in General Education* in the article by J. J. Schwab). In our slogan conscious world, courses of this second type have come to be known as "block and gap." The emphasis in this program was on discussion and laboratory, although lectures were still used, but on a less frequent schedule. The objective of the new general course was to present biological science as an ongoing process of inquiry into the world of living things. As such, biology has dealt and continues to deal with certain basic questions, such as how complex organisms develop ontogenetically and phylogenetically. How the patterns governing such development are transmitted and actuated from generation to generation. How simple organisms carry out their life functions. How complex organisms carry out their life functions (the latter including societal, behavioral and ecological considerations). How fundamental research in biology is related to problems such as health and disease. What the major theories and concepts in biology are and how they help explain and relate the basic problems here mentioned. How are developments in the biological sciences related to developments in the physical sciences, both conceptual and practical (i.e. — instrumentation)? How and why does one theory supplant another, and what are the tests of "truth" in science — which is itself constantly changing?

In order to develop these themes, textbooks and authoritative lectures were used primarily to provide basic background information. The brunt of the educational process was borne by selected and, where necessary, edited versions of the original scientific writings that represented the actual inquiries or syntheses dealt with in the courses. These were made available in syllabi prepared by the teaching staff. The laboratory was used to provide an acquaintance with phenomena, organisms, or methods pertinent to the readings. Some of these consisted of actual projects conducted cooperatively by the students, but the most important pedagogical device was the discussion. Here the student was taught how to read, analyze, and relate the materials in the syllabi.

These courses at Chicago differed in several important respects from other "block and gap" courses. Although they often followed a chronological sequence within a discipline, they were not primarily history of science courses. Nor were they philosophy of science courses. Neither were they attempts to integrate science with the social sciences and humanities. These functions were performed in our curriculum by separate "integration" courses. The materials studied were not excerpted to provide examples which were analyzed as models in the syllabi, as was done in some of the "case studies" used at other institutions. So far as possible, the instructor and the students had access to the complete texts. The analysis was done by both, working together in the classroom. Finally, this was never a pejoratively "liberal" or "general" program about biology for the non-biologist. It was required of everybody, biology concentrator and non-biologist alike.

In 1950, the physical and biological sciences were administratively united as a natural sciences staff, with the author as chairman. A three year sequence was developed consisting of a year of physical sciences, a year of biological sciences, and a year in which two quarters were devoted (at the student's option) either to atomic-molecular theory as an integrating theory in the physical sciences, or to gene theory as an integrating theory in the biological sciences. The third quarter was common to both groups and consisted of relating what is currently known of the structure of genes to modern theories of matter, and exploring the relations between the physical and biological sciences at this overlapping frontier. The format and philosophy of the natural sciences program was largely that of the second point of view. As previously, advanced standing in the program for an entering student was detemined by placement examinations, and accreditation was achieved through anonymous comprehensive examinations in a manner analogous to that described for the earlier survey courses.

The recent (1958) reorganization of the College has divided the natural sciences administratively into a physical sciences section and a biology section. The program for the former is described in this volume by Professor Robert Palter, who, in 1957, became chairman of the predecessor natural sciences program. The program for biology, which the author now heads, has been fundamentally reorganized under what was termed in the introductory paragraph, the third point of view.

The changes in our thinking came partly from external pressures, and partly from internal considerations. The two major external pressures were time, and a change in public attitude towards the importance of science, as well as towards its role in a liberal education. The internal considerations were the result of experience with the strengths and shortcomings of the earlier programs which now came under the scrutiny of an enlarged faculty.

In a four year curriculum geared primarily to the high school graduate, it was no longer possible to have a program demanding four to six quarters of biology from everyone. Nor was it sufficient to demand the kind of understanding of science as process of inquiry, which was the major objective of the previous program. The change in public attitude demanded a more technically adequate background from the point of view of brute coverage of facts, while at the same time wanting both the depth of understanding that was previously emphasized in our general courses, and an ability to continue one's scientific education as a layman beyond the college years. This latter was always a hoped for by-product at all stages of our curricular evolution.

These objectives can be achieved partly in proportion to the upgrading of the high school science curricula. In biology, this process is on the march. Better source materials are being made available; institutes are being held to bring teachers abreast of modern developments; up to date movies are being prepared in all major biological fields with the advice of competent experts; college biologists are visiting high schools, and high schools are, themselves, improving their courses and encouraging abler students in a variety of special ways. Part of our problem at the college level arises from the fact that our students are variously prepared both in terms of the quality of the training they have had, and in terms of the areas of biology covered. There is much more uniformity, at least in this latter regard, in chemistry, physics and mathematics. In order to cope with the problem of wide disparities in preparation, our new courses are flexible in the sense that though most students will be required to take a standard package, some will be able to substitute alternative courses on the basis of special preparation. Some will, of course, have a reduced program because of advanced standing due to superior high school background. The problems of proper placement and advanced standing within the program are handled by special examinations administered when the student arrives on campus. The so-called placement examinations are used to determine the particular courses he will be required to take. If these (and the high school record) show unusual knowledge and sophistication in any major area of biology, the student is invited to take an additional examination to qualify for acceleration through advanced standing in biology. In such cases he is actually accredited in the appropriate college course.

The new biology program retains several important features of the old ones. It is *in* science rather than *about* science and, as such, the same beginning courses are required of the major and the non-major alike. It has drawn upon the experience of the various techniques employed in the old programs and has attempted to incorporate them with maximal effectiveness in the new. This has resulted in varying emphases on lecture, laboratory, discussion, textbooks, original source materials collected in syllabi, and library assignments, according to the stage of the program and the type of subject matter being covered; thus replacing the more or less monolithic format of discussion and original readings with a more flexible approach. Examinations are broken up into shorter units of two and three hours each, and given at the end of each one-quarter course. Essays, laboratory practicals, and objective formats are used.

The normal sequence of one quarter courses in biology is as follows:

Biology 111, the introductory course, seeks to impart a common body of knowledge to all students by means of textbook assignments, three lectures per week, and a three hour weekly laboratory. It emphasizes comparative aspects of morphology, physiology, biochemistry and ecology of plants and animals. Stress is placed on the problems faced by living organisms and the adaptations that have been developed to solve their problems. A knowledge of chemistry equivalent to that gained in the physical sciences introductory sequence is prerequisite to the course. Its pace is rapid, and it develops a technical terminology as well as acquaintance with a broad sampling of techniques and phenomena in the laboratory.

Biology 112, assumes the technical background imparted by 111. It deals with the development of current theories of heredity and evolution, primarily through the use of original readings including both classical and modern papers. The course thereby provides an introduction to the analysis of scientific literature in a subject matter area where the literature lends itself particularly well to such treatment at this level. A laboratory project is also required and use is made of the Museum of Natural History. Most of the objectives of the old Natural Sciences 2 course may be found in 112. It meets for six hours per week (one lecture and five hours of laboratory-discussion, divided into two 2-hour and one hourly period).

Biology 111 and 112 are obligatory for all students (unless placement and accreditation tests indicate otherwise) and form the core of a three quarter introductory sequence. The third quarter requirement may be met in a variety of ways. It may be elected from among seven one-quarter courses, one of which, Biology 150, is required of biology concentrators, and all of which (including Biology 150) may be elected in any desired number, sequence or combination by any student who has had Biology 111 and 112 or equivalent background.

These courses are designed to cater to the student's special interest in some areas of biology as against others. Pedagogically (with the exception of Biology 150) they emphasize independent library work and a seminar approach in the classroom. They constitute an attempt to give the student training and practice in informing himself regarding areas of biology in which he is especially interested. Obviously, this is impractical in the mass courses (Biology 111 and 112) where several hundred students are involved. All of the courses in the entire sequence, beginning with Biology 111, are taught by regular staff members who are present in the laboratories as well as the discussions and lectures. Most of the elective courses meet as a three hour weekly seminar. The field biology course has additional time scheduled for field trips, and Biology 150, which is the first specialized course for concentrators, meets for six hours of laboratory work and three hours of lectures weekly.

Biology 113-118 are also designed to provide elective opportunities for non-biology majors who may have an interest in certain areas of biology and want to inform themselves beyond the three required quarters in the general program. The prerequisite arrangements (see above) make them open to general election by all students in the College.

The elective courses consist of the following:

Biology 113. Population Biology. A seminar emphasizing the interrelations of ecological, genetic, evolutionary and biogeographic principles for the understanding of population biology. (It includes such problems as the appraisal of the current status of knowledge regarding possible deleterious effects of increased short wave radiation on future biological characteristics of populations.)

Biology 114. Problems of Embryology and Humoral Regulation. A seminar emphasizing the methods and concepts used in attempting to arrive at an understanding of the dynamics of developmental processes, including the role of hormones and other chemical substances in plants and animals.

Biology 115. Physical-Chemical Aspects of Biology. A seminar dealing with the problem of physical and chemical concepts and techniques in the understanding and explanation of biological phenomena.

Biology 116. Behavior. A seminar providing a survey and analysis of theories and approaches to the study of behavior in animals and men.

Biology 117. Philosophical Aspects of Biology. A seminar dealing with selected topics in biology and philosophy with emphasis on the implications of each for the other.

Biology 118. Field Biology. An introduction to animal and plant communities in the Chicago area, consisting of field trips, seminars, and discussions dealing with the relations between the concepts developed in Biology 111, 112 and the materials observed in the field.

Biology 150. Vertebrate Biology. A lecture-laboratory course emphasizing the morphology, development, physiology and evolution of the vertebrates. The adult structure, function and development of the major organ systems are studied in detail.

For those who wish to major in biology, both B.A. and B.S. degrees are offered. The former (and, indeed, many programs in the latter) is conceived to be appropriate to the education of the student who wants a cultural major in biology in the sense that he is more interested in this area than in any other, but is not planning a professional career in biology. The B.A. is not thought of as a spurious degree in the sense that a biology concentrator with professional ambitions in biology would not be advised to take it. It reflects the curricular position that both the future professional biologist and the "cultural" major should have a broad and liberal education in several representative major areas within biology, and in the humanities, social sciences and physical sciences as well. To these ends, the program attempts to be broad as well as deep within the sciences, and to leave sufficient room in the student's curriculum for other disciplines. It also encourages individual work in biology through an honors program for which any student with an adequate grade point average who has completed five quarters of work in appropriate biology courses may apply.

Biology concentrators must take at least two intermediate level biology courses beyond Biology 150 from a sequence of four courses broadly covering the areas of botany, zoology, general physiology and biochemistry, to all of which Biology 111, 112 and 150 are prerequisite. Finally, four additional biology courses of a more specialized nature must be taken on an elective basis from among those offered by the departments or committees in the Division of the Biological Sciences. Thus, the concentrator in biology may be required to take as few as nine biology courses out of the total of forty-two courses normally constituting a four-year program; ten more are recommended in the areas of physics, mathematics and chemistry; and the remaining twenty three are potentially available for work in other areas.

It is our hope that the new biology curriculum at the general course level will *first,* give the student a knowledge of the more fundamental concepts and conclusions of modern biology, including an acquaintance with techniques, phenomena and technical vocabulary (Biology 111); *second,* develop an ability to read scientific literature and to follow the development of a few major concepts in biology in terms of the actual researches from which they arose (Biology 112); and *third,* provide practice, through the use of the library and individually prepared seminar reports, in getting biological information, and in understanding and organizing it in relation to knowledge already acquired (elective general courses). In addition, for those who wish to go further, the intermediate level courses, the specialized electives, and the opportunities for individual honors work, provide a rich curriculum for anyone interested in deeper, more extensive knowledge, whether for preprofessional or other reasons. The total program has been planned with an eye to achieving adequate literacy and background in mathematics and the physical sciences as well, while, at the same time, leaving at least half of the four year curriculum available for courses outside the natural sciences.

chapter 5

THE PHYSICAL SCIENCES IN GENERAL EDUCATION AT THE UNIVERSITY OF CHICAGO

*Robert M. Palter**

1. Context

The current general education physical sciences program at the University of Chicago reflects certain recent changes in the structure of the College, most notably the relocation of the bachelor's degree and the introduction of "majors" in various subject-matters. Briefly, the undergraduate curriculum is now standardized to a length of four years and the great majority of students are expected to specialize in some particular subject during their third and fourth years. (For a more detailed history of the natural sciences programs in the College of the University of Chicago, see the opening pages of the article by Professor Benson E. Ginsburg in this volume.) One important consequence of these changes for the undergraduate program in the physical sciences is the fact that all students no longer take the same introductory courses in the physical sciences: physical science majors take more or less conventional physics and chemistry courses; biology majors (including pre-meds) take a special physics course; non-science majors take a general education course in the physical sciences. It is this last course which will be described in this article. However, it should be emphasized that science majors are also expected to develop the

---

*The Author is Associate Professor of the Physical Sciences, The University of Chicago.

broad and critical outlook on science characteristic of the general education science courses, at diverse points in their academic careers and by diverse educational means. Thus, for example, *all* students regardless of major take a more or less identical introductory biology course of the general education type (for details see the article by Professor Ginsburg mentioned above). Also, science majors are urged to study the history and philosophy of science in a series of specially constructed courses. Eventually, by means of comprehensive examinations over the main areas of knowledge, it may be possible to set up minimum standards of achievement for *all* students in each of the areas; and I personally shall urge that in the area of the physical sciences, due attention be given to historical and philosophical questions.

The current general education physical sciences courses are in the tradition of the natural sciences curriculum developed in the College of the University of Chicago during the past fifteen years (and described in the first edition of the present volume); in particular, the currently offered Physical Sciences 105-106-107-108 is closely related to its immediate predecessor, the old Natural Sciences 1 (which itself evolved considerably over the years). However, Physical Sciences 105-108 has been adapted to meet the new educational requirements of a new College and hence is not entirely identical either in objectives or in content with any of its predecessors. Among the important factors influencing the construction of Physical Sciences 105-108 are the following: (1) only non-science majors take the course; (2) the course is normally a terminal one in the physical sciences for all students who take it; (3) students in the course may be expected to have studied algebra and geometry but not necessarily any science in high school; (4) the course may be taken simultaneously with or even prior to the required introductory mathematics course. Because of factors (1) and (2) the course must, we feel, include a representative sampling of some of the most important modern theories and methods of the basic physical sciences (chemistry and physics). Because of factors (3) and (4) no mathematics beyond high school algebra and geometry may be employed in the course. It is clear that there is a fundamental conflict between the demands of these two sets of factors. Our response has been, of course, to compromise — between the demands of contemporaneity and rigor on the one hand and the demands of pedagogy on the other. We can only hope that we have sacrificed neither the essentials of science nor the ability to communicate with our students.

2. Objectives

The objectives of Physical Sciences 105-108 are twofold: (1) to develop in the student a critical understanding of a significant sample of current knowledge in the physical sciences; (2) to teach the student something of the methods and techniques used to obtain such knowledge. Of crucial importance for an understanding of our objectives is our belief that they can be achieved most easily if they are achieved together, as by-products of a study of the integral whole which is ongoing scientific inquiry. Thus, we consider the achievement of (1) to be incompatible with the use of conventional college textbooks as primary reading materials; and we consider the achievement of (2) to be incompatible with the use of any standardized account of "scientific method." Instead, our reading materials consist mainly of original scientific writings; these writings — edited and annotated by our staff — are grouped into units designed (a) to convey some genuine insight into the methods and conclusions of significant areas of the physical sciences, and (b) to stimulate reflection upon the nature and scope of such methods and conclusions. It must be emphasized that we do *not* dwell on so-called "methodological" or "philosophical" issues but simply try to analyze the actual arguments of the readings together with (if necessary) their implicit presuppositions. (Incidentally, we have nothing *against* "philosophy of science"; we simply believe it should be taught in a distinct set of courses.)

Physical Sciences 105-108 is "historical" in character only in a rather attenuated sense. The choice and arrangement of readings are influenced primarily by the systematic structure of our subject-matter and by the intellectual preparation and capacity of our students. We *never* select readings because they are antique, "philosophical," or important for the history of ideas. We teach science, not *about* science. We do not ignore problem-solving or laboratory work, but we do attempt to give these aspects of science education their due weight, and no more. Perhaps the greatest difficulty involved in constructing our course has been the inevitable tension between *coverage* and *depth;* it is a constant struggle to avoid the extreme of a superficial "survey" course and the extreme of a narrow, over-specialized "professional" course.

3.   Content

The content of Physical Sciences 105-108 may be very briefly (but most inadequately, even misleadingly) summarized as: astronomy of the solar system, Newtonian mechanics and gravitation, conservation of energy, structure of atoms and molecules, and kinetic molecular theory. The inadequacy of this bald listing of topics springs from an essential characteristic of the course, namely, its special way of treating the "topics" to be "covered." The point is, that in order to secure both depth and coherence in the treatment of a few selected topics, we choose, on the one hand, to dwell very lightly on certain topics which generally bulk large in conventional introductory physical sciences courses and, on the other hand, to include certain topics generally reserved for more advanced physical sciences courses. I shall attempt in the following discussion to illustrate with examples, but I may as well state here my belief that a full appreciation of the course requires at the very least a direct acquaintance with all of its actual reading materials. What is uniquely characteristic of our course is, we believe, not the mere use of original readings — there are now numerous courses of this kind, differing among themselves in various respects, in colleges throughout the country — but just how these readings are selected and how they function in the teaching-learning process. Thus, one feature of our course to which we attribute great importance is that the structure of the course is not simply presented to the student as a finished product which he is asked to remember along with the details which fill out this structure; rather, the significance of each reading and the interrelations of the readings considered as examples of scientific inquiries into the physical world must be actively sought out by each student for himself, aided of course by such devices as classroom discussion, homework assignments, and examinations.

I begin with the obvious question: why mechanics and the structure of matter? The answer is, I believe, also obvious — on historical, logical, and pedagogical grounds. In the first place, modern physical science is concerned, clearly, with three different realms of phenomena: the microscopic (atoms, protons, electrons, etc.), the macroscopic (ordinary physical objects and their constituents), and the cosmic (solar system, stars, galaxies, etc.). Surely, any introductory physical sciences course must attempt to convey some insight into each of the three realms and into their interrelations. And if this insight is to be at all profound, then the sampling of all three realms must be "significant" (see objective [1] above). This implies, first, that a sufficient number of topics which are central to contemporary physical science be selected for study and, second, that the topics be studied in such ways that this centrality can be understood by the average student. Thus, the interpretation of cloud-chamber photographs requires the principles of conservation of momentum and of energy, two of the central principles of classical mechanics; the explanation of the chemical properties of any substance requires the concepts of valence and atomic number, which can hardly be understood without referring to Mendeleef's periodic table and the concept of atomic weights; the study of distant galaxies requires an extrapolation of certain properties of our own galaxy, and these properties in turn depend upon extrapolations from the solar system. In short, as these examples indicate, if contemporary science is to be studied with some chance of genuine understanding, the indispensable prerequisites are an understanding of: Newtonian mechanics; the conservation principles for mass, momentum, and energy; the astronomy of the solar system; and those chemical properties of matter basic to atomic weight determinations. Rather than leave our students either hopelessly confused or with the pleasant illusion that they really understand modern science without having mastered the "indispensable prerequisites," we prefer to begin by emphasizing the fundamental classical theories, and then to treat as much contemporary material as possible in the remaining time. We hope in this way to prepare our students for their continuing task of understanding and evaluating contemporary scientific evidence and conclusions.

The readings for Physical Sciences 105-108 are collected in three volumes titled, respectively, *The Motions and Interactions of Bodies*, *The Nature of Matter*, and *The Structure and Motions of Molecules*. The first volume is designed to give the student some insight into the meaning, the modes of application, the value, and the limitations of classical mechanics. The ideal here would be to develop in some detail an abstract axiomatic formulation of the laws of mechanics and then to show how derived theorems can be applied in various important static and dynamic contexts, including examples of gravitational, electromagnetic, and other types of forces. Since it is manifestly impossible to accomplish anything like this in a course of our type, we use a rather different approach: each of the basic concepts of classical mechanics — in particular, velocity, acceleration, mass, force, work, energy — is first treated more or less intuitively by means of simple examples. Students are in this way expected to develop some facility in the use of these concepts in a variety of mechanical contexts and to overcome those conceptual difficulties which seem to beset every beginning student of mechanics (including the great founders of the subject, Kepler and Galileo and Descartes). Following this piecemeal study of the concepts of mechanics, the student is confronted with Newton's systematic treatment of the laws of motion, including the application of these laws to the discovery of the law of gravitation. Finally, an alternative to the Newtonian analysis of mechanical systems in terms of force and acceleration is introduced in the form of the principle of conservation of (mechanical) energy.

More specifically, the contents of *The Motions and Interactions of Bodies* are as follows. The volume begins with a consideration of the five simple machines, emphasizing their common features and terminating with the work principle which applies to all of them. In the course of this discussion of the simple machines, the concept of vectors is introduced in connection with forces and components of force. Stevin's proof of the law of the inclined plane is studied, which introduces the principle of the impossibility of a perpetual motion machine. The role of friction in the operation of machines is pointed out, the two fundamental laws of friction are formulated, and the recent explanation of these laws in terms of adhesive forces between solid surfaces is studied in a review article by F. P. Bowden. Our brief study of friction (usually neglected in elementary courses) is designed to accomplish two things: first, to remove some of the mystery which surrounds the notion of friction in the minds of most beginning students, by replacing their idea of friction (as a malevolent demon somehow responsible for the melancholy fact that the nice simple laws of physics never seem to apply in the real world) with an appreciation of the "naturalness" of frictional forces when they are interpreted in the light of current research on the nature of solids; and second, to prepare the way for an understanding of the principle of inertia and thereby of Newtonian mechanics (many students disbelieve the principle of inertia because they persist in refusing to classify friction as a force in the Newtonian sense).

Forces have now been examined in some detail in static contexts; before introducing forces in dynamic contexts, the general problem of how to analyze motion is raised by means of the examples of falling bodies and of the motions within the solar system. We study Galileo's account of the numerous factors (or "variables") involved in the behavior of falling bodies and see how the problem becomes dramatically simplified in the case of free fall in a vacuum. The apparent motions of the heavenly bodies are described (a trip to the Adler Planetarium helps here); the calculation, on the basis of the moon's parallax, of the distance from the earth to the moon is explained; the heliocentric hypothesis is shown to account for none of the main irregularities in the apparent motions of the planets (retrogression); Kepler's laws of planetary motion are formulated; and finally, there is a brief sketch of later developments in astronomy based on telescopic observations.

With the foregoing factual basis in mind, the student begins to learn of some of the more important concepts and principles that have been devised for unifying and explaining terrestrial and celestial motions. Fairly lengthy excerpts from the writings of Galileo form one of the principal materials for study here. Especially important are Galileo's illustrations of, and arguments for, the principle of inertia. Also, Galileo's insistence on the fundamental similarities between terrestrial and celestial phenomena — including a far-reaching application of the principle of relativity — is seen to facilitate an understanding of falling bodies, on the one hand, and of planetary motions, on the other, so that the possibility of a universal science of motion is at least adumbrated. We turn next to two of the further elements required for the actual completion of this universal science of motion, namely, the quantitative expression of the forces involved in circular motion and of the laws of impact — both due to Huygens. With some editing and annotating Huygens' own account of circular motion serves admirably for introducing students to the difficult notions of centripetal force and centripetal acceleration (Huygens imagines a man attached to a rotating wheel and holding a lead sphere by a thread which is severed, thereby permitting the sphere to fly off tangentially). Huygens' own derivation of the laws of impact, based in part on the principle of relativity, also serves well not only to bring out the scope of each of these laws (conservation of momentum is universal, conservation of relative velocity and of *vis viva* [mv²] energy only hold for perfectly elastic impacts) but also to clarify the systematic interrelations of these laws (any one of the three laws is a consequence of the other two; conservation of *vis viva* — or at least the impossibility of an *increase* in *vis viva* — is a direct consequence of the impossibility of a perpetual motion machine). Also, in each of these investigations of Huygens the concept of mass, as distinct from weight, begins to emerge with some clarity.

The climax of our study of mechanics comes, of course, with Newton's axiomatic treatment of the laws of motion. Here the student finds summed up in a small number of definitions, axioms, and corollaries to the axioms, the entire previous discussion of statics and dynamics. Furthermore, he finds new principles emerging in the form of theorems which may be deduced from the axioms, e.g., Newton's result that centripetal forces always lead to motions in which equal areas are swept out in equal times, and conversely. The two latter theorems together with several others are shown to play a critical role in Newton's discovery of the law of universal gravitation. The speculative character of this law as Newton derives it is emphasized. Furthermore, it is pointed out that the simple algebraic statement of the law conceals some very important and complicated problems. In particular, the restriction of the law to pairs of mass points is seen to require special mathematical techniques (essentially, the integral calculus) for dealing with the gravitational interaction of real extended bodies; and the gravitational interaction of more than two bodies is shown to be an extremely complex affair not amenable to simple mathematical analysis. Two of the most surprising confirmations of the law of gravitation are studied briefly: the precession of the equinoxes and the tides.

The concept of work is now generalized in a natural way from static to dynamic contexts. This permits the formulation of the law of conservation of mechanical energy, which is shown to lead to the same predictions as Newton's laws of motion in cases where both can be applied. Also, the energy principle is shown to have applications where the laws of motion would be practically impossible to apply.

The Nature of Matter begins with a more or less straightforward exposition of the following topics: fundamental chemical reactions involving mainly the elements oxygen, hydrogen, nitrogen, sulphur, phosphorous, and the halogens; the gas laws; and the simpler phenomena connected wtih static and current electricity, including Faraday's own account of his electrochemical laws. There follows a section dealing with the development of an adequate method for determining atomic weights from data on combining weights, and culminating in Cannizzaro's "A Course of Chemical Philosophy," which sets forth essentially the current method for determining atomic weights. Throughout this discussion it is emphasized that the "atoms" whose relative weights are being determined are purely hypothetical entities whose existence remains doubtful but at the same time heuristically very suggestive. Mendeleef's account of the periodic table of the elements serves as a transition from the problem of determining chemical atomic weights to the problem of determining the nature (including the mass) of the individual atoms themselves. This latter problem is pursued in selections from J. J. Thomson on the discovery of the electron, Rutherford on the evidence for the nuclear model of the atom, and Aston on mass spectra and isotopes. The complex character of the inferences leading to the conclusion that an atom resembles a miniature solar system is stressed throughout; and simple calculations are introduced to illustrate these inferences. It is pointed out that the Bohr atom (very briefly described) is incapable of explaining whole ranges of phenomena, and the kind of theory which replaces it (in wave mechanics) is indicated. Finally, students read a description of how the periodic table of the elements is explained by Pauli's exclusion principle, in an article by H. R. Paneth from *Penguin Science News*.

The Structure and Motions of Molecules deals first with the question of the orientation in space of the atoms which constitute a molecule. The phenomenon of isomerism (structural, optical, and geometrical) is studied, in selections by Kekulé, Frankland, Pasteur, and Van't Hoff, for the light which it can throw on the structure of molecules; and a brief description of the various kinds of chemical bonds is presented. The volume continues with a study of the motions of molecules, including a simple derivation of Boyle's law from the basic postulates of kinetic molecular theory. The conservation of energy principle is extended to include heat as a form of energy, and a mechanical basis for this extension is supplied by the kinetic molecular theory of heat, studied in selections by Clausius and T. G. Cowling.

Nothing has been said so far about laboratory instruction. This omission was deliberate, since the laboratory exercises and classroom demonstrations in the course are explicitly designed to illustrate and to clarify the readings. In general, it may be said that we attempt to avoid the extreme of expecting our students to imitate research scientists working on a new problem and the extreme of expecting them to obtain predetermined experimental results. We supply enough information on the techniques and background of a given experiment to orient the students but not so much as to remove an element of the unexpected, even of the inexplicable in their experimental results. Typical experiments include the use of Atwood's machine to illustrate Newton's second law of motion and the influence of friction; the collection of data to illustrate Boyle's and Charles's laws; the identification of radicals and functional groups in organic and inorganic compounds; the determination of molecular weights by vapor density; the determination of specific heats with a calorimeter.

The most significant subject-matter omission in Physical Sciences 105-108 is light. It seems to me that the course would possess a higher degree of completeness and coherence if we could include a study of optics, electromagnetic radiation, and spectra. But serious treatment of these topics would require an additional quarter of work. In fact, just such a course was offered as part of a second year's work in physical science in the old natural sciences program. Our plan now is to offer this additional quarter as elective for interested students. Similar elective courses on other topics (e.g., solid state physics, relativity and cosmology, relation between chemical properties and structure) may also be offered.

4. Administration

At the outset of his academic career in the College of the University of Chicago each student takes a battery of placement examinations to determine his general education requirements in the areas of English Composition, Foreign Language, Humanities, Social Sciences, Mathematics, Biological Sciences, and Physical Sciences. On the basis of his placement score in the Physical Sciences examination (which is divided into two parts, one in chemistry and one in physics) the student is required to register for two or three quarters of Physical Sciences 105-108, or he may place out of the Physical Sciences requirement entirely. We assume that an exceptionally good high school chemistry course (or some equivalent preparation) will enable a student to place out of one quarter of the course, and similarly for physics. To place out of the entire course, unusually good preparation in physics, chemistry, and astronomy (not normally a high school subject) is required. Although such preparation is perhaps not unusual among students who decide to major in science, it must be emphasized that we are concerned only with non-science majors.

The annual enrollment in Physical Sciences 105-108 is 200-250 students; sections average 20-25 students. Each student normally takes three other courses. Classes in Physical Sciences 105-108 meet three times a week: two eighty-minute discussion periods and one two-hour laboratory period. Occasional lectures (perhaps one every two weeks) to the entire student body of the course have in the past often formed part of the formal instruction — but more recently such lectures have been all but abandoned. The elimination of lectures reflects our strong conviction that in an elementary physical sciences course which is also terminal, it is *absolutely essential* that the instructor be continuously confronted with his students so that their understanding can be challenged and possible misconceptions rectified. Students are provided with regular weekly homework assignments which include numerical problems, queries for discussion, and essay topics. (Specimens of each of these will be found in the Appendix to this article.) Numerous short quizzes and a longer quarterly examination consist of both numerical problems and short discussion questions, with a serious attempt being made to integrate these two types of examination items.

Appendix

SPECIMEN HOMEWORK AND EXAMINATION
QUESTIONS

1. a) A 3 lb. brick remains at rest on an inclined plane 130 in.
        long and 50 in. high. What amount of frictional force
        prevents its sliding down the plane?
    b) If the brick were turned so that a side of different area
        came in contact with the plane, what ought to happen?
        Explain your answer. (Assume that the texture of the
        surface of the brick is identical on all sides.)
    c) How much work would be necessary to push the brick up
        the entire length of the incline, provided that the friction
        had been made negligible?

2. Outline Galileo's argument that the earth must be the cause of
    the secondary light of the moon ("earthshine").

3. One of the consequences of the Copernican (heliocentric) sys-
    tem of the heavens was that it predicted the phenomenon of
    parallax for the so-called "fixed" stars.
    a) By means of a diagram and a brief discussion show how
        this parallax becomes a consequence of the Copernican
        system.
    b) How do you account for the fact that for many years
        astronomers failed to observe any parallax of the stars
        whatsoever?

4. Show that the horizontal launching speed for a satellite in a
    circular orbit near the earth is about 5 miles/second. Why
    must the launching be horizontal for a circular orbit? (Recall
    the formula for centripetal acceleration in circular orbits.)

5. Show that, according to Newton's law of universal gravitation,
    Galileo's law of falling bodies should be approximately but not
    exactly true for bodies falling near the surface of the earth.

6. Investigate what happens to the *speed* of an earth satellite as
    the radius of its circular orbit diminishes due to the frictional
    resistance of the atmosphere. Hint: Study the relationship,
    for circular orbits, between kinetic energy (T), potential energy
    (U), and total energy (E); in particular, show that $E = U
    + T = - T = U/2$. Then, assume that the net effect of the
    frictional resistance is to diminish the total energy of the
    satellite.

7. Why is one hydrogen atom in the ethyl alcohol molecule con-
    sidered different from the others?

8. Determine all possible isomers of butane (C_4H_{10}). Assume that the valence of carbon is four, of oxygen, two, and of hydrogen, one.

9. Essay assignment.

In the Preface to the first edition of the *Mathematical Principles of Natural Philosophy* (1687), Newton wrote:

> "I wish we could derive the rest of the phenomena of Nature [i.e., those phenomena not accounted for by New-ton's law of gravitation] by the same kind of reasoning from mechanical principles, for I am induced by many reasons to suspect that they may all depend upon certain forces by which the particles of bodies, by some causes hitherto unknown, are either mutually impelled towards one another and cohere in regular figures, or are repelled and recede from one another. These forces being un-known, philosophers have hitherto attempted the search of nature in vain; but I hope the principles here laid down will afford some light either to this or some truer method of philosophy."

That is to say, in Newton's view all effects in nature are ultimately traceable to the motions of particles which attract or repel one another with forces depending only upon the characteristics of the particles and the distance between them.

From this point of view, the general task of science in studying natural phenomena is to discern the dependence of the phenomena upon the motions of underlying particles, and then to discover the laws of force which govern that behavior. Of course, in the process of investigation, a direct study of the relationships of observable characteristics, whose dependence upon the motions of particles is not known, may be useful and necessary as a preliminary stage. For instance, Copernicus and Kepler may be said to have established the explanation of certain phenomena (the motions in the sky of those points and areas of brightness that we know as stars, planets, sun and moon) in terms of the motions of bodies in three-dimensional space. Newton then established the fundamental law governing the forces between those bodies and thereby their motions — and he traced the law back to a corresponding one governing forces between every two bodies and therefore presumably every two particles in the universe.

(a) To what extent do the investigations of energy, elec-tricity, and chemistry studied so far conform to the program laid down by Newton? In particular, explain in what sense these in-vestigations fail to deal with the characteristics (such as inertia and electric charge) and motions of the ultimate particles of matter.

Your answer should include references to at least three of the following: the conservation of energy principle, Coulomb's law, Ohm's law, Faraday's laws of electrolysis, the atomic-molecular theory.

(b)   Nevertheless, each of the above investigations does lead to the formulation of important truths about natural phenomena. How is this accomplished?   In particular, what new concepts in addition to Newton's force, mass, and motion are introduced?   Can these new concepts be related to the Newtonian concepts, e.g., can one learn anything about the motions of bodies and the ultimate particles of which they are composed from the laws of energy, electricity, and chemistry?

chapter 6

GENERAL EDUCATION IN SCIENCE AT COLGATE UNIVERSITY

*Clement L. Henshaw and Robert E. Todd**

ɔpecial courses for general education have been a part of the curriculum at Colgate University for thirty years, beginning with "surveys" which were recommended by a Faculty Committee in the late 1920's. First introduced experimentally, they were soon required of all students until World War II. Besides a language and a year of English, four one-semester courses in physical sciences, biological sciences, social sciences, and philosophy and religion, were taught in the freshman year. A fifth course in the fine arts followed in the sophomore year. The virtual displacement of the normal academic program by special courses for naval trainees during 1943-45 provided a natural occasion for reviewing the curriculum, particularly the requirements for general education. The outcome of this study was the adoption of an enlarged program of general courses in addition to a language requirement, which would extend through the four years as follows:

Year	Course	Credits
Freshman	Poblems in Physical Science	4
	Problems in Biological Science	4
	Problems in Public Affairs	6
	Problems in Philosophy & Religion	6

---

*Clement L. Henshaw is Chairman Department of Physics and Astronomy, Colgate University.

Robert E. Todd is Chairman of the Department of Zoology, Colgate University.

Sophomore	Area Studies (one of eight)	6
	Communication	3
	Music and the Visual Arts	3
Junior	Literature	3
Senior	American Idea in the Modern World	3
	Total	38

After a few years of experience, a feeling developed in the faculty that, desirable though these courses might be, the total requirement was too large a fraction of the 120 credits for the B.A. degree, and was too heavily concentrated in the freshman year. Accordingly, in 1954 the core curriculum was revised to the list below.

Year	Course	Credits
Freshman	Problems in Physical Science	3
	Problems in Biological Science	3
	Problems in Philosophy & Religion	6
Sophomore	Music and the Visual Arts	3
	Literature	3
	Communication	3
	Area Studies	3
Junior	American Ideals and Institutions	6
Senior	America in the World Community	3
	Total	33

Students may be exempt from any of these courses by passing a special examination. In addition, a student who takes a year laboratory course in any science may omit one of the two core science courses. This provision was adopted not because of duplication but because it will help a student concentrating in science to obtain a much needed breadth in his program.

Organization and Conduct of the Courses

At the time the core curriculum was launched in 1946 it was the Faculty's intention that the general education course in the natural sciences be a single year course, with some problems selected for study which cut across the traditional division between the physical and biological sciences. It soon became clear that it was quite impractical to organize and staff a unified year course of this type. The University was fortunate to have remaining on its staff after the war a nucleus of several people who had broadened themselves by teaching in the science surveys, but few were willing or qualified to delve to the proposed depth into problems in so many diverse fields. Accordingly, the division was made into separate semester courses taught twice a year. This had a number of organizational advantages. Students could take the courses in either sequence, thus evening out the teaching load for the departments from which the staff was drawn. Class and lecture room space, as well as teaching aids and materials, could also be employed more efficiently.

This institution, as a liberal arts college, is committed to the extensive use of small classes and student participation. Accordingly, the two science core courses were set up for three discussion meetings a week of about 25 students each, and one general meeting when all sections came together. When the reduction from four to three credits was made the total number of meetings per week dropped to three, with general meetings coming less often. Most general meetings are lectures in which background material is presented or the line of reasoning of a problem is reviewed. Appropriate demonstrations and films are found valuable if an effort is made to tie them closely to the material presented. The lecturer is the staff member who is best prepared in the particular topic.

Staff for these courses is drawn from the regular science departments with occasional assistance from a man in some other area who had adequate background. Each instructor carries his section throughout the entire semester, a policy which may be hard on the instructor at first, but essential, we believe, for good teacher-student relations and for effective teaching. No instructor is asked to carry more than two sections, equivalent to half his load.

With assorted instructors teaching a course which is different in both subject matter and approach from conventional science courses, certain provisions are needed to prevent too wide a diversity in interpretation of the objectives and standards of performance expected of the students. The most important of these provisions is a weekly staff meeting and coffee hour. Here, in an informal atmosphere, there is a free interchange of ideas, comparing of experiences and discussion of teaching problems. Led by the member who has the greatest competence in the particular area, the staff also takes up the advance material to clear up questions or uncertainties and to plan the broad method of attack to be used. These discussions, particularly if the problem is a target of current re-search, inevitably bring in advanced information on recent developments. Much of this may be too detailed or difficult for presentation to the students but it serves to enrich an instructor's background and maintain his interest.

Since the two courses have had largely separate staffs (one instructor, a paleontologist, teaches regularly in both), a certain amount of divergence in evolutionary development has occurred, as might be expected. The description of the physical science course is given below in some detail. Then in the section on the biological science course the differences will be noted.

Physical Science Course — Core 11

OBJECTIVES

At the time the core curriculum was launched in 1946, a detailed list of objectives of Core 11, as the physical science course is now called, had not been made. The basic plan was to gain greater depth of penetration in limited areas than was achieved in the physical science survey, and also to introduce an emphasis upon how scientific knowledge is arrived at. Hence the suggestion of approaching selected topics as scientific problems seemed eminently suited to the purpose. As experience has been gained with this method, the objectives can now be more clearly stated. They are:

1. To avoid superficiality by exploring the chosen subject matter to greater depth than customary at the freshman level.
2. To develop by actual experience some skill in critical thinking and logical reasoning with data and principles of science.
3. To break the students' habit of relying *solely* upon the authority of textbook or teacher, replacing it in part by reliance upon the authority of facts and logical reasoning.
4. To convey some understanding of science as an enterprise, as a means of getting knowledge and solving problems.
5. To acquire knowledge in certain areas, some skill in using it, and an appreciation of the interrelatedness of knowledge in science.
6. To give a few glimpses into the evolution of ideas in science.

Obviously there are real limits to the degree of achievement of broad objectives such as these. But it should be noted that effort directed at one does not preclude progress toward two or three others at the same time. At present, those objectives higher up on the list are considered to be of somewhat greater importance than those lower down.

TEXT MATERIALS

No single book can serve as a text for a course of this type, nor is a single source consistent with the objectives of the course. As explained below, when taking up a topic as a scientific problem, the student needs access to factual information as well as certain expository material covering related principles. This material is supplied to the student in two ways. First, he purchases a manual for the course which contains explanations of how each problem will be approached and reproductions of useful articles from sources like the *Scientific American*. The second means is for the student to consult portions of several selected texts or popular books on science. Multiple copies of these are kept on reserve in the library. Experience has shown that some of these library readings are of greater value than others. Those which are largely dogmatic contrast awkwardly with the more investigative attitude which is striven for in the classroom. So they are being replaced with appropriately written exposition in the manual. There is no plan at present to eliminate *all* library readings. The necessity for consulting varied sources has distinct advantages. Students benefit from differing viewpoints, and they are less likely to regard a single volume as the sole and final authority on all matters.

THE PROBLEM APPROACH

The greatest and most obvious weakness of the problem approach for teaching science in general education to non-specialists is the lack of broad coverage of subject matter. Staff members who taught in the former survey course at Colgate found it quite a wrench to shift to a course which omitted large blocks of material they had thought valuable or important. Obviously, such omissions are justified only if the teacher can bring himself to believe that greater ends can be substituted.

Several advantages of the problem approach have come to light as a result of the experience at Colgate. First, for the study of how scientific knowledge is gained, it is a more natural and reasonable procedure than abstract discussions of logic and methodology. Obviously impressed with the tremendous advances in scientific knowledge, philosophers have for years described and analyzed what they call "the scientific method." Many educators have thus taken their cue to summarize into four or five simple steps what this "scientific method" is. Yet research scientists see little resemblance between this summary and their own efforts or those of their predecessors. They claim there is no *single* method for solving all scientific problems; there are many methods. The common factors which appear in all scientific investigations are not steps of procedure, or method, but principles of scientific thinking, such as the requirement that any acceptable hypothesis be consistent with all the available evidence and that such evidence be based upon "publicly verifiable" observations or experiments. If real scientific problems are studied it is possible to bring out frequently the tentativeness of hypotheses, and the bases for their acceptance or rejection, and still note that the procedural steps are far from identical.

A course which discusses scientific procedures and stresses principles of scientific thinking sounds like a course *about* science rather than a course *in* science. This criticism can be avoided with the problem approach because the students can have some active participation in the solutions of the problems. They read about some of the relevant facts and hypotheses proposed and in class discussion they consider the degree of support different facts lend to different hypotheses. This is why discussion meetings are so important for this method of teaching. The educational process of getting the student actually to participate in the reasoning process is quite different from the one in which he merely tries to *remember* the steps of reasoning followed by someone else, which he hears presented to him in a lecture.

A third advantage of the problem approach is its ability to capitalize upon the natural interest of the student in recent developments. Not every problem currently under investigation lends itself to a course at college freshman level, but there are plenty that are incompletely solved in which students show keen interest. And by selecting problems from a variety of science fields, some breadth is gained by the sampling process, even though the degree of coverage achieved in a survey course is not possible.

SELECTION OF PROBLEMS

If a person contemplates designing a freshman science course around a group of problems currently under investigation his first reaction may be one of dismay. What prospect is there for young college students, who are not science specialists, to handle the mathematics and grasp the concepts used in current research problems in the physical sciences? In the fields of straight physics and chemistry the prospect is dim indeed. But we have found that there is a wealth of usable problems in the observational sciences of astronomy and geology, and in the inter-science fields like geophysics and meteorology. The necessary mathematics can be kept simple enough and they serve well for the objectives mentioned above.

Of the five problems now dealt with in Core 11, three are of the type which are under current study. One of these, very popular with the students, asks, "How did the solar system originate?" This problem immediately follows the one on celestial motions, described below, in which are noted the features of the system which imply a common origin for the family of planets. We devote about two weeks to a historical review of the more important hypotheses, winding up with some discussion of recent proposals of Whipple and Kuiper. In this problem students can see how an appealing hypothesis is later discarded on new evidence or more careful study.

From the currently active area of geophysics, rich in unsolved problems, we have developed a unit on the interior of the earth. Here students begin to appreciate how inaccessible the region is and how interrelated the many factors are of density, temperature and composition. Yet they also learn new respect for the detective skill of the seismologist in unscrambling the welter of wiggles upon his seismograph record, revealing significant changes in properties of the earth at great depths.

Finding an answer to the question, "What was the origin of the Carolina Bays?" would have little effect upon the welfare of mankind. But this small problem from geology has been used since 1946. The Sass article, "When the Comet Struck," from the *Saturday Evening Post* of September 9, 1944, convinces all the students of the near certainty of a meteoritic origin. But Douglas Johnson's careful systematic analysis[1] persuades most of them that the explanation is probably not so simple. In recent years we have included in the manual a reproduction of Prouty's article[2] to give a fuller statement of the arguments for the meteoritic point of view. It makes a striking contrast with the Johnson article in style of scientific writing.

The problem approach need not be confined to those under current investigation. Former President Conant developed the case study method at Harvard University in which the solutions of real problems of an earlier period in history are studied. We have found it possible to enlist student participation in working out anew the solution to problems which have already been solved. One of these is stated, "Why does the temperature of the air decrease as one goes to higher altitudes?" The solution is as much a mystery to the students as any current problem We find it necessary, in the four weeks devoted to it, to review a number of physical principles relating to hydrostatics, convection, properties of gases, and radiation. We discuss the nature of heat and develop some of the kinetic theory before the solution is complete. At the end, some application is made to meteorology in the vertical stability of air masses.

PROBLEM ON CELESTIAL MOTIONS

The fifth problem now included in Core 11 is, "What is the best explanation for celestial motions?" All college students before entrance, have been given a fairly complete description of the solar system and its mechanics. But few, if any, would be able to reconstruct it from the available observations. In some general education courses the history of man's efforts to work out this scheme is studied in some detail. We have approached it from the other end. This problem is taught early in the fall semester but fairly late in the spring, in order to have best weather for student observing.

The instructor begins by pointing out that the student derived his knowledge of the solution from a respected authority, an essen-

[1]Douglas Johnson, *American Scientist*, 32, 1-22 (January, 1944)
[2]W. F. Prouty, *Bull. Geol. Soc. Am.*, 63, 167-224, (February, 1952)

tial part of education, especially at the lower levels. But that is not the way scientific knowledge is first gained, he explains. It must be gradually built up and figured out in ways which can seldom be predicted. He then proposes that the students put aside, temporarily, their reliance upon the experts, and endeavor as a class activity, to work out a solution to the question themselves. They may be able to make some of the needed observations directly, though there should be no objection to accepting observations from sources with better equipment and more time, for these observations can be and frequently are independently verified. But all inferences, proposed mechanisms, hypotheses or conclusions derivable from the observations will be made in class and not borrowed from others.

The first step is to agree upon what the motions are which need to be explained. Here most students are hazy. To promote the observational attitude they are asked to sketch portions of the night sky and horizon at the four points of the compass, and repeat these sketches from the same vantage point about 30 minutes later. Few sketches turn out accurate, but a synthesis of results for the entire class will show the systematic apparent east-to-west rotation of the entire sky or "celestial sphere" about the earth as a center. (In these days of artificial satellites the sphericity of the earth can be taken as demonstrated.) To explain this hour-by-hour motion two assumptions or hypotheses can be used. Either the entire sphere is actually revolving around the earth, or the earth is rotating in the opposite sense. The latter idea is less difficult to visualize mechanically but it would be more acceptable if it had the confirmation of some deductive test. A rotation of once a day is hardly enough to make a person dizzy. It might show up, though, in certain situations where moving bodies are partially free of the earth for limited periods. Here the students read about shifting tracks of satellites, and they see a Foucault pendulum change direction in the afternoon lecture. This confirms qualitatively the hypothesis of the rotating earth.

The period of this rotation seems to be about 24 hours. It makes a good laboratory project for the students to determine this time more precisely. On successive nights they watch and time a bright star disappearing behind the edge of a building when viewed from a fixed location. With care, some students can make this observation to a precision of a few seconds.

The next step is to consider the left-over motions not fully accounted for by the spin of the earth. The most noticeable is that of the moon (though many city-bred students are ignorant of it) which nightly shifts eastward about 13°, taking 27⅓ days to return to the same position in front the background stars. On stars maps in their manuals the students plot several positions of the moon, and current data from the American Ephemeris can also be supplied. It is a natural inference that the moon revolves around the earth once in that period, although no simple confirming test, like the Foucault pendulum, is available.

The sun also has an apparent motion relative to the background stars, though it is not directly observable. Many students are familiar with the seasonal changes in noontime altitude as well as the shift in rising and setting locations and times. This is evidence for periodic changes in declination. The eastward increase of right ascension may be inferred from various observations, such as the 4-minute difference they observed between the periods of the sun and stars, or the changing pattern of stars setting after sunset. The sun appears to be about the same size as the moon and only a little farther, so by analogy with the moon, the hypothesis is proposed that the sun likewise revolves around the earth with a period of one year, in an orbit inclined some 23° to the celestial equator.

Sometimes a clever student suggests that the *earth* should be assumed to revolve around the *sun* once a year instead. A common answer of the instructor is that such a scheme should certainly be investigated, but the student made no such proposal with regard to the moon and it is sensible to follow through the most obvious and plausible hypothesis first.

Attention is next directed to the planets whose motions upon the celestial sphere are not uniform like those of the moon and sun. They progress eastward most of the time but at certain intervals they appear to stop and move westward, then move eastward again. The character of these retrograde loops is made clearer to the students by having them plot monthly values for right ascension and declination for Mars and Venus on polar coordinate paper. Successive telescopic photographs of these plants are examined. They show not only large and progressive changes in apparent diameter but phase changes as well. If one discounts the thought that they are pulsating in size, it is evident that they must change their distance from the earth by large amounts. The progression from small to large in apparent size coupled with a phase sequence from full to crescent, then reversing, presents a convincing inductive argument that Venus is revolving around the sun. A homemade model shows that if Venus does this while the sun in turn revolves around the earth, retrograde loops of the correct frequency can be produced.

A similar scheme for Mars, except that it loops the earth as well, is shown to account quite adequately for its change in appearance as well as its retrograde motion. So with the proper choice of relative distances and periods, all the planets can be pictured as circling the sun which in turn carries them around the earth. This model, it might be pointed out, is quite different from the old Ptolemaic system of epicycles and deferents.

Here the students are baffled. They are confronted with a scheme which apparently is consistent with all the positional observations and yet it is contradictory to what they were formerly taught and have firmly accepted. But the instructor warns that they do not yet have sufficient evidence to transfer the model from the status of a hypothesis to that of an accepted theory. Other observations must be sought. Furthermore the whole scheme must square with what we know about the behavior of bodies and how they influence each other. Here Newtonian dynamics is assumed as demonstrable from laboratory studies, and gravitation is proposed as the force which keeps these bodies from moving off into space on tangent straight lines. It is also explained (by using a demonstration) that one body never revolves about the exact center of another. Rather they both revolve about their common center of mass. On this basis, and without the use of equations, the provisional scheme of the earth being the center can be shown to be contrary to simple laws of dynamics. That is, if the planets are to follow paths centered close to the sun, the earth must exert little influence upon them and hence be much less massive than the sun, which requires the earth to revolve around a point close to the center of the sun instead.

This contradiction required substantial revision of the initial hypothesis, although the parts describing the rotation of the earth and the revolution of the moon are unaffected. It becomes necessary to find a different explanation for retrograde motion of the planets and the result is the familiar heliocentric system. Finally there are two critical deductive tests, aberration and stellar parallax (we emphasize the latter), both due to motion of the earth in its orbit around the sun. These last effects have been observed but are extremely minute, of the order of a few seconds of arc or less, and historically were not influential in the acceptance of the heliocentric system.

After spending nearly four weeks wrestling with various phases of the problem as sketch above, the students are then asked to read something of its history. Although this review is sketchy, there is opportunity to consider Aristarchus' insight, why his ideas failed to be accepted, the success of another "erroneous" scheme, the Ptolemaic system, Copernicus' revival of the heliocentric approach, Tycho Brahe and why he rejected Copernicus' new scheme, and Galileo's and Kepler's important contributions which culminated in Newton's mathematical synthesis. The prediction and discovery of Neptune and Pluto serve both to give additional confirmation of the heliocentric theory, and to show how some discoveries are made in science. Students have indicated in various ways that such a historical summary, after they have grappled with the problem themselves, is both interesting and valuable.

More time than one would expect seems necessary before the students are really straight on what the motions are that need explaining. Skill in visualizing relative motion in three-dimensions comes slowly. Although the student manual provides detailed explanation with many diagrams we have found several mechanical models of great assistance. Particularly helpful is a three-foot diameter transparent plastic star sphere which can be rotated to simulate hourly motion, and on which successive positions of moon, sun, or planets can be shown with a sticker. Of assistance for supplementary reading is J. B. Sidgwick and W. K. Green, *The Heavens Above*, Oxford University Press, New York (1950). For the historical treatment, Gerald Holton and D. H. D. Roller, *Foundations of Modern Physical Science*, Addison-Wesley, Reading, Mass. (1958) is especially valuable.

TESTING

Each instructor is autonomous in his own classroom but all sections have common monthly tests. All staff members share in the preparation of these tests, and final forms are reviewed in staff meetings. We have found that formulating suitable test questions is the greatest headache of teaching a course which asks a good deal more of the students than remembering a body of organized knowledge. In a very real sense, the students recognize as the *empirical* objectives of a course those mental tasks they are called upon to perform for grading purposes.

To emphasize the objective of understanding how science problems have been or can be solved, questions are sometimes used which ask the students whether a given statement is: true by definition, plausible hypothesis, fact on the basis of scientific evidence, or inconsistent with known facts or principles. Another type asks whether a fact supports one, the other, both, or neither of two competing hypotheses. Historical questions depend less upon an accurate memory of dates and more upon placing significant events in proper sequence. Sometimes it is possible to present excerpts from a popular article on a scientific problem and test for recognition and understanding of important steps in the attack on the problem. When recall questions are used they require not simply the memory of facts but the recall of relationships, arguments for or against a particular hypothesis, or other elements of understanding. Sometimes students are asked to display their knowledge in a certain area and then in further questions to apply to it to an unfamiliar situation.

Between 30 and 40 per cent of testing time is devoted to free-response questions, requiring either brief statements or longer expositions. Here again, one of the objectives of the course is that the students be able not only to think in critical and logical fashion, but to express these thoughts orally and in writing. This objective is further supported by asking each student to write one or more papers during the semester which are analytical in character rather than descriptive or expository.

Biological Science Course — Core 12

The semester course in biological science is directed towards the same broad objectives as the course in the physical sciences. The subjects are presented in the form of problems and the student is confronted by a set of puzzling situations, each of which is designed to arouse his curiosity and challenge him to find a satisfactory explanation. Since, ideally, the motivation for the exploration of a problem should be derived as much as possible from the student himself, particular care must be attached to the phraseology of the question by which each problem is introduced. A question which is too ingenuous or one which is too abstruse will produce initial indifference.

The reading material which helps the student in his exploration of the problems is contained in a number of selected books on reserve at the Library. The titles range from conventional texts to books which were never designed to be texts at all. In many instances it has proved impossible to find readings which treat the subject matter in the intended way. The material may be either too abstruse, too brief, or it may be presented too dogmatically. Consequently a student manual is used which provides some essential material written in harmony with the aims of the course, and which also includes reproductions of some useful articles.

THE PROBLEMS

For the first few years after the inception of the course, five problems were considered. When the time alloted to the course was reduced, one problem was omitted, the one which impinged upon the field of evolution, "Why does the body contain useless parts?" Of the four problems currently considered, two may be classed as animal physiology, one as plant physiology, and the fourth is in the area of genetics. These problems are posed by the following introductory questions: "How is the circulation of the blood controlled?" "How is prenatal development regulated?" "How is skin color inherited?" and "How does life depend on light?" The order in which these questions have been considered has varied over the years. Since the course is avowedly of the block-and-gap kind, there is no special continuity running throughout the whole semester. However the problem on reproduction usually precedes the one on heredity.

The students quickly recognize the assumption behind the question "How is the circulation of the blood controlled?" and some time is devoted to considering how we know that blood does circulate. The first step is a clarification of the meaning of the phrase, "circulation of the blood." Experience has shown that few college freshmen — although categorically claiming that blood does circulate — can make an analysis of the circulatory system in clear, general terms. For example, the mere motion of the blood is frequently mistaken for true circulation.

In dealing with this problem, the instructor may play the part of a firm disbeliever, and the student is urged to assume the role of an investigator attacking an original problem. Taking nothing for granted, the students are asked to plan a series of observations and experiments which will produce as large a body of evidence as possible in support of the hypothesis that the blood does circulate. Many of the steps in this series may be suggested by the students' reading in William Harvey and some may be their own. With such a plan in mind, the students are given considerable opportunity to carry it out. Demonstration dissections of several types of vertebrates and preparations of the sheep heart and lungs are supplied for careful examination. Considerable time is spent observing the flow of blood through the web of the frog's foot and through the three-day chick embryo. Living frogs may be used to trace the course of blood through the heart and major blood vessels. The students' own arms are available for carrying out Harvey's directions for locating the valves which prevent the backflow of blood in the veins. A number of movies which reinforce and expand the students' own laboratory experiences are shown at the general meeting. Considerable time is allowed for reflection upon the reading, discussion, and laboratory experiences and for the exercise of critical judgment. A student is thus provided with an opportunity to understand, in a way not otherwise possible, the several factors involved in the establishment of even so fundamental a concept as the circulation of the blood. Incidentally, a considerable amount of factual information is necessarily acquired.

Having reviewed the argument for the circulation of blood and the historical development of this idea, the questions of why we suspect the existence of any controlling mechanisms and what is meant by the term "mechanism" are considered. In the process of thinking through the several physiological mechanisms, the interrelations, complexity and unity of the body become evident. In addition, the extreme difficulties that face the investigator in obtaining clear cut evidence with respect to the physiology of the circulatory system are apparent. The student finds that the heart does not speed up when we exercise because (as he often believes) the active muscles need more oxygen and food. The tendency of all of us to think teleologically comes up for appraisal and analysis.

The biological problem which undoubtedly arouses the greatest degree of spontaneous interest is the one which deals with reproduction. This problem is primarily directed toward exploring the hormonal factors which control the very early development of the individual. As is inevitably the case in biology, considerable descriptive material must be included. It is difficult to speak of the functions of such structures as the ovary, the follicle, corpus luteum, and pituitary in intelligible terms unless the students are acquainted with the positions, anatomical relationships, appearance and, to some extent at least, the cellular structure of these parts.

The problem is treated by the historical method, although its history, in comparison with that of many biological problems, is relatively contemporaneous. The question of reading material which is comprehensible to the students is solved by George W. Corner's book, *The Hormones in Human Reproduction*. This book presents, in a very human and understandable way, a firsthand account of the progress of representative biological investigation, not as it should have occurred according to arbitrary scientific precepts, but as an actual case history illustrative of biology as it really operates. Much of the experimental work involved is described in sufficient detail to permit a considerable amount of critical discussion and appraisal. In following this account of the investigation of the role of the horomones in reproduction, a student's attention is directed to the many and often unpredictable variables associated with life which the investigator must constantly take into consideration, the way in which the results of previous work sometimes lead into sterile paths and the human incidents which constitute such a poignant part in the progress of science. The material of this book is supplemented by consideration of some of the more recent experimental work in this field.

In the laboratory the students are given an opportunity to see the actual effects of sex hormones upon the vertebrate body. Frogs are injected out of breeding season after the method developed by Roberts Rugh so that it is possible to demonstrate ovulation and the passage of the eggs down the oviduct as well as fertilization and subsequent development. These observations are supplemented by the excellent motion picture *Fertilization Studied through a Mi-*

croscope and *Ovulation in the Frog,* which show aspects of these processes which it would be otherwise impossible to demonstrate.

The problem introduced by the question, "How is skin color inherited?" has proved an interesting one. Of course the question could be phrased to focus attention on eye color, hair color, intelligence or almost any other of a number of characters. But the attempt here is to relate biological science to a sociologically significant area with a view to contrasting opinion, prejudice and rumor with more objectively determined, varifiable knowledge. In this problem there is an excellent opportunity to weigh scientific evidence against preconceived and often biased notions. Before the specific matter of skin color can be judged, the students need to review our present day concepts in the science of genetics and their origins. Then arise the questions of what physiological and anatomical features account for a particular skin color, and can one color be sharply distinguished from another and measured objectively. And, to be sure, how does one study inheritance in humans, since man studying the genetics of man is faced by certain notable handicaps.

Several problem areas have been used in the past with some success but have been placed in abeyance for the time being. One of these, "Can life arise from nonliving substances?" concerns the origin of life in recent times. As man's knowledge of life progressed from the level of the organism to that of the cell and finally to the molecular level, there has been a successive modification of his ideas about life's origin. As a result, the boundary between the animate and inanimate has become less clear. The problem leads inevitably to a consideration of the virus which seems to melt indistinguishably into the "twilight zone of life."

TESTING

The same remarks as made previously on the testing program in the physical science course apply to this course. It is the experience of the staff that the construction of straight recall questions is relatively easy. In the field of biology more of this type of item may be justified and necessary since so very much of the subject matter is unfamiliar to the general student at an elementary level. With the best of intentions to eliminate extraneous terminology, there is a large body of vocabulary. However, this vocabulary is so interwoven with the conceptual values of the subject that questions which seem superficially to test merely recall of a term really demand more understanding than they appear to. A text book definition may be learned with little or no appreciation of the meaning, but if a question is properly phrased, the student must have an understanding of the concept and the associations involved in order to give an acceptable answer. He must also have thought with sufficient depth and gained sufficient orientation to see the implications of the question.

Nevertheless, it is most difficult to construct questions which are "fool proof." Words being what they are, almost any phrasing of a "thought" question is open to several interpretations — or misinterpretations — on the part of various readers. Students who have penetrated the subject most thoroughly will see exceptions to statements which are intended to be general characterizations of a situation, and will claim with some vigor that the question is ambiguous. Objective questions become "objection" questions. Not all the testing in this course is on the basis of objective items. Free response questions are frequently used, and an essay type of examination is often employed in conjunction with the Functional Writing Program, a coordinated effort to emphasize effective English expression and elimination of mechancial errors.

Evaluation

To construct a significant objective evaluation of a college course is a formidable task when the course aims include much more than the recall of knowledge. The only study at Colgate which approached objectivity took place incidental to a wider effort. This was the Cooperative Study of Evaluation in General Education, of the American Council on Education, in which sixteen institutions participated.[3]

The Science Committee of this study prepared four tests under the general title of, "A Test of Science Reasoning and Understanding." Two tests were in Natural Sciences and there was one each in Physical Science and Biological Science.[4] They were designed

---

[3]Paul L. Dressel and Lewis B. Mayhew, Editors, *General Education: Explorations in Evaluation*, American Council on Education, Washington, D.C., (1954).

[4]Most of these are out of print. Some may still be available from the Office of Evaluation Services, Michigan State University, East Lansing, Michigan.

to measure some of the other outcomes of science teaching besides
subject matter knowledge. Each contained about 50 items based
upon four or five readings passages in the test. The questions
asked students for example, to recognize whether statements quoted
from the passages were statements of a problem, a hypothesis,
a test of a hypothesis, a conclusion, etc.

In the course of this study the Natural Sciences — Form C
test was administered to two Colgate freshmen classes at entrance
and again to many of these same students at the end of the sophomore year. (At this time there were wider exemption privileges
from the science cores for students enrolled in the AFROTC Program, so some students went through without either science core
course.) The results of this evaluation study are summarized in
the Table below. There are no other comparative data on these
groups, such as scholastic aptitude, so the interpretation of gains,
especially for the small groups, is difficult.

It seems clear that the maturing process of 20 months in
college enables a student to make a higher grade when he repeats
a test of this kind. His vocabulary is larger and he has learned
to read more carefully and perhaps more critically. But the science
core courses, even when taken a year before the post-test, seem
also to make an additional contribution to whatever abilities this
test measures. It is also gratifying to note that the average gains
shown in the table are substantially greater than the average gain
for 790 students in six colleges of the Cooperative Study, which
was 3.37 points on a similar Form A of the test. Finally, the
table shows that when one section of Core 11 is composed of students selected from the top 10 per cent of the class in overall
ability, and taught by an instructor who is skilled in pursuing the
objectives of the course, the gain can be larger than for any other
group. This experience has been the same when the test in Science
Reasoning and Understanding — Physical Sciences, has been used
as a pre-test for Core 11 and incorporated in the final examination as a post-test.

Not all evaluation can be accomplished objectively. There
is room for subjective appraisal and it is hoped that a more thorough review of the two courses will be undertaken in the not too
distant future, aided by an outside observer. Meanwhile opinions
of individuals who have taught in the course are of some interest.

Experience with A.C.E. Test of Natural Science Reasoning and Understanding, Form C at Colgate University

Group taking:	Class of 1956 Mean Scores				Class of 1957 Mean Scores			
	No.	At Entrance	Sophomore Gen. Exam	Gain	No.	At Entrance	Sophomore Gen. Exam	Gain
Core 11, not Core 12	23	25.3	34.5	9.2	17	27.1	35.4	8.3
Core 12, not Core 11	28	26.6	35,6	8.6	21	26.0	32.6	6.6
Both Core 11 and Core 12	130	27.2	35.7	8.5	204	27.7	36.3	8.6
Neither Core 11 nor Core 12	51	27.5	34.2	6.7	38	26.7	32.8	6.1
Total	232	26.9	35.2	8.3	280	27.4	35.5	8.1
Selected section of high general ability (Core 11 and Core 12)					18	30.9	41.4	10.5

The very limited use of laboratory has been criticized by a number of teachers, particularly in the biological science course. They feel that direct observation of materials keeps the student from letting his mental constructs wander too far from reality. On two or three occasions in Core 12 students do have opportunity to examine an elodea leaf under a microscope, study a sheep's heart or look at the web of a frog's foot. But the lack of space which can be set aside for laboratory work in this course has prevented adequate use of the laboratory approach. In the physical science core course laboratory activities also are limited. This is due partly to lack of space and partly to the nature of the problems. Worthwhile projects are done in astronomy but even if space were available it is hard to conceive of much significant laboratory work which would aid the study of the earth's interior or the Carolina Bays. If laboratory is to make a genuine contribution to general education objectives and not slip into standard routines, much creative effort is needed, according to the experience at various institutions.[5]

When a college course tries to get students to think about new ideas in unconventional ways confusion is almost certain to arise. Even though a careful explanation is made in a *Foreword* in each manual, and reviewed in the first meeting or lecture, students slip easily into old habits and attitudes. They have difficulty realizing that studying the readings so they can remember the important points, although necessary, is not sufficient in these courses, and they are surprised to find test questions which ask for more than recall of knowledge. On two or three occasions in past years the students have voiced dissatisfaction with the testing in Cores 11 and 12 through their elected representatives on a Freshman Council. In every instance when a delegation of the Council had opportunity to converse with the staff and to understand the aims of the course clearly, the complaint was withdrawn. This is only one kind of evidence to indicate that the success of any semester of teaching in Cores 11 or 12 is closely related to how fully the students are made aware of the unique objectives of the courses, kept in sympathy with them, and shown how best to work toward them.

[5]C. L. Henshaw, "Laboratory Teaching in General Education Courses", *American Journal of Physics*, Vol. 22, pp. 68-75, (1954)

One of the obvious weaknesses of courses of this type is the large number of areas of science which are *not* explored, by the very nature of this method of teaching. Nor is it possible to develop very well the interwoven logical structure of a subject like physics when a course is composed of often loosely related samples. In spite of these shortcomings, real advantages seem to have emerged. The problem approach makes possible a definite break from authoritarian teaching and it also is a successful means of conveying an appreciation of the nature and spirit of science. Furthermore there has been little concern with the overlap between the content of the science cores and other science course a student might take, especially in Core 11 where the problems are drawn from astronomy, geophysics and the like. The weakness of limited coverage could be diminished if each course were extended to a year in length allowing more areas of science to be explored, but there is little prospect now of such a change being accepted by the Faculty. The strongest arguments for additional time for these courses is not so that more problems could be studied. Rather the need is for more time to teach the students how to read, understand, analyze and evaluate popular scientific writings. We can never hope to close the gap between the extent of scientific knowledge and our limited time to explore samples of it with our students. But if we can develop in them a critical skill and lasting interest then they will be able to carry on for themselves a continuing education in science for the rest of their active lives.

chapter 7

BIOLOGY I & II AT DRAKE UNIVERSITY

Leland P. Johnson*

General education at Drake University was first officially recognized in 1939. At that time, courses in general biology and in western civilization were offered. These courses grew out of vigorous discussions for a period of two years. The development of western civilization was an outgrowth of history 1 and 2. Biology was an integration of botany and zoology, in which biological principles were stressed through the use of plants and animals. At this early date, the climax of the course was the laboratory study of the cat. Other emphases have changed, and a more experimental approach is now stressed, but the study of the cat remains an important segment of the course.

Over the years, there has been a change in general education requirements. At present, all liberal arts students are required to take English 1 and 2 and a year of foreign language. If a student proves proficiency by examination he may omit a part or all of these requirements. Physical education is required of all. In addition to these, each student must now have twelve hours in the humanities, twelve hours in the social sciences, and twelve hours in the sciences. Until this year, the requirements have been fifteen hours in the area of English and foreign languages, fifteen hours in the social sciences, and fifteen hours in the sciences. The science program has consisted of biological sciences 1 and 2, eight semester hours, and physical sciences 1 and 2, eight semester hours. The requirement for non-science majors can now be met by either bio-

---

*The Author is Professor and Department Head Biology, Drake University

logical sciences 1 and 2 or physical sciences 1 and 2, followed by
four semester hours of biological science 51 or physical science 51.
If the student elects biological sciences 1 and 2, he completes his
science requirements with physical science 51. The sciences numbered 51 are special courses designed to complete a science experience.
The methods, scope, limitations of science, as well as subject material in both the biological and physical sciences are emphasized in
the twelve hour program.

General Biology

General biology is the course to be presently considered. For
approximately seven years, the pre-professional students were taught
in a separate biology course but both non-majors and majors are
now taught in one course. It has been the feeling of the staff that,
as we changed the general course to fit better the needs of the non-
science major, it also better meets the needs of pre-professional
students.

The objectives of the biological sciences at Drake University
are intimately associated with the aims of Drake University and the
College of Liberal Arts. The aims focus upon the continuing
growth of the individual student's personality. It assumes that we
recognize where the student is when he comes to us and builds
upon this background. General Biology objectives may be placed
in four major categories:

(1) The development of personal abilities. This involves
the development of a basic biological vocabulary, the perception of
kinds of biological data, and the ways of obtaining biological
knowledge. In addition, it involves the ability to critically analyze
biological information and to express judgments in both written and
oral form. Intimately coupled with these is the development of a
student's ability to identify and pose biological problems.

(2) Development of orientation in the cultural experience of
mankind. The primary aim is the development of an understanding of biology and its relationship to the physical and social
sciences with stress upon the scope and limitations of science. An
acquaintance with the history of biology through the growth of
an idea is stressed in the manner of Lovejoy's "The Grand Chain
of Being." A desired outcome is an understanding of the natural
interaction of scientific ideas and society.

(3) The development of fundamental personality traits. This involves the development of an awareness concerning living things in an environment, that man is a biological being in a physical and philosophical universe. This awareness is commensurate with awareness of man's intellectual and emotional potential. Because of man's great intellectual capacity, he possesses abilities to control his environment. Therefore, man must always be cognizant of the resources which he controls, as well as his goals and purposes.

(4) The expression of social attitudes through the establishment of responsible relationships. Students in biology may become more willing to accept and contribute to the realization of biological ideals in society and the resolution of some of our problems in health, conservation, population, food, etc. In addition, the student, because of his biological understandings, may endeavor to establish more wholesome relationships in family and community.

These aims are to be accomplished in the course through:

(a) stressing intellectual content rather than the compilation of facts,
(b) mutually emphasizing student and content, not one at expense of the other (Man is a part of an environment and knowledge is essential if he is to cope adequately with it),
(c) promoting analytical thinking, not just memorization,
(d) aiding the diligent, sincere, and inquiring student in every way possible,
(e) teaching what is not known as well as what is known,
(f) anticipating developments within the next scope of years,
(g) acquaintance with current biological literature for the laymen,
(h) providing experiences which can stimulate curiosity, create critical attitudes, and demand perserverance.

The mechanics of the course involve three hours of lecture per week and two one and one-half hour laboratories or two two-hour laboratories. Students not planning to use biology professionally take three hours of laboratory per week; those planning to use biology professionally elect four hours per week. In the laboratory taken by the pre-professional students, terminology and laboratory techniques are stressed to a greater degree. The lectures are used to develop broad concepts, and the laboratory to obtain information to substantiate these concepts and as a place for exploration of new concepts. It is assumed the student has a chance to develop scientific methods after basic laboratory techniques have been mastered.

The student obtains a textbook, *Biology*, by Villee; a *Laboratory Guide for General Biology*, by Johnson and others; and "Plant Life" and "The Bestiary" from the Scientific American Series. In addition a comprehensive reserve library list is available for student use and assignments are made to these sources.

No attempt is made to cover in detail all aspects of biology but the course is separated into a series of correlated units forming a continuum for the whole course.

The first unit involves an introduction to science, the methods of science, the cell, metabolism, and adaptations. In the laboratory, the student is introduced to the logic of biological terminology by stressing prefixes, suffixes, and roots of both Latin and Greek derivation. An effort is made to show how this information may be applied to other situations. The student is introduced to the microscope and an exercise is devoted to recording biological data. This involves written descriptions as well as drawing, labeling, and measuring. A variety of cells is studied with constant emphasis upon living cells. This unit is terminated with a study of growth and mitosis.

Unit two consists of a survey of the plant kingdom and emphasizes invasion of land by plants and spermatophyte adaptations. The laboratory, during this period, includes one session involving the use of the library to stress the techniques that a biologist would use to obtain background in preparation for professional research. It introduces the student to the location, purpose, and use of the card catalog, the stacks, encyclopedias and dictionaries, indices, guides, and periodicals. This is preliminary to the assignment of a short paper upon a subject of the student's preference, based upon source material from the library. The paper is due approximately eight weeks after its assignment.

Representative Thallophyta, Bryophyta, Pteridophyta, and Spermatophyta are studied in the laboratory. After completing their study, the students are presented with a series of unknowns which are used as food products. They are asked to describe the part of the plant which is used as food and to give the critical reasons for their identifications. For example, in the onion the primary parts used for food are leaves. This is based upon the reasoning that the edible parts are attached to a structure, the stem, which bear outgrowths, in the axils of which are buds or leaves.

Unit three deals with invertebrates and ecology. In the lecture are discussed major characteristics of invertebrates and a skeletal phylogenetic series is presented. The laboratory involves the ecological study of a laboratory pond. The pond is made with a series of six aquaria. The water is continually moved from aquarium to acquarium by a suction air pump placed between two of the aquaria and a series of siphons. It is thus possible to study different ecological niches in the laboratory. Immediately prior to this study, additional organisms of the type found in the various aquaria are added so that the students will not lack for material. They identify and describe in detail one or two organisms listing the characteristics of the environment in which it is found. By this process the student is introduced to taxonomy and adaptations. Students are encouraged to share their information and as organisms are found they are listed on a chart. Students in any one laboratory are held responsible for knowing the important characteristics of each organism listed. A summary of the invertebrates terminates this laboratory study. It includes a demonstration of the biogenetic principle and a phylogenetic tree.

Unit four concerns heredity and environment. After a basic introduction to genetics in the lecture, the typical patterns of inheritance are studied. This is terminated with discussion of eugenics and euthenics, radiation and genes, and genetics in politics. The laboratory involves the study of monohybrid inheritance, probability, including the use of the binomial, and the study of approximately a dozen human characteristics with determination of their phenotypic and genotypic frequencies in the class population.

Unit five concerns the chordate and focuses upon the human organism. The structure and physiology are approached, essentially as exemplified in Carlson and Johnson's *The Machinery of the Body*. The laboratory work includes dissection of the cat and physiological demonstrations using turtle and frog material. Two students work with each cat. The cat is selected because of its large size. It has been our experience that the reluctant student becomes acclimated after two laboratory periods and usually is enthusiastic about the dissection.

In Unit six the lecture deals with evolutionary fact and theory, and its philosophical implications. In addition, the philosophical implications of science and especially of biology are reiterated. The course is terminated following discussions of the future of biology and the possibilities of human migration to the planets of other solar systems.

The last six weeks of the laboratory consist of a cooperative investigation to emphasize the activities of a scientist. The study begins with the development of the problem in such a way that an answer may be obtained. The problem typically is in an area of the laboratory instructor's major biological interest. The instructor presents a series of questions in a most general form. The students limit these to a single problem. The laboratory group then surveys the literature in a simplified manner. Each student is held responsible for surveying certain areas of biological abstracts concerning their problem. The instructor is available to direct this search. The data so obtained is then used to properly state the problem to be studied. Since 24 students are normally in each section, the problem is broken into twelve different units including the necessary controls. Twelve students will be responsible for the study of different aspects of the problem. Another twelve students will perform the same series of experiments independently. The experiments are so planned that the students may collect three or four sets of data. By duplicating the data through having another student independently perform the same investigation, it is possible to point up one of the important aspects of science, that data should be capable of reproduction. Each individual reports on and writes a simplified report of his part of the total project. These reports are made available to the whole laboratory section and the instructor leads discussions for drawing major conclusions.

In essence, the student performs the activities of a scientist. He states a problem, he develops methods for getting an answer to his question, he collects data, he interprets his data and prepares a report fashioned on the model of a scientific paper he has read. For example, individuals doing an exercise upon the influence of the toxicity of detergents upon *Paramecium caudatum* would go to the Journal of Physiology to see how physiological papers are written. Typically, the student's report would include the following headings:

(a) the reason for the problem
(b) appropriate history
(c) methods and procedures
(d) data
(e) interpretation of data or discussion
(f) summary or conclusions
(g) literature cited

The course is designed to impart biological facts and theories. It is also designed to develop an understanding of biology and the biologist, by acquainting him through participation with the problems and difficulties inherent in research, as well as the stimulation and satisfaction that comes from trying to obtain answers not to be found in a textbook to simple questions they have learned to phrase.

Students are evaluated by several means. Quizzes which demand short answers or responses involving paragraphs of written material are given in the laboratory. Practical examinations are also given. Both objective and free response examinations are given over the lecture discussion portion of the course. One major examination each semester requires a discussion type answer. In addition, a short paper the first semester, the research report, and weekly abstracts of current magazine articles during the second semester insures that each student must complete a considerable amount of writing. This part of the program is a small attempt to counteract the charge legitimately made against college education today that students do not sufficiently practice communication skills and may graduate unable to express their ideas in written form. The six weeks and final examinations are typically objective type examinations involving a variety of approaches.

Final evaluation of the students is made with an approximate ratio of 60 per cent weight for major departmental examinations, covering discussion, readings, and laboratory, and 40 per cent weight for laboratory work, including quizzes, ingenuity of approach and quality in laboratory work, written reports and individual conferences.

chapter 8

THE COMPREHENSIVE SCIENCE COURSES AT THE UNIVERSITY OF FLORIDA

*H. L. Knowles**

The general education program at the University of Florida is one of the oldest in the United States. It has been in continuous operation since 1935. With a very few exceptions, all of the key personnel who initiated and directed the earlier development of the program have been replaced by others. The University of Florida has grown and is developing more and more in the direction of technical and graduate training. Never-the-less, the original purposes of general education, its administrative organization, and its basic philosophy have remained remarkably constant.

The program is conducted under the administration of the University College. All freshmen and sophomores — now numbering over seven thousand — are enrolled in this college. Each student, on the average, devotes over half of his time during these two years to study in seven comprehensive courses, one of which is in the physical sciences and one in biological science. The comprehensive courses are intended to embrace the core of knowledge with which every educated person should be familiar. In several areas students are now permitted to substitute for the comprehensive course the elementary course in a professional field.

Looking back over nearly a quarter of a century we realize that the integrity of the program has been maintained against the opposition of new key personnel but also this opposition has brought change that has strengthened rather than weakened gen-

---

*The Author is Chairman of the Department of Physical Sciences.

eral education at the University. The program as a whole and each course has experienced some degree of change, from slight to profound. Probably the physical science course has been the most difficult to construct and the biological science course the most involved with extraneous outside pressures.

The Physical Science Course

The general education course in physical sciences, designated as C-2, is a two-semester course carrying three hours credit each semester. There are three recitations and one demonstration-lecture weekly. The recitation sections average thirty students to the section and the demonstrations have about one hundred.

The annual enrollment in the course is about two thousand, which is somewhat over one-half of the freshman class. At the time the program in general education was inaugurated, it was expected that all freshmen, except those with superior entrance qualifications intending to major in science, would take C-2. Superior students wishing to do so could substitute general chemistry or general physics. In practice, however, the substitution of general chemistry for C-2 has not been limited to superior students, and while this procedure may be questionable from the standpoint of those who believe that a specialized course is not a suitable substitute for a general education course, it does permit the University to accelerate the specialized programs of students majoring in science.

THE COURSE PRIOR TO 1949

At the time the previous article[1] was written concerning the course in physical sciences at the University of Florida, the original attempt at an integrated approach to the course had been abandoned and a survey type of course had been adopted. The reasons for this change have been set forth in that article. However, subsequent administrative changes as well as encouragement given by Dr. Earl McGrath following his visit to the campus indicated to the C-2 staff that a renewed attempt at the integrated type of course might be successful. Consequently in the spring and summer of 1949 the material originally used in the integrated course was entirely re-worked.

---

[1]*Science in General Education.* Edited by Earl J. McGrath. William C. Brown Company, Dubuque, Iowa, 1948.

The material for the integrated course[2] had originally been arranged in two study guides, one for each semester, which contained library references and a minimum discussion of subject matter, together with sets of daily study questions and problems. The problem approach was definitely emphasized, since it was believed that only through the deductive reasoning employed in answering hundreds of questions would the student incorporate and use in his everyday living the principles he had learned.

In reworking the original material, the scope of the course was reduced somewhat, principally by cutting down on the discussion of the technical processes by which the materials of our environment are converted into various manufactured products, such as paper, nylon, and steel. The reduced course content was designed to be covered in one semester.

The original study guides had contained daily library references. With more than one thousand students attempting to obtain library books for the preparation of daily assignments, considerable strain on library facilities developed. The daily library assignments were also awkward for those students living away from the campus. In revising the course material, it was decided to include in the text all the necessary subject matter together with the sets of daily study questions.

PRESENT COURSE FOR THE FIRST SEMESTER

The text[3] now being used for the first semester's course, C-21, is an integrated approach built around the theme of the physical factors in our environment which have influenced the development of civilizations. These factors have been listed by Hedger[4] as:

"(1) climate, including precipitation, temperature, winds, and barometric pressure;
(2) natural resources, including soil, minerals, waters, natural vegetation, and native animal life;
(3) landforms; and
(4) space relationships, of which relative and fixed location, size, and form are the important aspects."

---

[2]Ibid.

[3]*Our Physical Environment.* L. W. Gaddum and H. L. Knowles. Houghton Mifflin Company, Boston, Massachusetts, 1953.

[4]*An Introduction to Western Civilization.* G. A. Hedger. The Odyssey Press, New York, 1949, page 72.

The material was re-arranged in six parts. Part 1, Space and Time, deals with the determination of location on the earth's surface through the use of latitude, longitude, and maps and then considers the space and time relationships of the earth, moon, and the polar and zodiacal constellations.

Part 2, Weather and Climate, develops the physical concepts, such as insolation, pressure, humidity, winds and air masses, which form the basis for a study of weather. The world climate pattern as determined by physical controls — insolation, pressure cells and their resultant wind and ocean current patterns, and topography — is then studied.

Part 3 on native vegetation follows closely the world climatic pattern and furnishes a connecting link between the biological and physical sciences.

A study of topography is covered in Part 4. This includes a consideration of the composition of the earth's crust and of the processes of vulcanism, diastrophism, and gradation which cause the formation of the various topographic features. The distribution of these various features on the earth is also discussed.

Part 5 considers the material resources of the earth's crust and atmosphere and how these raw materials are converted into the many products that enter into our everyday living. This section starts with a consideration of the nature and composition of matter and the processes by which materials are changed from one form to another. Included are discussions of metallurgy, the carbon and nitrogen cycles, and compounds of carbon. A chapter on soils is closely related to the previous work on climate and vegetation.

The transformation and utilization of energy resources discussed in Part 6 starts with the elementary principles of dynamics. The concepts of work and energy and the convertibility of heat into work precede a discussion of prime movers. This is followed by the transformation of mechanical work into electrical energy, and the transmission and distribution of the electrical energy. In conclusion, new sources of energy are considered.

The foregoing approach to the physical sciences differs in several respects from other similar courses. The material is built around a definite theme: the physical factors in the environment that have affected the development of civilizations. Topics, such as galaxies, which are irrelevant to the theme have been omitted.

Obviously a discussion of environmental factors without relating these factors to the world map would be pointless. Consequently successful completion of the course presupposes a knowledge of place location, and continued use of a world atlas by the student is essential.

The material covered is taken from the fields of astronomy, physical geography, geology, meteorology and climatology, chemistry, and physics, but these materials are viewed in their relations to the central theme, and not as separate compartments of knowledge. No attempt has been made to survey these fields, and the usual over-emphasis on physics and chemistry has been minimized.

The problem approach has been emphasized throughout the course, as it is felt that the student becomes familiar with the basic concepts only as he applies them in reasoning through specific situations. As used here the word "problem" does not necessarily refer to a numerical relationship, but is applied to a situation where certain facts, some perhaps irrelevant, are stated, a question is asked, and by the application of basic principles, a logical conclusion is to be reached.

Each assignment in the text contains an average of about eight pages of text material, in which a few basic principles are discussed, and a set of twenty to twenty-five study questions of the multiple-choice type. In general the first part of the problem list is made up of relatively simple and straight forward applications of principles discussed in the current chapter. The remaining questions are of a more involved nature, often of an integrated type combining in review various principles previously discussed. It is expected that the student will have studied the text material and worked as many of the problems as possible before coming to class. Student participation is encouraged in the recitation sections and much of the class time is spent in helping the students clear up difficulties they have encountered in trying to solve the problems. Two examples will indicate the type of question used.

Page 107 is a typical question involving climatic controls.

A glance at the temperature distribution should show the student that the place is located in a middle latitude in the southern hemisphere. The relatively low annual variation in temperature indicates a west coastal-location where winter temperatures are kept mild by the prevailing on-shore winds from the high pressure cell over the ocean centered at about 30° south latitude. Winter rains would be frontal. Mild summers would again be due to the off-shore cool ocean current, and the dry summer indicates the encroachment of the horse-latitude drying effect as the sun's declination becomes more southerly. These conditions are all satisfied by (5) central Chile.

	Temp.	Prec.
January	67	0.0
February	66	0.0
March	65	0.6
April	61	0.2
May	59	3.5
June	56	5.8
July	55	4.8
August	56	3.2
September	58	0.8
October	59	0.4
November	62	0.1
December	64	0.3

The climatic pattern at the right is typical of a certain place A. In which one of the following regions might the place A be located characteristically? (1) northern coastal Chile (2) central coastal California (3) western Tasmania (4) southeastern Australia (5) Santiago region of central Chile.

The other answers may be eliminated as follows: Answer (1) northern coastal Chile having a latitude of about 20° S is under the drying influence of the horse latitudes throughout the year where winds from the high pressure cell over the ocean constantly blow on-shore across the cool ocean current and are warmed as they move inland. This would produce a desert with no appreciable rainfall, since air must be cooled if precipitation is to occur. Answer (2) central California is in the wrong hemisphere. Answer (3) western Tasmania at a latitude of about 40° S would have frontal precipitation throughout the year, and the temperatures are too high. Answer (4) southeastern Australia would have warmer summer temperatures and would show a summer peak of convectional rainfall from moist air received from the offshore warm ocean current.

The inclusion of an answer in the northern hemisphere in the foregoing problem may seem pointless. However, a surprising number of freshmen have difficulty in differentiating between northern and southern hemispheric locations. This may be illustrated by one student who when confronted by a set of climatic data showing higher temperatures for December than June remarked that there couldn't be such a place, since no place had higher temperatures in winter than in summer!

An example of the integrated type of question is the following: Taken from the narrative of a world-traveler: ". . . As we glided to our anchorage in the harbor the quarter moon, nestling in the 'sickle' of the constellation Leo, hung low on our meridian. We had a fine haul of fish aboard and, as the other boats of our fleet were already unloading, our captain was naturally anxious to get ashore. The storm had delayed us many hours and since about three hours remained before sunrise I hurried ashore. . . . ."[5] In which one of the following regions might the above have occurred?

(1) New Zealand   (2) southern coast of Cuba
(3) coastal Mozambique   (4) Norway
(5) coast of central California.

A quarter moon on the meridian "before sunrise" gives the local time as about 6 a.m. Since three hours remained before sunrise there are approximately six hours of daylight. From a chart of the zodiacal constellations, it is easily determined that Leo is on the meridian at 6 a.m. in December. Six hours of daylight in December indicates a latitude of about 60° N. The answer is thus (4) Norway.

THE WORK OF THE SECOND SEMESTER

After shortening the original material to a one-semester text, it was necessary to employ temporary measures for handling C-22, the second semester course. For this purpose three variants were established and available texts were adopted. The variants were extensions of three of the parts into which the work of the first semester had been divided. One concerned the geomorphology and physiography of the United States, another was a continuing study of the earth as a planet and of the natures and relationships of other celestial bodies, and the third was a continuation of the study of the transformation, transmission, and utilization of energy.

While the variants offered in C-22 were quite acceptable to most students, principally because the students were allowed a free

---

[5]*Monsieur Passepartout.*   R. S. Chenille.   Paris. 1840.

selection, it has been felt by the staff that the best interests of general education were not being served. If general education is a body of knowledge that every educated person should know, it is hardly defensible to divide it up and allow selection. There is also a strong tendency for a divided general education course to degenerate into a number of specialized courses, each reflecting the particular training of the specialist in charge.

For these as well as administrative reasons the staff began about two years ago to develop a new approach to the work of the second semester. The material of the first semester is based largely on the phenomena of our physical environment. But physical science is much more than phenomena. It is a human endeavor which originates within the minds of men and is carried on by men. Hence it was desired to present a more complete picture of physical science, with its interplay of experiment and theory, its relationship to the beliefs and culture of the times, its heritage from the past, and in particular to show its very human side. Accordingly, the core of the textual material chosen consisted of carefully selected excerpts from the original works of a few great scientists. Even freshmen can learn much about scientific procedures as well as the concepts themselves by reading the actual words of the creators of physical science. The popular idea that a scientist can solve any problem by donning a white coat, going into a laboratory, and applying "the scientific method" is pretty well shaken after the student sees the difficulties which such mental giants as Galileo encountered in recognizing and formulating those fundamental concepts which now seem so elementary to us today.

There is no attempt at "coverage" in C-22. It is the feeling of the staff that our students have acquired a comprehensive factual knowledge of their physical world in C-21. After considerable soul-searching it was decided to select four fundamental problems, each from a different area in physical science. Excerpts were chosen and textual material was written to show the nature of a scientific problem, the growth of understanding, and the actual methods of working and thinking used by scientists. Fortunately this material can be arranged in direct chronological order so that the student can see it as a continuing story.

The subject matter of C-22 is divided into six blocks. Part 1 is a short introduction to pre-Greek technology and sets the stage for Greek science.   Part 2 illustrates a typical Greek science by presenting parts of Ptolemy's *Almagest*.   After a review of the apparent motions of the sky, the straight-forward and common-sense thinking of Ptolemy is presented as a theoretical structure of the universe. In Part 3 the astronomical discussion is continued with the reawakening of Western science in the work of Copernicus, Kepler, Brahe, and Galileo. Excerpts are used from the *Commentariolus* and *De Revolutionibus, Epitome of Copernican Astronomy,* and *The Sidereal Messenger.* At about this point the student has become acquainted with three hypotheses concerning the nature of the universe, the Ptolemaic, the Tychonic, and the Copernican, each equally successful in explaining the observed apparent motions in the sky. This situation is illustrative to the student of a common situation in science where more than one explanation is consistent with the known facts, and a decision as to which explanation is "true" must be deferred until new or more accurate observations are obtainable. Galileo's invention of the astronomical telescope allows one hypothesis, the Ptolemaic, to be rejected on observational grounds. The philosophical and theological controversy between the Tychonic and the Copernican systems is resolved later by the work of Newton.

It should be apparent to the student that the choice between the proposed systems of the world made by an educated seventeenth-century man was determined in good part by his views about physics.   Accordingly, Part 4 opens with Galileo's attack on Aristotelian mechanics in his *Two New Sciences.*   The attack continues with excerpts from Newton's *Principia* which culminates in Newton's creation of modern mechanics and the triumph of Copernicus and Kepler in Newton's "new grand synthesis" in which, by the addition of a universal law of gravitation, physics and astronomy become temporarily one and the same.

Some of the ideas of the atomic structure of the world held by the Greeks, Galileo, and Newton were included in the preceding material.   Now in Part 5 the atomic theory as developed by the chemists is traced.   This part begins with Dalton, who was strongly influenced by Newton, and continues with some of the work of Gay-Lussac and Avogadro.   The section is concluded by the essentially modern ideas of Cannizzaro.

Part 6 considers the development of the principle of uniformitarianism in geology which assumes, among other things, that the same astronomical, physical and chemical processes have continued in the past as they now do in the present. The unfolding of this principle by Hutton, Playfair, and Lyell makes up most of the text of this section. This final part is concluded by Chamberlin's theory of multiple working hypotheses which has a great deal to say about the nature of present day theorizing in any branch of physical science. Thus the theory of Chamberlin, a geologist, makes a fine "capstone" with which to end the course.

Although the ideas developed throughout the course are the fundamental ideas of physical science today, considerable care has been taken to bring the student up-to-date in factual knowledge within each area. This up-dating process is most conspicuous in astronomy where factual horizons have widened considerably since the seventeenth century. The arrangement of material is similar to that of C-21 with daily text and problem assignments. Problems are of both the multiple choice and open-end type.

TESTING PROCEDURE

Tests in both C-21 and C-22 are prepared by the staff and are administered and scored by the Board of Examiners. Students are graded on the basis of two or three one-hour progress tests and a three-hour final examination. The tests contain about fifty multiple choice questions per hour. The student is furnished with certain supplementary material such as a "blank" world map showing outlines of continents (but not countries) and with a few parallels and meridians, a zodiacal chart, humidity tables, and a periodic table of the elements. In so far as possible, the test questions are intended to emphasize reasoning ability rather than just memory. A file of questions having from twenty to one hundred variants of most of the questions in the texts, as well as others, furnishes a supply of nearly fifteen thousand questions from which test items may be taken. Final grades are set on the basis of achievement using a semi-fixed scoring system.

The gradation and abundance of questions in the texts give the superior student ample opportunity to exercise his talents, and few if any students are found who are able to reason their ways through all of the more difficult problems. It is very seldom that a superior student gets a perfect score on a progress test and never on the final examination. For those who wish to pursue certain topics further, supplementary references are listed and are available at the library.

CONTINUING ADMINISTRATIVE PROBLEMS

In spite of gaining considerable maturity during the past quarter of a century, the general education course in physical sciences here at the University of Florida is still beset with certain administrative problems largely centered around acquiring and keeping a qualified staff. The present staff of eighteen full-time members includes from one to four specialists in each of the fields of physical science. Half of these hold doctor's degrees and the others have completed graduate work beyond the master's degree.

It is felt that in general staff members should have Ph.D. degrees in science and should be individuals whose qualifications are acceptable to the Upper Division departments of their specialties. It is essential that they be genuinely interested in general education. In these days of shortages of physical scientists together with the high salaries paid by industry, the problem of staffing a general education department in physical science is not an easy one. To interest a qualified candidate, it is usually necessary to assure him an adequate salary, a teaching outlet in the Upper Division, and facilities for research. To be adequate, salaries should be at least on a par with those in the Upper Division to induce instructors to leave the security of the well-established (and entrenched!) departments of their specialities for the greater uncertainties and lesser prestige of a relatively new program for freshmen and sophomores.

To obtain teaching outlets in the Upper Division and research facilities, a working agreement between the University College and Upper Division is necessary. Such cooperation has administrative blessing but at times needs administrative coercion. Upper Division departments with overloaded teaching schedules are often willing to allow University College instructors to teach advanced classes for which they are qualified, but these departments are seldom willing to return staff time of comparable quality or quantity. The furnishing of research facilities in physical science for staff in the University College has also remained a largely unsolved problem. It would appear that the Upper Division has much to gain through the use of specialists from the University College, but experience has shown instead that the services or even the presence of outstanding specialists in the general education program often are not welcomed by departments of the Upper Division.

During the spring of 1957 as the general education program at the University of Florida was nearing the quarter-century mark, the administration invited a panel of nationally known experts[6] in the fields of general education to come to the campus to evaluate the local program and make recommendations.   Concerning the program as a whole their report stated: "The University of Florida is to be congratulated in having established a strong program in General Education, and for having been able to sustain it at a high level of efficiency. . . . We believe the program as a whole is sound."   With regard to C-2, the panel stated in its conclusions that "we believe this to be a good course heading in the right direction."

---

[6]Harry J. Carman of Columbia University, Sidney J. French of the University of South Florida, John A. Moore of Barnard College, Lennox Grey of Columbia University, Harold Fawcett of Ohio State University, and Paul L. Dressel of Michigan State University

chapter 9

THE COMPREHENSIVE BIOLOGICAL SCIENCE COURSE

*C. Francis Byers**

The biological science course is one of three courses constituting the science portion of the general education program at the University of Florida. The other two are a year course in physical science and a semester course in mathematics. There has been little attempt made to co-ordinate the materials taught in these three courses. The problems of each are different and have been solved — to the extent that they have been solved at all — in a somewhat different way. In the biological sciences the nature of the subject matter, the homogeniety of the area covered, and the history of the development of biological teaching have made our problems less difficult than those encountered in the physical sciences.

The details of the biological science course as taught and administered today (1959) are the result of study, evaluation and change since 1947 as the opinions of an ever changing staff and needs of a large student body seemed to indicate. In many instances they are a compromise between widely differing view-points and interests. The integrity of the course as a unit has been maintained through (1) a common textbook, (2) a common set of examinations, (3) weekly staff meetings, and (4) the over-all structure of the University College. The course is given as a year course (6 hours credit) divided into two semesters. Both halves of the course are given each semester and during the summer ses-

---

*The Author is Head of the Department of Biological Science and Assistant Dean of the College of Arts and Sciences. (Retired 1959)

sion.   Two sixty minute objective examinations are given each semester and a three hour comprehensive examination is given at the end of each semester.   The course is given without a laboratory though it is supplemented by demonstration material — specimens, lantern slides, movies, museum displays.

To fulfill its functions in a general education program, the biological science course must develop attitudes and informed opinions regarding man as an animal and the world of life of which he is a part.   We hope to accomplish this through the proper emphasis and integration of selected materials.   This, we believe, would enable the student to see the world about him and his part in it with more complete perspective than can be achieved through narrow specialization in any one of the biological sciences.

It is hoped that the course developed will be of sufficient substance and consist of enough basic biological material that other elementary courses in biology will not need to cover the same ground, but rather, will find it advantageous to build their professional curricula upon it.   While we are primarily constructing a course in general education in the biological sciences, we will make every effort to meet the desires of various Upper Division Departments by including materials which they deem appropriate.

We strive to present biological science not as a technical elementary course suitable for students majoring in the field, but rather as a comprehensive treatment of the living world accurate and detailed when necessary.   A University graduate should know about Darwin as well as about Shakespeare; should know about scientific principles as well as about ethical or political ones.

COURSE MATERIALS

Criticism has been made that over the years courses in general education have become more standardized and conservative than their counterparts in the professional departments they represent. This criticism has been made in biology more than in any other area.   Certainly the experimentation that characterized the early days of general education seems to be less in evidence as more and more courses in biology resort to the use of a textbook and discard the earlier "study outlines," syllabi, and day-by-day lesson plans. The nature of the general education course in biology depends today on the contents and arrangement of material in the textbook adopted.   Increasing numbers of students, large and variegated staffs. and the methods of grading and examination has made this almost inevitable.

The history of the general education course in biological science at the University of Florida as far as materials are concerned is practically a history of textbooks.   As indeed, is much teaching of biology on the first year college level.

Pioneer work in what later was to become the field of general education was done for the biologist by A. Franklin Shull[1] of the University of Michigan.   Dr. Shull's insistence that elementary biology should be taught as a series of integrated concepts or principles and not as a study of individual representative animals paved the way for the establishment, years later, of comprehensive courses in biology for general education.

The course at the University of Florida was strongly influenced, in its beginnings, by the Shull tradition.   It was necessary to extend the principles idea to cover a wider field and to encompass factual material that we felt the student needed to support pertinent ideas and concepts that we wished him to take away from the course.   But, as many of the desirable possibilities in such a program had been worked out by our predecessors, we were able to start wtih a reasonably well integrated course.

Our initial efforts proved the student with a syllabus and study guide which was an outline of the topics to be considered and a series of questions to direct his attention to material supplied by assigned readings in textbooks and library reference sources.

We found the syllabus and assigned readings unsatisfactory because it was difficult to write examination questions that would be fair to all students in all sections of the course unless they had some common core of knowledge and common experience in class. With hundreds of students each taking the same examination, many instructors, and a long list of reference works, this was not possible.   The only solution that suggested itself was to write our own textbook.[2]   This book, first published in 1942, was used as the basis of the comprehensive course in biological science at the

---

[1]*Principles of Animal Biology*.   Shull, LaRue and Ruthven.   McGraw-Hill, New York.

[2]*Man and the Biological World*.   Rogers, Hubbell, and Byers.   McGraw-Hill Book Co., New York, 2nd Edition 1953.

University of Florida (and, incidentally, in a fair number of other schools) until 1958-59.

Necessary revisions of *Man and the Biological World* — which are now in progress — made it desirable to adopt a new textbook.[3] The new textbook has changed the emphasis of the course to some extent. Previously the course was man-centered (not Human Biology) and heavy on natural history. Today there is more stress on physiology and cellular biology, with such themes as evolution, genetics, and man woven into the story as strands in a rope.

Curiously the fever for change that characterized general education two decades ago has shifted to the biology curriculum in the Upper Division Departments. The advent of Sputnik I has caused a re-evaluation in all science programs at all levels in the United States. The biologists have been as active as representatives of the other sciences in this respect — witness the program of the *Biological Sciences Curriculum Study* of the *American Institute of Biological Sciences*. Restlessness is most marked on the high school level and the first year college biology level. That general education will remain uneffected seems unlikely.

The first year biology course in the more traditional — non-general education — programs has taken material freely from the general education biology courses, as well as giving materials to general education. So much of this two-way exchange has taken place that it is difficult to separate the two programs. Dr. Simpson, in the preface to the textbook, *Life*, resolves the difficulty by stating that the two are the same. Proposals have been made to place this general education-elementary biology course in the twelfth grade in high school and relieve the colleges of the responsibility of considering them. Other proposals of a very different kind have also been made. How these will be resolved at the University of Florida remains for the future to determine, but marked changes in the general education program in biological sciences may be anticipated.

Problems connected with the Course

In the 1948 edition of this book, we listed four problems that had not been worked out in a satisfactory manner. Ten years

---

[3]*Life.* Simpson, Pittendrigh, Tiffany. Harcourt, Brace Co., New York, 1957.

later these same problems remain and two have been added: (1) adequate examinations to measure the achievement of the objectives established by the course; (2) a program and set of curricula for the selecting and training of teachers in biology for general education; (3) curriculum adjustments between our course and other university units offering instruction in the biological sciences; (4) adjustments necessary to meet the demands of professional programs, especially in medicine, dentistry, and agriculture; (5) establishment of laboratory experiences meaningful for general education; and (6) selection of course materials and procedures to clearly differentiate general education from professional biology. The first four of these were our earlier problem; we have since added the two latter ones.

1. *Adequate examinations.* Because of the large number of students taking this course (2,000 to 2,400) and a limited amount of staff time, it is necessary to give machine graded, objective examinations. It is easier to construct items for these examinations that test only for facts. The course is more interested in ideas and concepts than in facts alone. We have never been able to resolve this difficulty to our complete satisfaction though many variants of the objective test have been tried and various combinations of subjective and objective testing have been attempted. This problem still remains a perpetual challenge.

2. *Teacher training.* As the student body increases, new staff members — not always easy to get — are required. By selecting well trained (Ph.D.) biologists we are apt to neglect the peculiar requirements of the teacher in general education. The staff that we selected in the past and new additions currently being selected have had to be trained in service. In general education broadness of viewpoint, sympathetic understanding, tolerance, a wealth of experience in outside fields, liberalism, and a bit of the missionary spirit are matters to be considered. We must expect our faculty to possess those same values that we tell our students they will acquire from a general education program. General education has broken with tradition not only in its re-evaluation of subject matter, but in the qualities that it expects in its teachers as well. We recognize, of course, that there is danger here. Superficiality and a pleasing personality may be selected in place of solid worth.

Adequately trained teachers is still one of our most pressing problems.

3. *Curriculum adjustments.* Some of the courses in the general education program are mainly used as parts of the core curriculum; others may serve, in addition, as prerequisite courses for advanced study in their respective area. Until very recently, the course in biological science had the dual responsibility of meeting the requirements of both general education and the Upper Division Departments interested in the biological sciences. Even more disturbing are the situations caused by upper-division units which by-pass this course and substitute one of their own limited, technical, and traditional courses in its place, thus defeating the purpose of the general education program. With changes in the headship of these upper-division units these two problems are constantly before us. Currently, there is a strong feeling that students majoring in any of the biological sciences (if such students can be identified in their freshman year) should be permitted to omit the general education course in biological science from their courses of study. Many people interested in general education do not agree with this viewpoint.

4. *Preprofessional training.* The problems here are closely allied to those indicated under "curriculum adjustments." The chief one has come about through the desirability of the biological science course serving as the "general laboratory biology" requirement for entrance to medical and dental schools. For many years the Department of Biology of the Upper Division has helped with this problem by offering a laboratory course without lecture, based on our course. Through this device we can offer our course either with or without laboratory. The current tendency within the upper division units of offering their own elementary courses and substituting them for the general education courses has greatly weakened this curriculum arrangement and may eventually do away with it entirely.

5. *Laboratory.* A laboratory period has never been a part of biological sciences course *per se* (see No. 4 above). From the beginning there has always been a division of opinion as to whether there should not be a laboratory. This problem has been thoroughly studied and discussed by the staff. Assuming that practical difficulties (time, space, and funds) could be mastered, it

seems to be the prevailing opinion today that laboratory experience might well be a legitimate part of general education and would tend to strengthen and augment the goals of the biological sciences in this area. To be effective, however, such laboratory experiences would need to be very different from those given in the regular first year biology courses. The dissection of earthworms and the superficial anatomy starfish would not suffice. No published laboratory manuals would be satisfactory. That there are general education values to be obtained from laboratory experience, and from laboratory experience alone, most of us would not deny. The challenge is to write a set of laboratory exercises that will bring out these values. To some of us, this is the single greatest challenge in general education today and could well be the factor that will eventually separate general education in biology from the traditional first year biology courses.

6. *Selection of course materials.* As indicated under the section of this report on "materials," there is current confusion and unrest regarding the course contents of the various kinds of introductory courses in the biological sciences from high school through college. The methods of presenting the general education course are fairly definite but the material to be presented is not. The survey idea has long been discarded, but even with the block-and-gap method some coherence must be given to the course — some emphasis. There is a modern trend toward biochemistry, physiology, and cellular biology. Against this trend are those who have been brought-up in the natural history tradition. While neither of these need to exclude the other, on which would the emphasis be placed to best accomplish the objectives of general education? The staff of the biological science course at the University of Florida has pondered these matters for some years. They remain unresolved.

chapter 10

AN APPROACH TO GENERAL EDUCATION
IN PHYSICAL SCIENCE AT HARVARD UNIVERSITY

*Gerald Holton**

1. Introduction

In Harvard College, the relationship between the specialized science courses and the general education courses in the natural sciences is shaped by unique local conditions: Our whole general education program is still relatively young and in flux; there are six introductory courses in the natural sciences to choose from; and the prospective science concentrator is not obliged to take any of these at all.

The views of any one of the instructors hardly reflect the full range of opinions, but the experience of having taught both in the general education program and in conventional physics courses has gradually convinced me of several propositions:

(1) In the long run, an effective general education program in physical science depends for its survival upon the active interest and support of the specialists on the science faculty. If only for this reason, three conditions are necessary, though perhaps far from sufficient: the course must be headed by an instructor whose professional training and commitments lie in the physical sciences; the

*The Author is Professor of Physics, Harvard University.

Permission has been given by the editors to quote extensively from the *American Journal of Physics*, Vol. 25, No. 7, 425-429, October 1957, and the *College and University Bulletin*, Vol. 9, No. 9, February 1957, and No. 10, March 1957.

level of the course must be as significant, rigorous and honest in scientific content as any introductory departmental course, though the coverage and emphasis may differ; and it must be demonstrably clear that the student in a general education course benefits at least as much as if he had taken some routine departmental introductory course, such as elementary physics.

(2) If adequate communication and rapport exists between staffs of general education and departmental science courses, a very useful effect may be observed, again at the faculty level: the fresh and searching approach of a good general education course is likely to influence the teaching of routine science courses, which are traditionally considered to be among the less adequately taught courses in our colleges. The self-education and broadening of viewpoint that often takes place when specialists in science take on the task of teaching general education courses is another healthy, related effect.

(3) The benefits to science concentrators in a good course using the general education approach to science can be great; not the least benefit is to see, by concrete example, the unity underlying related sciences, e.g., of physics and astronomy in the examination of the dynamics of planetary systems, or of physics and chemistry in the consideration of atomic theory. But the timing and type of such a course must depend on the institution and the available staff. At Harvard College, for example, the course *Foundations of Modern Physical Science* (Natural Sciences 2) has been so adjusted that the freshman or sophomore taking it can thereby fulfill the premedical physics requirement of most medical schools. Also, concentrators in the physical sciences may, in their junior or senior year, choose for physics credit the course *Modern Physics and its Historical and Philosophical Background* (Natural Sciences 120).

2.   Type of the Course

The introductory course here outlined is directed to students in the liberal arts and in the nonphysical sciences. It contains many features which I have tried out for several years, as well as some new ones in which I have confidence. In colleges where there cannot be three separate courses — one for physics and engineering majors, another for premedical students and science majors not in physics or engineering, and a third for nonscience majors — this type of syllabus could accomodate in one course the last two or these three groups. At other colleges it could be identified with the third type of course, including the physical science course for liberal arts students and the integrated or general education course.

3. Aims and Approach

My principal aims are (a) the sound presentation of the key concepts and theories of physical science, and (b) the development of intellectual tools for the student's orientation in an age where science has become a dominant cultural force. Physical science is therefore studied both as a body of rigorous and structured knowledge and as a living process of investigation which can have large-scale consequences.

The center of the course lies in physics, although connections are made to other physical sciences whenever appropriate. Instead of adhering to the ancient but rather arbitrary division of physics into rigid categories (e.g., mechanics, heat, etc.), I let the historical and philosophical development of science suggest the organization and unification of the material. Like others who have tried it, I have found that this approach has several advantages. Occasional well-chosen references to the original work of great scientists can provide the excitement of looking over the shoulder of the originator at his work. A careful study of the meaning of fundamental concepts brings out that feature of science which has made it the proverbial model for effective thinking. And the occasional analysis of procedures and tools of working scientists may help to formulate the student's attitude toward problem situations in general.

However, the main strength of any science course lies in its scientific subject-matter content, and the most important experience we can give a student comes when he finds that he can enjoy and solve a difficult but important problem in science, although it be on the introductory level. This is the prerequisite to an understanding of the physical universe. And if the student does not reach this stage first, attempts to teach the "meaning" or nature or structure of science can hardly succeed. Therefore, I avoid following the historical line wherever it does not help to clarify the scientific content.   In short, in this course the history of science is thought of not as a subject of main concern, but as a pedagogic aid.

Encyclopedic coverage — the great stumbling block in elementary courses — has also been discarded; instead of giving a general (and therefore perhaps shallow) survey, I have elected to spend the time on a more careful study of a number of key topics.   This choice need not imply a set of unconnected cases; they can be arranged to form a continuously developing story from early beginnings to contemporary research, from Galileo's law of free fall to thermo-nuclear reactions.

The guiding principle in the selection of subject matter for this form of block-and-bridge course is that each main topic should fulfill two purposes: it must be of interest and importance in its own right, and it must have important links with the rest of the story.   For example, the laws of projectile motion are discussed first in connection with Galileo's contribution to kinematics, but are taken up again several times later: as examples of vector addition, as a special case of motion under Newton's law of universal gravitation, and in connection with the motion of charged particles in the cathode-ray tube and the mass spectograph.   The same selection principle gives one courage to omit many topics which usually have been regarded as indispensable in the classic type of preprofessional physics course (e.g., photometry, lens abberations).

Another important aim in my course is to refer at least from time to time to the links which connect physical science to the rest of our culture — topics such as the effect of philosophical school on scientific work and the converse, the social effects of science and technology, the organization of science itself.   With these students perhaps more than others, we have a serious responsibility to indicate the place, the power, and the limits of science.

4. Length and Level

The course is intended to be taken in the freshman or sophomore year; it meets three hours a week for demonstration lectures, once a week for a $1\frac{1}{2}$-hour discussion in smaller groups, and about every other week for a three-hour laboratory session.   (This distribution of time is dictated not by some inherent necessity, but by our local circumstances.)

(a) MATHEMATICAL LEVEL

No special mathematical prerequisite or aptitude is required of the student.   Nevertheless, we have found it quite feasible to introduce all students to the use of some calculus in our course.[1] One really needs to make only a relatively small investment of time to make the main points (delta process, differentiation and integration of 3 or 4 functions), and the effects on the range of examples and on penetration are considerable — not to speak of the effects on the morale of the staff.

(b) LABORATORY WORK

The laboratory is so designed that it covers material not otherwise elaborated upon in the course; thereby each experiment is endowed with additional student interest, and more lecture time can be given to other topics.   Moreover, if the course is to serve a double purpose, the specific experiments can concentrate on topics which one expects a premedical student to be familiar with (e.g., geometrical optics, electric circuits).

5. Topics for Lectures and Discussion Periods

The time allowance indicated below for each of the eight parts of the course is only approximate.   I have indicated by asterisks those topics which might be discussed in abbreviated form if the local situation should make it necessary to prune the content even further to permit a lengthier treatment of the rest.

Part A: Kinematics (3 weeks)

1. Speed and Acceleration.   (Measurement and "errors"; motion with constant speed; instantaneous speed; equations of motion for constant acceleration; mathematics and the description of nature.)
2. Galileo and the Kinematics of Free Fall.   (Qualitative vs quantitative science; free fall; experiment and theory.)
3. Projectile Motion.   (Simple trajectories; vector algebra; general projectile motion; Galilean relativity*.)

---

[1]For a description of a successful course with the same point of view, see Arnold Arons, J. Higher Educ. 26, 75-82 (1955) and Am. J. Physics Vol. 27, No. 9, 658-666 December 1959.

Part B: Dynamics (2 weeks)

4. Newton's Laws of Motion.   (First law; force; second law; mass and weight; third law; Mach. experiment*.)
5. Rotational Motion.   (Uniform circular motion; centripetal force; absolute and relative space*.)

Part C: The Astronomy and Dynamics of the Planetary System.   (3 weeks)

6. Greek Astronomy*.   (From Plato to Ptolemy.)
7. The Copernican Theory.   (Heliocentric system; what is a good theory?)
8. Kepler's laws.   (The universe as mechanism; the three laws.)
9. Galileo's Contributions to Astronomy.   (What is scientific evidence?   Interplay between philosophic position and scientific theory.)
10. Newton's Law of Universal Gravitation.   (Newton's "Rules of Reasoning"; derivation of the law; tests.)
11. Some Consequences of Newton's work. (Value of G; mass of celestial bodies; shapes of planets*; tides*; the effects of the great synthesis outside physical science.)

Part D: The Conservation Principles. (4 weeks)

12. Conservation of Mass.
13. Conservation of Momentum.   (Collision; explosion*; open and closed systems; angular momentum*.)
14. Conservation of Energy in Mechanics. (Work; energy; application to previous topics.)
15. Heat Phenomena.   (Temperature; fluid theory of heat*; specific heat capacity; change of state.)
16. First Principle of Thermodynamics.   (Joule's and Mayer's work; applications.)
17. Second Principle of Thermodynamics*.   (Entropy; direction of heat flow; efficiency of heat engines.)

Part E: Origins of the Atomic Theory. (3 weeks)

18. Laws of Gases.   (Laws of Boyle, Charles, Gay-Lussac; gas models.)
19. Atomic Theory in Chemistry. (Dalton*; law of multiple proportions*; atomic weights; Avogadro's hypothesis.)
20. The Periodic System of Elements. (Valence; Mendeleeff's work; the modern table of elements.)

21. The Kinetic Theory of Matter and Heat.   (Plausibility arguments; derivation of pressure formula; meaning of temperature; other successes; failures of the theory.)

Part F: Theories of Fields in Electricity and Magnetism. (4 weeks)

22. Origins of the concepts of Field and Charge.   (Fluid theories*; force-distance law; Coulomb's experiments.)

23. Electrostatics. (Electric field strength; potential.)

24. Electric Currents. (Ohm's law*; electrolysis; magnetic fields; current-field interaction.)

25. The Electron. (Cathode rays; e/m measurement; measurement of e; determination of Avogadro's number.)

26. Electromagnetic Waves. (Wave motion in general; electromagnetic waves; Hertz's experiments*.)

Part G: Quantum Theory of Light and Matter. (5 weeks)

27. Some Optical Principles. (Light; Huyghens' principle; interference; continuous spectra.)

28. Quantum Theory of Planck and Einstein. (Blackbody radiation; photoelectric effect; measurement of h; photon-wave dilemma.)

29. Discrete Spectra.   (Emission; absorption; Balmer series and others.)

30. Rutherford's Atomic Model. (Scattering experiments; nuclear charge and size.)

31. Bohr's Theory of the Atom.   (Energy levels; atomic size; emission and absorption spectra; correspondence principle; periodic table; valence; anomalous specific heats*; x-rays*.)

32. Matter-waves and Indeterminacy.* (De Broglie matter-waves; electron diffraction; reinterpretation of electron orbits; particle-wave duality; complementarity concept; indeterminacy relation.)

Part H: Nuclear Atom and Nuclear Energy. (5 weeks)

33. Radioactivity and Isotopes. (Discoveries of Becquerel and the Curies; nature of α, β, γ-radiation; radioactive series; half-life; isotopes; mass spectography.)

34. Nuclear Model.   (The proton; artificial transmutation; neutron; induced radioactivity.)

35. Mass-Energy Equivalence.   (Exothermic and endothermic processes; elements of special relativity theory; con-

servation principle of mass-energy; pair formation and annihilation*; neutrino*.)

36. Nuclear Energy.   (Discovery of fission; fusion; binding energy; nuclear forces; recent models of the nucleus*; elementary particles; reactors and other applications.)

37. Retrospect.   (Conditions for the growth of science; science and the bases of our culture.)

6. Reading

The textbook on which the course is based[2] contains additional material on the conceptual methods of physical science, which may be assigned as independent reading for interested students.   It is also very instructive to make supplementary reading assignments on specific technical topics in other introductory physics texts. For further historical and philosophical background material I have found selections from the following references of particular interest and use to students: Herbert Butterfield's *Origins of Modern Science*, E. A. Burtt's *Metaphysical Foundations of Modern Science*, J. H. Randall's *The Making of the Modern Mind*, Lewis Mumford's *Technics and Civilization*, P. W. Bridgman's *Logic of Modern Physics*, and Philipp Frank's *Einstein*.

7. Laboratory Experiments

We recognize that physics, as a body of knowledge, is now far too extensive to receive adequate general coverage in an introductory course.   Space for the program outlined above has been won by giving little or no attention in lecture or discussion to a number of traditional topics (and favorite, hard-won lecture demonstrations!), for example in hydrostatics, thermal expansion, musical sound, lenses and mirrors, magnetostatics, alternating currents, vacuum tubes.   For some students, high-school courses in physics will have covered this material.   But whether or not such a background can be assumed, the laboratory experience can well concentrate on some of these topics.   The following fourteen experiments, which can be done in this course. correspond to experi-

---

[2]Gerald Holton, *Introduction to Concepts and Theories in Physical Science* (Addison-Wesley Publishing Co., Reading, Mass., 1952); or G. Holton and D.H.D. Roller, *Foundations of Modern Physical Science* (Addison-Wesley Publishing Co., Reading, Mass., 1958.)

ments usually found in the repertory of the traditional type of college physics course. In the laboratory manual we have been using, the theory of each topic is presented in a fairly self-contained manner.

1. Motion with Constant Acceleration: Free Fall.
2. Newton's Laws: Reaction Car Experiment.
3. The Laws of Statics: The Crane.
4. Rotational Motion: Centripetal Force.
5. Conservation of Momentum and of Energy: Ballistic Pendulum.
6. The Mechanical Equivalent of Heat.
7. Vibration of Strings and Air Columns.
8. Electric Currents: The Potentiometer.
9. The Cathode-Ray Oscilloscope.
10. Alternating Current Circuits
11. Electronics: The Triode.
12. Lenses and Optical Instruments.
13. Spectroscopy.
14. Radioactivity: Half-Life of Thoron.

There are, of course, many roads to the goal we set ourselves in this course. But whatever the road taken, when one's class has read the last page and done the last experiment, and one reflects upon the fact that this is probably the last time these students will have any formal contact with physical science, one must be able to face the question: have we used this short year to the best advantage to help them know what science is?

chapter 11

THE GENERAL EDUCATION COURSE IN PHYSICAL SCIENCE AT THE UNIVERSITY OF KANSAS CITY

*Norman N. Royall, Jr.**

The general education course in the physical sciences at the University of Kansas City is known as the Foundations of the Physical Sciences 110-120. It is a two-semester sequence meeting for four fifty-minute lectures and one two-hour laboratory session each week from September until June. For this study the course carries a credit of ten semester hours.

The Foundations course is not required for graduation. The university does specify that a minimum of ten semester hours in the physical sciences shall be completed by all candidates for the bachelor's degree, but this requirement may be satisfied by any total of ten semester hours embracing at least two different physical sciences with appropriate laboratory work. For example, a five-hour course in chemistry together with a five-hour course in geology would meet the graduation requirement. All of the regular science majors at the university meet the requirement in this manner, and some of the non-science majors also follow this procedure. The great majority of the non-science majors, however, satisfy the requirement by completing the Foundations of the Physical Sciences 110-120, and the course has been designed with their interests in mind.

---

*The Author is Professor of Mathematics and Physical Science. University of Kansas City.

Although the course is technically on the lower college level, this is not practically the case. There is a large transfer problem at the University of Kansas City — common to many urban universities having large numbers of students transferring in after one or more years of college study elsewhere. This means that the Foundations course must, in fact, be regularly presented to a class of about one hundred and fifty students almost equally divided between the four classes.

This student distribution presents a severe pedagogical problem. It is met by keeping the technical level of the course as low as possible and the conceptual level as high as possible. For example, it is not assumed at the outset that any one in the course has real facility with logarithms, but the lectures do not flinch from mature discussions of methodology and epistemology that are usually found on the senior or graduate level. Thus the freshmen are at times "put to it" in order that the seniors not be bored.

On the other hand, the technical level is steadily raised throughout the course. Elements of both trigonometry and conic sections are taught, and the course closes with a discussion of the Restricted Theory of Relativity which is almost wholly mathematical — being based upon detailed analysis of the Lorentz-Einstein Transformations.

In view of the above remarks it would be well before continuing a general discussion of the course to display its technical content in detail. For, the special feature of the course is *not* this technical content, and failure to appreciate the really large technical content can lead to a misunderstanding of the nature of the course when the emphasis — as in what follows — is placed upon non-technical aspects of the course.

TECHNICAL CONTENT

A general education course in the physical sciences will usually give some attention to the four principal physical sciences: (1) physics, (2) chemistry, (3) astronomy, and (4) earth science [geology and geography]. In addition, if the study is not to be entirely descriptive, some attention must be given to (5) mathematics. The following listing isolates the material of these five disciplines that is actually taught in the course:

Physics

The kinetic-molecular theory of matter; the Bohr-Rutherford theory of the atom; hydrostatics, specific gravity and buoyancy; vibrating strings and the physics of the musical scales; the simple pendulum and the Foucault pendulum; the dynamics of freely falling bodies; elementary kinematics and kinetics of accelerated motion of bodies; kinetics of circular motion; the concepts of work and energy; motion of projectiles in a parabolic path; heuristic development of the inverse square law of gravitation; reflection and refraction of light; the general lens equation and the optics of the telescope; diffraction, polarization, and interference of light; Michelson-Morley experiment; the Lorentz-Einstein Transformations and the restricted theory of relativity; the mass-energy relation.

Chemistry

Boyle's law; Gay-Lussac's law of combining volumes for gases; the law of definite composition and the law of multiple proportions; Avogadro's hypothesis and the concept of the molecule; gram-molecular volume and the calculation of atomic weights; chemical equations and formulas; oxidation and reduction as inverse processes; the Periodic Table and the early form of the Periodic Law; the Bohr-Rutherford theory and its relation to the later form of the Periodic Law; protons, neutrons, electrons, the nature of the chemical bond, ions, electrovalence and co-valence.

Astronomy

Fundamentals of positional astronomy, right ascension, declination, equinoctial colure, zodiac, precession of the equinoxes. Cosmologies of Eudoxus, Heraclides, Ptolemy, Copernicus; Kepler's Laws of Planetary Motion and Newton's Law of Gravitation; the theory of comets; cosmogonies of Buffon, Kant-Laplace, Chamberlin, Weiszacker and Hoyle; theories of stellar evolution; Herzsprung-Russell diagram; novae; implications of relativity theory for astronomy.

Earth Science

Fundamentals of historical geology, age of the Earth calculated from salinity of the oceans, from sedimentation data, and from radio-activity of rocks; principles of mapping and correlation of geological strata; the geological time scale and the geological eras, principal structural events of the geological eras; structural history of the

Grand Canyon region; principle biological events of the geological eras, elementary paleontology and the theory of organic evolution; meteorology of the general wind system on the Earth, Coriolis Effect; climatic distribution and Koeppen's classification of climates; climates, climatic change and human history.

Mathematics

The foundations of geometry, definitions, postullates, and axioms; the Pythagorean theory of the figurate numbers and of the regular polyhedra; the problem of the Application of Areas; the Pythagorean theorem and the discovery of irrational magnitude; ruler and compass constructions and their restrictions in Euclidean geometry; the three unsolvable problems of classical geometry; the conception of geometry as an "ideal" science, classical conceptions of the nature of geometric reality; logic of proof and logic of inquiry, geometric paradoxes and their significance; Zeno's paradoxes on motion; elementary theory of the parabola, ellipse and hyperbola; ancient and modern definitions of the conic sections and proof of their equivalence; Menaechmus' property for the parabola and its use in solving the Delian problem; properties of parabolic mirrors; calculations with Roman numerals, binary arithmetic and the "place position" conception and its importance for modern high speed computers; elements of trigonometry, functions of the special angles, use of trigonometry for solving right triangles.

The above technical content is not isolated and presented as five discreet disciplines. Nor is it organized by the so-called "block and gap" technique. Let us now turn to the principle of organization used in the course.

ORGANIZATION OF THE COURSE CONTENT

The course is organized historically. This is true in both a narrower and a wider sense of the term "historical."

First, using the term in the narrower sense, the technical material is usually presented in the sequence that would be described as the actual chronological order of its development in a history of science itself, conceived of simply as a history of ideas logically connected internally without relation to a wider world of ideas with which it inter-acts — a view of the history of science which I do not endorse, however, except in a limited sense. For example, in this first sense of the term "historical," the geometry of the conic sections is presented prior to the presentation of the Galilean dynamics and the Keplerian astronomy which make use of this geometry. And the mechanistic world picture of Renaissance astronomy and physics is presented as essentially completed by Newton prior to the rise of chemistry under Lavoisier, Dalton, Avogadro and Mendeleev. Relativity theory as another chapter in physics is presented after this material in chemistry, and the Bohr-Rutherford theory of the atom is developed as a chapter in physics whose implications for modern chemistry are then pointed out.

Continuing to use the term "historical" in its narrower sense as applying to the history of science, the technical material within each of the sciences is *not* presented in the dogmatic logical order — the method hallowed by textbook authors — but in the non-dogmatic psychological order in which it actually developed. For example, dynamics is usually introduced in technical courses by announcing Newton's three laws of motion, adducing some evidence in support of them, and then proceeding forthwith to the solution of problems involving these laws. This is not the method here. Instead, the Aristotelian theory of motion as a received "common sense" theory is presented, Galileo's destructive analysis of this theory is then shown in detail as given brilliantly by him in his *Dialogues On Two New Sciences,* his use of the pendulum and the inclined plane in groping for the foundations of an adequate theory is set forth, and the celebrated Law of Inertia is shown emerging at last as it does after more than two hundred pages in the *Dialogues.*

A similar method is followed in chemistry. The usual textbook begins a dicussion of chemistry by an outline of the kinetic-molecular theory of matter, then announces the atomic theory and the gas laws, out of these develops the systematic structure of chemical theory, and finally applies this to the explanation of various phenomena such as, for example, oxidation and reduction. This order is reversed in Physical Science 110-120; for, it was reversed in the actual development of the science of chemistry. Instead, the discussion opens with the received "common sense" theory of the four elements and of "phlogiston" as they related to the problems of metallurgy and combustion faced by Lavoisier and others. It then moves to Lavoisier's experimental developments which replaced this older system by a new one only partially structured and without a systematic theory of the fine structure of matter. The debates over the nature of elements and of mixtures and compounds is next presented in some detail, the role of the gas laws in clarifying some of these debates is then shown, and the atomic theory of Dalton and Avogadro then emerges as an intellectual construct which rationalizes a mass of data, this rationalization being the principal warrant for its acceptance. The researches of Mendeleev and of Bohr are then shown as leading to a periodic law which is seen as an impressive "gestalt" embracing the entire elementary theory of the subject.

The reasons for adhering to this historical manner of presentation are psychological, logical, and philosophical. First, if students see the problems as they were actually seen by creative scientists in the throes of original research — unstructured, confused and contradictory — they sense some of the excitement that accompanies genuine research. Second, they move from this psychological plane to the logical plane by understanding logical developments as they were actually considered in the context of a logic of inquiry and not "blindly" as justifications in a logic of proof. Third, by adhering to this procedure the philosophy of science known as "naive realism" is destroyed in the student by cutting it off at its tap root.

This last remark is important. The very method of presentation of most undergraduate science courses encourages students to believe that the research activity of scientists consists essentially of the "discovery" of structures antecedently "in nature," followed by exegesis upon what is "found" by "looking" at these structures. In other words, it encourages what is known technically as naive realism. This is a false philosophy of science and of scientific method. The history of science itself presents sufficient evidence of its falsity. But it is a philosophy of science not without its uses for reactionaries. For, if science is possible only in the presence of little hard objects with antecedently given structures to be discovered, then the methods of intelligence associated with science — theory as hypothesis, public evidence from experiment as warrants for belief, etc. — are not relevant for the solution of social or moral problems whose locus is not in little hard objects. This conclusion then allows persons with vested interests

— who do not wish those interests subjected to critical review —
to pre-empt the social and moral domains for their own favorite
methods based upon tradition, authority, revelation, intuition, or
some persuasive combination of the foregoing.

The course is also arranged historically in a wider sense of
the term. That is, it is arranged so as to present the natural history of the universe prior to man's appearance as this natural
history is understood by scientists today. The course opens, therefore, with the problem of origins — that is, with scientific cosmogony. The views of Buffon, Laplace, Chamberlin, Weiszacker
and Hoyle about the origins of the Earth and the solar system are
set forth at the very beginning of the course. This implies, of
course, that one must present some recent scientific theories such
as those concerning stellar evolution before the students have all of
the background desired in chemistry and in relativity theory.

The lectures on cosmogony are then followed by ones on
historical geology, thus carrying forward the natural history without a break. The historical geology leads quite naturally to the
subject of organic evolution and finally to the question of the
natural emergence of man.

Once the threshhold of recorded literate civilization is reached,
the course proceeds generally by the narrower principle: Bronze
Age technology is seen as leading ultimately to the idea of theoretical science in early Greek civilization, the subject of classical
geometry then emerges in its proper background from a rational
point of view, and from this point onwards the history of science
becomes a part of the general history of ideas and of the growth
of the mind of man.

Thus, the weight of the study of astronomy, geology, and
mathematics falls in the first semester. The second semester carries
the main load of instruction in physics and chemistry. But in no
case is the order rigid. For example, Archimedes' hydrostatics —
a topic of physics — is treated in its proper historical place in the
first semester. This enables one to raise at their proper point
certain epistemological questions, and to explore why the classical
and medieval worlds — with much of the technique of the experimental philosophy in their hands — stood for centuries on the
threshold of modern science and did not cross over.

It is in such explorations of the interactions between formal
science and the larger social scene that much of the general educa-

tional value of the course is to be found. It becomes appropriate, therefore, to discuss at this point the connective material and the integrating themes within which the major insights are sought and which finally give to the course a certain unity.

CONNECTIVE MATERIAL AND INTEGRATING THEMES

Transitions are made between bodies of systematic technical content by certain connective material. For example, at the end of the opening discussion of the scientific cosmogonies, the question is raised concerning the compatibility or incompatibility of these views with the Story of the Creation in Genesis. The difficulty of simple interpretations is pointed out — for example, there are *two* creation stories in Genesis, and the explanation of this fact requires historical scholarship. This leads quite naturally to the question of the historical sources of Genesis itself. At this point I present a lecture outlining the essentials of the historical scholarship concerning the Book of Genesis as given by Graf and Wellhausen. In spite of this material now being classical, I have found that the undergraduates are quite ignorant of it — even the literature and history majors, in general, have no acquaintance with it.

The isolated character of the religious account of origins is contrasted with the cumulative and corrective character of the scientific cosmogonies from Buffon to Hoyle. This contrast is shown to rest logically upon the fact that scientific concepts are defined around referents in a public domain of the senses and are logically inter-connected with one another so that deductions from one of them have logical consequences for the others; whereas, the principal explanatory concept in the religious account — the Will of God — has no referents of this character. Hence, although this religious concept presumably has great honorific dignity, a high price is paid for it: it is logically isolated and nothing can be deduced from it.

A discussion such as the foregoing introduces the students to questions of method and of epistemology in a context which has the merit not only of being important and exciting, but of being closely tied to actual examples fresh in their minds from the recent lectures on cosmogony.

The so-called Argument from Design is next raised as a possible point of compatibility between scientific and religious outlooks. Hume's searching analysis of this argument in his *Dia-*

logues on Natural Religion is then brought to the attention of the students and the analogical superficiality of the argument for an ethical monotheism is made plain.

Hence, the students are not encouraged to seek compatibility between scientific views and those aspects of the religious tradition which are essentially mythological. To do otherwise would be to make too great a compromise of intellectual integrity — this latter being a primary value that is held before the students at all times throughout the course. On the other hand, much later in the course the question of whether the scientific method of inquiry is compatible with the genuine spirit of high religion is raised in another context wherein the students are acquainted with the type of thinking done by Dostoyevsky in the *Legend of the Grand Inquisitor*. Here matters appear in a somewhat different light. But this all requires time; for, the students — though of good intelligence — have a greater ignorance of high religion than they do of science.

Another example of connective material is that provided by anthropology. The lectures in historical geology are, of course, meaningless unless accompanied by some paleontology, and this leads at once to the theory of organic evolution. This brings up at once the question of the evolution of man. And the question is welcomed. Insights are not obtained by avoiding issues, but by sharpening and clarifying them.

The great controversy surrounding the names of Darwin and Huxley is set forth in a few lectures in all its dramatic detail. The story of the principal predecessors of *Homo sapiens* is then told. Thus a link is provided between natural history and human history by a few lectures in anthropology, and the geological time scale is seen merging into the time scale of pre-history.

All of the connective material is treated with the same seriousness and attention to detail as are the other parts of the course. For example, the students have a laboratory session in physical anthropology. In this they use a collection of plaster models of the skulls of the seventeen so-called "missing links" to measure and calculate Calvarial Height Index and run correlations much as might be done in a regular course in anthropology. Thus *Pithecanthropus erectus* becomes more than a passing word in a lecture.

The material in climatology is used to place a large naturalistic framework around certain aspects of human history, and the students are introduced to the type of thinking done by Ellsworth Huntington and others. Thus, without stressing climatic determinism the students are encouraged to seek broader and richer contexts in which to interpret regular history courses.

This possible intellectual contact with other courses in the curriculum is always in mind. For example, at the appropriate point the impact of the first birth of the idea of natural causality and theoretical science on the Greek mind is discussed. This phenomenon underlies the entire sophistic age of the Attic Enlightenment. At this point a lecture is devoted to tracing this development in the thought of Aeschylus in *Prometheus Bound* and of Sophocles in *Oedipus Rex*. This is done deliberately to make contact with a course in World Literature which is also part of the general education program at the University of Kansas City. It is at such a point as this that freshmen unacquainted with the Greek tragic dramas must simply possess their souls in patience. Sometimes insights are obtained in retrospect and one does not go ultimately without reward, however.

One of the major themes in the first semester is the relation between geometry and idealist thought. After they have completed the technical material in geometry, it is brought home to the students that certain conceptions about geometric reality and how it is known underpin the system of Plato. This is shown explicity by a discussion of his *Meno* dialogue; the ultimate connection of these conceptions with the "logos doctrines" of medieval theology is then pointed out. The fact that classical geometry breathed the spirit of scholasticism a thousand years before scholasticism was born comes as an insight to the undergraduates which enables them to appreciate the deeper continuity between the mind of antiquity and that of the medieval world.

The foregoing is achieved without any emphasis upon mentalistic Hegelian historicism. Quite the contrary is the case. The richness of the context of both scientific and non-scientific developments and their constant interaction is kept constantly before the students.

This stress upon the great classical philosophies of science enables the students to appreciate in a genuinely competent manner in the second semester the extent to which the rise of modern physics and chemistry was a fundamental break with the systems of Plato and Aristotle. Thereby they come ultimately to perceive near the close of the course the essential unity in the process of the formation of the modern mind and the decisive role of science in that formation. Since this modern mind — it is hoped — will also be their own, it is only by such self-conscious critical awareness of its roots that they can become autonomous individuals with a real possibility of giving leadership in transcendence over the dilemmas that now confront their modern world.

This last remark now brings me to an explicit statement of the larger philosophy of education which underlies this course.

BASIC PHILOSOPHY OF EDUCATION OF THE COURSE

All courses have underlying them — either tacitly or explicitly recognized — a fundamental assumption about the relation of the individual to the culture. The fact that education is concerned with the time-binding process, and that this process is meaningless apart from the concept of culture, is sufficient proof that this is the case. The fundamental assumption usually involves a value judgment about what the relation of the individual to the culture *should* be and the role of the particular course in bringing this about.

Three general positions can be distinguished. And all of them have some merit.

One assumption is that of *the individual as a functionary of a culture*. In general, this view — which we may call for convenience viewpoint A — takes the culture for granted and attempts to give the individual technical competence in a role. This is the view of all professional faculties. The great merit of this view is the clarity and concreteness of its aims. It can identify a body of relevant subject matter easily. It has great appeal to the majority of faculty members who have received the usual professional graduate school training, whether in engineering, law, mathematics, English literature, or philosophy is of no particular importance. They key concept is "efficiency" and the shibboleth is "high standards." Obviously, there must be much of this type of education A if a culture is to remain intact and function.

The great weakness of viewpoint A is its rather simple-minded view of both the culture and the individual. Its conceived roles for the functionaries are constantly being imperiled by the unhappy discovery that both the individual and the culture are far more complex than its theory allows.   Hence, there arises within this viewpoint A what sometimes passes for general education. New courses may be introduced into the pattern provided it can be persuasively argued that they will contribute to the "efficiency" of the now more broadly conceived role of the functionary.   Thus, engineers may take English in greater quantity when it is discovered that they have not been literate enough to write reports.   Or, a mining engineer may even study world history if it will make him more efficient on an assignment in Peru.   At times the discussions within this viewpoint A take on the sound of the rhetoric of the next position B.   There is much stealing back and forth of symbols and rhetoric between all of the positions.

The typical general education program of this viewpoint A is the "distribution requirement."

The second viewpoint B conceives of *the individual as a functionary within a culture*.   The difference of preposition is all-important.   This view is far more aware of the complexity of the individual and of the culture than is viewpoint A.   It realizes that efficiency in limited roles is not easily achieved in a complex culture where an individual is forced to play many roles.   In the modern world one needs driver education even if he is not going to be a truck driver, for all will play the role of motorist with varying degrees of peril to themselves and others.   The key concept is "adjustment" and the shibboleth is "democracy."   A merit of this view is it kindliness; a demerit is its sentimentality.   A fatal defect of this view B is that it often attempts in the name of education many activities that would be better left to other institutions of the culture which can do them in a more capable manner.   This is based upon its presumption that a desirable activity is necessarily a desirable *educational* activity — a nonsequitur.

A major weakness of viewpoint B is that, although aware of the complexity of the culture, it is essentially uncritical of it. Thus, all aspects of the culture are received with equal approval, there is no discriminative principle within its selection of curriculum material, it is torn to pieces in a complex industrial world and its energies dispersed in trivia.

The typical general education course of viewpoint B is the "survey course."

The third viewpoint C conceives of *the individual as a critic of the culture*. It is even more sharply aware of the complexity of the individual and of the culture than is viewpoint B. But its vision is not of adjustment to the culture. Rather its view is one of adjustment of the culture by autonomous individuals who are morally responsible. The key concept here is "criticism" and the shibboleth is "breadth." A peril in this position is aestheticism and a certain aristocratic withdrawal. At its best the great strength of this position is its vision of transcendence and its strong moral responsibility.

I have tried to fashion the Foundations of the Physical Sciences 110-120 around the best in viewpoint C as I understand it. I consider it the most urgent type of education needed in our colleges today, for it seems to me that what the culture desperately needs above all else now is informed critics and not mere functionaries.

Whether one chooses to call this viewpoint C a type of general education is of little importance. I have known some of the prime objectives of the Foundations of the Physical Sciences 110-120 to be achieved by professors of geology or professors of astronomy, for example, who managed in their regular departmental courses to create the divine discontent and the transvaluation of values that lay at the heart of what used to be known as "liberal education." But that was long ago, before the faculties of Arts and Sciences — under the spell of the prestige of the Graduate Schools — had embraced a form of professionalism of type A.

I close upon a note of pessimism. I do not anticipate a spread of the type of course I have here described. There seem to be both practical and ideological forces against it. There is no suitable textbook. None exists. The students have had to be provided with voluminous mimeographed notes and directed to read in the original sources. In this the "paper backs" have helped. But the temper of the times seems increasingly conservative, and many of our faculties do not seem to embrace as a primary value the increase of rational and critical attitudes toward man and society. Indeed, it comes as a melancholy discovery to realize that many of our faculties regard so old-fashioned a course as Foundations of the Physical Sciences 110-120 as something dangerously new.

chapter 12

GENERAL EDUCATION IN THE PHYSICAL SCIENCES AT KANSAS STATE COLLEGE OF PITTSBURG

*W. H. Matthews**

For the baccalaureate degree at Kansas State College of Pittsburg the required General Education program is composed of eight semester hours of English Communication, eight semester hours of Humanities, thirteen semester hours in the Social Sciences and thirteen semester hours of Natural Sciences and Mathematics, making a total of forty-two semester hours. Special general education courses are given to meet these requirements and most of the students take these courses. However, for transfer students and in special conditions for some of our own students field courses in these areas are allowed in lieu of the regular general education courses.

The requirement in Communications may be met by taking two integrated courses of four hours each or by offering six hours of written ocmposition and two hours of speech. Beginning with the Fall semester of 1959 it will be possible for the student superior in English usage to receive credit by examination to meet this requirement.

The requirement in the Humanities area includes three hours of literature and five semester hours chosen from fine arts, philosophy, and general religion. In literature and the fine arts special courses of a general education character are offered. While the

---

*The Author is Prof. of Physics, Rtr. with an introducton by Ernest Mahan, Dean of Instruction Kansas State College of Pittsburg.

three hours of literature are prescribed a student may offer foreign language for the other five hours if it is required in his curriculum.

In the Social Science area five hours of American Heritage, which is a historical approach course, and five hours in American Problems are offered and most students take these general education courses. However, transfer students and some of our own students may offer field courses in history and the allied social sciences in lieu of American Heritage and American Problems. Three hours of general psychology are prescribed.

In the Biological Sciences the general education courses are General Biology on the freshman-sophomore level for five hours or Life Science on the junior-senior level for five hours. Five hours of botany, bacteriology, or zoology may be substituted. In the Physical Sciences the general education course is titled Fundamentals of Physical Science and is offered on the freshman-sophomer level and on the junior-senior level for five semester hours. Chemistry or physics may be offered in lieu of the general education course. Mathematics is taken for the remaining three hours in this area. The course given for general education experience is called Modern Mathematics but the student may elect to offer any other course in mathematics to meet this requirement.

Fundamentals of Physical Science

The course Fundamentals of Physical Science is offered for college students who do not intend to make science their life work and have entered college with little or no training in this field. The specific purposes of the course are to orient students in the physical science field, to give him or her an appreciation of scientific method, and develop an understanding of the contributions of the physical sciences to the solution of contemporary problems. As a comprehensive presentation of the relationships and widely used applications of the physical sciences, Fundamentals of Physical Science seeks to furnish a basis for correct scientific thinking, and to impart knowledge of present-day science and industry and their social implications. In any such course the aim is to present all principles in language simple enough for the uninitiated. A text is chosen which presents the material in such a manner that the instructor can devote the greater part of his time to lectures, demonstrations, and leading class discussions.

Fundamentals of Physical Science 61 and 161.

Students may enroll in the junior college course 61 or the senior college course 161. Each course offers 5 semester hours of credit. The time allotted for instruction in either course is seven hours per week and so divided that students meet three hours for lectures, demonstrations and discussions and four hours for laboratory work and group conferences. Students who transfer to Kansas State College from other colleges, especially the junior colleges located in Southeastern Kansas and adjacent states; teachers who receive a part of their college training during summer sessions and others who for various reasons prefer to pursue the course as a senior college subject enroll in course 161. It is quite obvious that the two courses are quite similar as the fundamentals of any science are the same whether studied in either the freshman or the senior year, however the courses are different in many respects. Students enrolled in course 161 are required to complete more group discussion forms than those enrolled in course 61, they receive more library assignments, their quizes and final examination not only cover a greater area but they are more critical in evaluating each individuals ability in science reasoning and understanding. Due to the fact that so many students transfer to Kansas State College of Pittsburg from junior colleges in Kansas and from those near by Missouri, Oklahoma, and Arkansas, a greater number of students select course 161 than do course 61, as is indicated by "The fall semester 1959 schedule of classes," which shows as course offerings, one section of Fundamentals of Physical Science and three sections of 161.

COURSE OBJECTIVES

During the years 1950-1954 the author of this course description served on the Natural Science committee of the cooperative study of Evaluation in General Education of the American Council in Education, a program directed by Dr. Paul L. Dressel assisted ably by Dr. Lewis B. Mayhew. The committee in regular sessions devoted considerable time to the exchange of ideas about important aims of science courses in General Education; and effective methods in achieving them. Of the many objectives discussed the following seven were seriously considered.

To extend the students ability

1. in applying science knowledge to new problems and situations.
2. in the reading and evaluating news articles and popular writings on scientific development.
3. to understand the point of view with which a scientist approaches his problems, and the kinds of things that he does.
4. to analyze scientific data summarized in maps, tables, curves, charts and graphs.
5. to understand the role, importance and limitations of science in the modern world.
6. to face facts, to revise, judgment and to change behavior in the light of appropriate evidence.
7. to recognize the need of additional science knowledge in a situation and the ability to acquire it.

All of the objectives seriously considered by the committee are acceptable as the objectives for the course Fundamentals of Physical Science.

A CONFERENCE METHOD OF TEACHING

For approximately ten years the author of this article and his colleagues have been experimenting with the approach indicated by the heading above, not with any thought of replacing lecture and laboratory presentation.   On the contrary, the conference method of teaching is used as a supplement to them.   The class is divided into groups of six students each, with an effort made to have in each group as wide a representation as possible of varying course programs and vocational interests.   When the topic is "Sound," the person whose major subject is music makes many worthwhile contributions, as do those from the industrial arts department, when machines or electricity is under discussion.   The journalism student make contributions when popular science news articles are being evaluated etc.

The groups meet around laboratory tables under the chairmanship of one member, either elected or appointed by the teacher. As soon as a certain block of subject matter is partially or fully covered, the students are given copies of a form which asks for a variety of answers or judgments.   Instead of submitting individual responses, they are expected after exchange of ideas to arrive at a *group* decision on each of the items in the form.   The varied backgrounds and interests frequently lead to mutually profitable discussions. To illustrate the conference method of teaching, a unit on illumination and color is described.

Each student is presented two articles on the topic "illumination." The students are asked to make a study of the articles before meeting with the conference group, then after meeting with the group to submit on one form a group rating of the two articles. In making their evaluations of the two articles the students follow the instructions contained in the form which are as follows:

> After you have read the two articles on illumination carefully, try to agree on a rating of each one according to the following six criteria. Use the four grade letters A, B, C, and D with their usual meaning. Mark the article number in the box below, the rating you agree upon. For example, if article 1 rates B and article 2 rates D, you would record "1" and "2" as shown in the first rating blocks.

Example.

A	B	C	D
	1		2

1. Reasonableness, credibility, and authenticity.

A	B	C	D

2. Freedom from attempts to influence the reader illegitimately.

A	B	C	D

3. Freedom from incorrect reasoning and minor contradictions.

A	B	C	D

4. Facts presented in contrast to opinion.

A	B	C	D

5. Important assumptions and implications omitted from the article.

A	B	C	D

6. Article follows through and tells what it promises to tell.

A	B	C	D

After you have judged the articles according to the above criteria or standards, grade the articles by averaging the separate ratings.

Score-Article (1) ....

Score-Article (2) ....

On a second form the students make a group appraisal of several objective statements pertaining to the articles, the response to each to be selected from the following key:

1. The statement is based upon incorrect reasoning.
2. The statement is a reasonable hypothesis.
3. The statement is warranted.
4. The statement is an opinion stated as a fact.
5. The statement is a fact.

Previous to the presentation of a form related to "color," certain important principles such as refraction, diffraction, interference, polarization, etc., are taken up and demonstrated. It is stimulating to the students to see if they can identify the cause or causes of color which they see in variety around them. The form contains twenty items under the following key:

The color may result ———

1. when a substance is heated to a high temperature.
2. selective absorbtion of light.
3. interference of light.
4. selective scattering of light.
5. unequal refraction of light waves.
6. diffraction of light waves.
7. selective absorption of some polarized light waves as viewed through an analyzer.
8. high voltage electricity passing through a gas or vapor.
9. ultra-violet light falling on certain ores, dyes, salts or solutions.

In addition to the forms described above, students in their conference groups complete two forms during the time alloted to the subject "light." One based on a magazine article "light control," the other upon "air glow," an article that describes an experiment to be preformed and then the results of the experiment.

When the block of subject matter is "Geology" the students in their conference groups complete three forms based on three chapters of Lincoln Barnett's book "The World We Live In," namely the Earth is Born, The Pageant of Life, and The Age of the Mammals; one based upon a research bulletin "Strip Mined Lands of the Western Interior Coal Province" by Nelson F. Rogers

— Central States Forest Experiment Station, Columbia, Missouri, and one related to a Field trip (Geology).

During the time that geology is being studied, the students complete a form that was summarized from a chapter "The Natural Sciences in General Education" in the fifty-first yearbook of the National Society for the Study of Education, part 1, written by Dr. Louis Heil, Director, Office of Evaluation and Educational Research, Brooklyn, New York.

The form used by the students contains criteria that are kept before them throughout the entire course, not just in conference but in the lecture room, the laboratory and during quiz periods. Its title is objectives dealing with interpretation, and is stated as follows:

1. Observation and terminology — The principles and concepts of science, as well as the general method are solidly anchored to the starting point of observation and terminology.

2. Relativity of theory and concept — One of the major contributions which science instruction can make is a person's need for a satisfying world picture and a workable philosophy of life is the idea of relativity of theory and concept.

3. Cause and effect — The scientist is fully aware that the interpretation of material phenomena on a "cause and/or effect" basis has resulted in many errors and misunderstandings.

4. Teleology, plan, and order — As an outcome of general education, students should be able to identify assumptions of teleology, plan and order in nature when formulating their own interpretation of natural phenomena or when judging the validity of interpretations made by others. They should also recognize that such assumptions are needless and that man's concepts, theories and scientific generalizations or principles are more nearly "within" the evidence.

5. Sampling and extrapolation — Cautious thinking demands care in the extension of data either from a specific item or from a series of specifics to a generalization or from a generalization to other specifics. A lack of caution in drawing a conclusion from a single case or too few cases has led to erroneous conclusions regarding many personal and social problems. The role of analogy in the thinking

process is, in a strict sense, restricted to the formulation of hypothesis; it does not apply to conclusions.

6. Authority — Although the scientist often relies on authority as a source of facts or evidence, he consistently invokes the appropriate criteria to evaluate the reliability of the source of authority from which evidence is sought.

In this form the students use the above criteria of six parts in responding to the validity of twenty-five statements and also to the classification of each as to the criterion that is illustrated. Each group is also required to formulate statements that illustrate each criterion — the statements to be either science or non-science.

In addition to the discussion forms described, students in group conferences complete during the semester other forms as follows:

> The Story of the Atchison cave.
> Hypotheses-Science and non-Science.
> The atom and its radiation.
> X-rays.
> Problems related to the building of atomic weapons of war.
> Atomic energy and peace
> Hiroshima.
> The strange death of Louis Slotin.   (Death from radiation poisoning.
> The worlds first atomic drugstore.
> Sound — High fidelity.
> Facts and fiction about high fidelity.
> How to buy Hi-fidelity.
> Breaking the sound barrier.
> Tornadoes.
> Lightning and thunder.
> Cold weather ahead.
> Long range weather predictions.
> Radio-active fall out.
> Geophysical year.
> Satellites.

Most of the discussion forms are based on articles that have appeared in such magazines as Life, Time, the Saturday Evening Post, daily newspapers and bulletins. However, several of the forms such as "Illumination," "Field Trip geology)," "The Atom and its Radiation," "Lightning and Thunder," and "Hypotheses-Science and Non-Science" are based on articles written by the author of this report.

The space allotted to this article does not permit a full discussion relative to each block of material contained in the course, hence a detailed description of one segment is given with the hope that it will convey to those who are interested at least better than a dim picture of the course content and how it is taught.

Kansas State College of Pittsburg has directly beneath it a geological formation known to geologists as the Cherokee shale, this formation is at the very bottom of the Pennsylvanian system. The Cherokee shale is approximately 450 feet thick and it embraces several coal seams; the economically important beds of coal are in ascending order: Columbus, Rowe, Weir-Pittsburg, Mineral, Fleming, Crowburg, and Bevier. Most of the population of the vicinity is located in ten towns situated along the outcrop of the Weir-Pittsburg seam, a formation that is largely responsible for the settlement of the area and the establishment of many of its industries. Within a distance of 5 miles from the college campus, six seams of coal have been or are now being mined at their outcrops by a method known as "stripping" (the overburden is removed by electric shovels). This method of mining not only exposes the coal to view but also its associated clays and rocks.

The character of the rocks and the kind of fossils associated with the coal measures indicate that the cherokee shale was deposited in a basin in which the sea advanced and retreated many times. When the sea covered the basin, limestone, sandstone, and shales were formed. While the sea was absent from the basin, nonmarine sandstone and beds of coal accumulated. The Weir-Pittsburg coal seam occurs at about 200 feet below the top or at about the middle of the Cherokee shale. This bed ranges between 34 and 42 inches in thickness and it has produced more coal than any of the other beds in Southeastern Kansas. Each coal seam has its own particular thickness and they differ in such properties as percentage of volatile matter, fixed carbon, ash and sulphur, and also in their calorific values.

Water erosion caused the anterior outcrop of each of the various coal beds. There are many creeks that have and are having a part in the erosion of the Cherokee shale, some flowing in a Northeast direction to the Marmaton river. Others flow to the Southwest to the Neosho river, however, most of the creeks flow in to the Spring river in the Southwest.

Pittsburg is supplied with water from a formation described in bulletin 38, State Geological Survey of Kansas as follows:

> "At the present time the local residents and industrial concerns are adequately supplied with water from a formation known as the Boubidoux sandstone, a porous water bearing sandstone that is exposed over a large area in southeast Missouri; where water inters the formation. At Pittsburg the water bearing sandstone is about 1,000 feet below the earths surface. The formation is the most common source of water for municipal supply in the tri-state district. The wells pumped by the Pittsburg City Water Department averages a yield of 2,000,000 gallons daily. However, during the hot summer days, the late drought period, the average increased to 2,800,000 gallons per day."

Within a distance of approximately 20 miles east of the college campus into Southwest Missouri and about the same distance to the Southeast at the very Southeast corner of Kansas the Pennsylvanian system has been completely erased by water erosion thus exposing the mississippian rocks. About 50 square miles of the mississippian system are exposed in the state of Kansas, all of it at the location mentioned.

At the location decribed 20 miles east of Pittsburg the Bartelsville sandstone outcrops. A formation that yields large quantities of oil, not here but in various places in Kansas. However, at the outcrop described, asphalt sand is quarried and used as road building material.

At or near the outcrop of the Mississippian twenty miles southeast of Pittsburg, lead and zinc ores are mined, tripoli is quarried, and other rocks such as calcite, iron pyrite, feldspar etc., are exposed and available.

West of Pittsburgh within a distance of 100 miles the Pennsylvanian system is over lapped by the Cambrian formation which yields such economic products as salt, clay, shales, building materials and gypsum.

The physical geology of the formations described, their common rocks and minerals, their economic products receive attention in class room reports and laboratory study, with maps and survey bulletins used as they are needed.

In the block of subject matter "Geology" students make a rather intensive study of three important geological periods that are located at about the very middle of the table of "Geological Ages" and they gain some knowledge of those that are older than the Mississippian and those younger than the Permian system.

It is revealed by tests that those who have completed the course have gained considerable knowledge relative to the geology of one particular area and it is our opinion that they know the proper procedure for acquiring such information about any other region in which they may become interested.

Other aspects of the "Block"

The block of information (geology) is based for the most part upon three chapters of Lincoln Burnett's book, "The World We Live In," "Kansas Geological Survey Bulletin," and four chapters of the text book, "The Physical World" by Paul McCorkle. The chapters are "The Earths Changing Crust," "The Hydrosphere," "Rocks and Minerals," and "Products of Rocks and Minerals." Three other chapters of the text book are used as references. "Matter Associated with Living Things," "Matter Associated with Chemical Energy," and "Water and Its Application to Daily Life." During the time allotted to Geology students are required to acquire or further their knowledge of density and specific gravity, temperature scales, heat units, oxidation, reduction and combustion, atomic and molecular weights, acids, bases and salts.

A week or so before the scheduled date of the field trip, the students are advised as to what they are expected to observe, such as the geology of the area and also its role as related to the shaping of the economics and sociology of the community.

By reading State Geological Survey of Kansas bulletins, and classroom lectures, the students learn that the first railroad into the area was completed from Kansas City in 1870, and that four years later the first shaft mine was operated to take coal from the Weir-Pittsburg coal bed. By 1890, four railroads were operating in the area, three of them interested for the most part in transporting coal from the area, one in carrying zinc ore to the zinc smelters located in the town of Pittsburg and its vicinity. (It was more economical to transport the zinc ore to the coal mining area than the more bulky coal to the zinc mines.

During the time interval 1874 to 1890, many large coal mines were put in operation and the growing industry attracted experienced coal miners from other coal mining localities in the United States and from foreign countries, many of them from the British Isles.   During a coal strike in 1892 negroes from Alabama and other southern states were brought into the area as strike breakers, this was repeated in 1907.   Mining operations were expanded tremendously at the turn of the century and hundreds of miners with their families migrated from foreign countries, principally Italy, to southeastern Kansas.

At Joplin, Missouri, and its vicinity, lead and zinc ores are mined in rocks that were formed during the Mississippian period, the methods of mining these ores are quite different to those used in coal mining.   To mine lead and zinc miners were attracted from other "hard rock" mining fields of the United States and foreign countries some of them from the tin mines of Cornwall, England.

In the coal mining region of Southeastern Kansas many industries are directly related to coal and coal mining, while in the extreme Southeastern corner of Kansas and Southwestern Missouri many of the industries are related to zinc and zinc mining.   In each region there is a direct relationship between its history, economy and sociology with a geological formation.

While the field trip is being planned the students using a map will determine the number of square miles of the earth's surface that are drained of rainwater by the three local creeks, they are also required to determine from a reliable source, the annual rainfall in inches over the area.   From these data plus some careful field observations and the criteria, "one third of the water that falls over the area is absorbed by the soil, a third evaporates and the remaining one third is carried away by streams," the students are expected to formulate an hypothesis supported by evidence that is based on the opinion — "that by means of a suitable dam placed below the locations where the streams join to make a single creek enough water could be empounded to supply a city the size of Pittsburg, Kansas."

THE TRIP:

Each student carries while on the field trip, a skeleton map of the area to be studied, the map to be completed during the study.

The completed map to show the locations of the various coal seams, the railroads in the area, the outcrop of the Fort Scott limestone and the streams that caused the outcropping of the various formations. Before the trip is started each group of 5 or 6 students is supplied with an aneroid barometer or an altimeter to be used in measuring the approximate difference of altitude from one formation outcrop to another, these values also to be shown on the maps. Each group also carries a simple hardness testing kit that has been assembled in the physical science laboratory. The kits are used by the students to aid them in selecting rock specimens that in their opinion might yield to polishing procedure. Students also collect such fossils as crinoid stems, brachiopods and sometimes others found in the Pennsylvanian system of rock.

The first observation on the trip is a large electric shovel uncovering two coal beds in a single pit, these seams are known to geologists as the Rowe and the Knifeton, they are located almost at the bottom of the Cherokee shales and near the bottom of the Pennsylvanian system. Under each bed of coal is observed a bed of white or light gray clay known to geologists as "fossil soil." The reason for the name given to the clay is that often times petrified tree roots and roots of other prehistoric vegetation are found imbeded in the clay.

LABORATORY (*Geology*):

Each student is supplied with seven sheets of mimeographed material titled Group Projects. The Projects introduced as follows—

> The following projects are based on samples of water and geological specimens collected on the field trip.
> Each troup will be assigned two or three of the projects. After the assignment is made each group will make laboratory investigations as directed and aid the group chairman in preparing a report relative to the results of the investigations.
> The chairman or some representative appointed by you as a group will then make an oral report to the entire class.

LABORATORY PROJECTS (*in condensed form*):

    1. A laboratory study to determine some uses that might be made of the local rock "Tripoli." (The bulletin, Kansas

Volcanic Ash Resources to be used as a reference for this project).

2. To determine the freezing point temperature of the highly mineralized acid "Kirkwood strippit water." This project is a laboratory evaluation of one of several hypotheses that stem from the question — "Why is it that even on the coldest days this pit never freezes over?"

3. Tripoli as an art material.

4. A study of clay samples from three different coal beds. References — "Clay Testing" survey bulletins and a process for extracting alumina from Kansas Clays — State Geological bulletin 47, Part 4.

5. Ceramic Glazes — In this study the students make a ceramic glaze by using a much used formula, however they use tripoli instead of volcanic ash and local clay in the place of Florida kaolin.

6. To determine the calorific value of a black shale that occurs with some of the coal beds, they determine the percentage of volatile matter, fixed carbon and ash in a sample of the shale and from these an approximate value of the B.T.U. content.

7. A study to determine the purity of the Fort Scott limestone.

8. Obtain sulphuric acid and iron oxide from iron pyrite samples collected during the field trip.

9. A. study of rock samples to determine whether or not they can be polished. (This experiment involves some study of hardness of the specimen, the hardness of abrasives, particle size, etc.).

10. An investigation based upon a local problem — extremely acid, highly mineralized water often flows from abandoned shaft mines located near the outcrop of the Weir-Pittsburg coal seam. This water flows into some of the local creeks, thus destroying the fish and vegetation.

11. A project based on another local problem — a chain of land locked bodies of water that result from strip mining extend for a distance of more than forty miles in a diagonal direction across Crawford and Cherokee counties, along the outcrop of the "mineral" coal seam. Some use has been made of these lakes by fishermen, swimmers and for boating. The water has been used as stock water and for a very limited amount of irriga-

tion, however, it is too highly mineralized to use as "boiler" water or for domestic use.

The student's investigations are to make a study of the hardness of the water, the amount of soluble material carried, whether it carries organic matter in any appreciable amount and how it reacts to various water treatments.

12. This project is a repetition of Henri Bequerel's historical experiment that resulted in the discovery that radium ores are radioactive, however, the students use the black nodules collected while making the field trip instead of the uranium ore and a double edged razor blade instead of a key.

The laboratory reference for this project:

"Composition of some uranium-bearing phosphate nodules from Kansas shales." Kansas Geological Survey Bulletin 102, Part 2.

Conclusion:

Students learn many facts and principles in the course, and it is our opinion that they get more satisfaction and a better understanding by applying them in group discussions and laboratory discussion than they would get by verifying known laws.

The course is built around five core topics: Geology, The atom and its Radiation, Light, Sound and Weather. When Geology is the topic, students must learn many physical principles and facts, when light is the subject it is very necessary that the laws pertaining to electricity, heat, etc, must be studied and applied. Similar comment would be made bearing on the relationship of many laws to the topics enumerated in this paragraph. It is not necessary to force physical principles and chemical laws into the course structure, they just naturally get into the "picture" as the course progresses. Experience tells us that the type of laboratory investigations used in the course provide a sense of creative work for some students, reading popular science news articles and group discussion bearing on the articles for others. The course is still experimental and will be undergoing changes always if it is to be kept dynamic and alive. New material must be added, hence some must be discarded, sometimes these changes must be made at a days notice especially at the time of a great discovery or a great scientific achievement.

One of the instructor's major concerns in this course is to make progress evident to the student, primarily by means of short objective tests which furnish conclusive proof to them that they know something about the subject, that they are improving their method of thinking and are acquiring a considerable amount of worthwhile information.   This course is so structured and administered that the students have a part in their own education.

chapter 13

SCIENCE COURSES FOR GENERAL EDUCATION IN THE COLLEGE OF ARTS AND SCIENCES UNIVERSITY OF LOUISVILLE

*P. A. Davies**

Science courses for general education in the College of Arts and Sciences are offered at two levels. Introduction to the Physical Sciences and Introduction to the Biological Sciences are primarily for freshmen, but sophomores are occasionally admitted by permission of the divisional chairman. These two courses and also Introduction to the Social Sciences (Problems of Modern Society) and History of Civilization in the Division of Social Sciences, the Humanities course (literature, art, music and philosophy), and freshman English are the basic required courses for general education in the Junior College.

An advanced, interrelated science course, History and Philosophy of Science given for seniors in the Departments of Biology, Chemistry and Physics is required for the A.B. and B.S. degrees in these departments. Occasionally a senior major in mathematics and philosophy or a junior in one of the sciences who has had sufficient scientific background will be admitted.

The general education science courses are one semester (17 weeks), three-credit courses and meet three times a week for fifty minutes each. Each introductory course is complete to the extent that it is neither prerequisite to nor integrated with any departmental course or courses in the college or any science instruction

---

*The Author is Chairman of the Division of Natural Sciences, University of Louisville.

received in high school.   A student may begin with either introductory course and follow with the other.   Prerequisites for History and Philosophy of Science are senior standing in a science
department and a competency in science.   However, because it is
required for the undergraduate science degrees and department requirements are so restricted, some seniors enter the course without
any college training in one of the science departments.

Both introductory courses are primarily for freshmen who
plan to major in divisions other than the sciences but need these
courses to meet their major requirements.   They also serve as
general education courses leading to the Associate of Arts degree.

A student may be excused from the introductory science
course requirement by any one of the following: (1) from the
physical science requirement by completing an equivalent course
in astronomy, chemistry, geology or physics, and from the biological
science requirement by a basic course in botany or zoology, with a
minimum grade of C; (2) by passing that part of the Freshmen
Admission Test containing Mechanics of Expression, Social Science,
History, Natural Science and a combination of Literature and
Fine Arts in the 50th or above percentile; or (3) by passing the
Natural Science section of the Sophomore Comprehensive Examination in the 25th percentile or above.   Should a student after
completing an introductory course desire, through change of major,
to take a basic laboratory course in a science department, he is
allowed credit for both courses, but if he has previously obtained
credit in an equivalent laboratory course, he cannot receive credit
for the introductory science course.

It is clearly recognized in our College that two types of basic
instruction in science are necessary to meet student needs, various
curricula and instructional requirements.   One type includes basic
laboratory courses in the different science departments with emphasis upon minute details and laboratory skills which are prerequisites
for advanced courses in a department, or as interdivisional courses
in the various departments for degrees.   The second type consists
of introductory courses for non-science majors which are not prerequisites to any advanced courses but are terminal in the sense
that they are usually the only science courses taken by non-science
majors.

From time to time pretests were given to students who had
just enrolled in the Introduction to the Biological Science course

to determine their factual scientific information, their understanding of biological principles and their ability to apply principles. The ratings were checked with the biology courses taken in high school. It was found that students with one or more high school biology courses had retained some knowledge of factual material but they had almost no understanding of scientific principles or the ability to apply them to new situations. The data obtained have been valuable in determining the instructional procedures for the basic course.

Recognizing and determining valid student needs in the field of science for non-science majors at the freshman level is difficult and requires constant effort. Home and school training, habits, interests, attitudes, abilities to formulate and apply principles, abilities to employ critical thinking, and skills vary and change, and so do the needs. Many sources have been explored, sifted for validity, and tested in actual situations. Needs were determined from national and local inventories in the physical and biological sciences, local health organizations, questions and suggestions by both undergraduate and graduate students, and the experiences and judgments of instructors in both science and non-science divisions.

In retrospect, the original determination of needs and the translation of the needs into valid materials and methods proved to be very sound and have formed the bases for improvements that have been incorporated into our present courses. Important changes that have gradually occurred in the introductory courses are: revaluation of aims with the placing of some of the original ones in primary positions and the delegation of others into secondary places, a more careful selection of subject matter, and the stressing of depth rather than breadth of the subject matter selected. If too broad a range of scientific subject matter is attempted the coverage will be superficial and the student will acquire a large acquaintance with the results of science and less understanding of the method of achievement. He will come away from the course lacking in experience of the way of science, of science as an intellectual discipline and as a method and way of life.

The thinking that promoted the establishment of introductory courses in science for general education and the desire to develop successful ones to meet ever changing-student needs have held steady during the twenty-six years since their inceptions and are today as strong as ever.[1]   Two fundamental and very important things have constantly needed revaluation to keep the course in progress: (1) scientific needs of individuals in order to live happily and successfully in a rapidly changing world and (2) scientific principles, concepts, methods, and the selection of basic facts to be employed in developing materials in introductory courses to meet student needs at the freshman level.

An abundance of visual aids is essential in science courses without laboratory at the freshmen level.   We have been very fortunate in obtaining an abundance of visual aids in the form of motion pictures, lantern slides and opaque projector equipment, demonstration apparatus, specimens, charts and models.   Part of these aids have been supplied by the various film libraries in Louisville, others from the Division of Natural Science budget, and the remainder on loan from the different science departments.   The courses could be greatly improved by the addition of numerous required laboratory exercises in which the student could experience the actual handling of equipment, observe living and non-living materials and solve simple scientific problems.   This has been hindered in the past by the lack of suitable laboratory space and equipment and the lack of experienced personnel, but the prospects for the future are encouraging.   During the past academic year, students in the Introduction to Physical Sciences had the opportunity on a voluntary basis to perform simple laboratory exercises on light and optical instruments and also on sound by using the oscilloscope. Trips were taken to a local observatory where the moon, sun and planets were observed.   They also had the opportunity to visit points of geological interest where minerals and fossils were identified.

An experiment concerning class size has been under way for the introductory science courses.   Classes of forty or fewer students meet for lectures and discussions three times a week for fifty minutes and classes of over one hundred students meet for lectures twice each week and then are broken into smaller groups for discussion and quizzes during a third period.   If the large classes with their smaller discussion and quiz groups are taught by experienced teachers, a high degree of success is obtained,

---

[1]J. J. Oppenheimer, "The General Courses in the College Program," School and Society, LI (1940). 518-22.

but if any part is conducted by instructors or graduate students who are inexperienced in the philosophy and aims of general education, they are less successful. The ideal class was found to be about forty students taught by experienced personnel. This number may be seated closely enough to the instructor to see clearly the demonstrations, and the questions asked by students are not so numerous but that they can be answered immediately without disrupting the progress of the class, while in larger lecture classes the answering of questions is usually postponed until the discussion section when they may seem less important to the student or are forgotten. The forty class size is large enough to develop a spirit of competition and retain the enthusiasm of the instructor while classes much smaller usually lack competition and enthusiasm for maximum achievement. History and Philosophy of Science, a lecture course, normally has fewer than forty students so it does not offer class size difficulties.

Introduction to the Physical Sciences

From the beginning, this course has had interrupted progress because different persons have taught it for only short periods. Each has introduced his own ideas, interests and philosophy which in certain cases were not too favorable. For the past two years, Dr. Carl E. Adams has assumed the responsibility for the supervision of this course and is participating in it with interest and enthusiasm. He brings to it the possibility of continuous supervision and participation and an understanding of the nature and needs of the physical sciences in general education for non-science majors at the freshman level.

The textbook used in the course is *Man and His Physical World* by D. E. Gray and J. W. Coutts. Assigned sources for additional reading are: *The World of Copernicus* by Angus Armitage, *The Universe and Dr. Einstein* by Lincoln Barnett, and the *Scientific American*. A term paper is required in which the student expresses himself on some topic of personal interest in the physical sciences.

PRINCIPAL AIMS

1. To acquire a fund of information about astronomy, chemistry, geology and physics.

2. To understand the scientific method and acquire practice in its application.
3. To establish an appreciation of man's accomplishment in discovering scientific facts and principles.
4. To acquire, through knowledge of the history of the physical sciences, a greater appreciation of the contributions of science.

SECONDARY AIMS

1. To develop a scientific attitude.
2. To know the major economic aspects of the physical sciences.
3. To be able to read and to discuss intelligently, scientific topics of interest to the layman.
4. To understand the role of science in modern civilization and to be aware of the problems that may be created and solved by it.
5. To enjoy science as a leisure activity.
6. To know the important sources of reference materials in the physical sciences.
7. To recognize the relationship of science to other fields of learning.

PRINCIPLES

Space does not permit the publication of the entire list of physical science principles used in the course, so a few were selected at random.

1. All substances are made up of small particles called molecules, which are alike in the same substance but different in other substances.
2. Energy cannot be created or destroyed but may be changed from one form into another.
3. Energy is involved in all chemical action.
4. All matter is made of atoms and molecules which are in constant motion.
5. The physical state of matter depends on the speed of motion of the molecules composing it and upon the attraction of the particles for each other.
6. Every body in the universe continues in a state of rest or uniform motion in a straight line unless acted upon by some external force to change that state.
7. The work obtained from a machine never exceeds the work put into it.

8. Light travels in a straight line in a medium of uniform density.

9. An electric current is directly proportional to the electromotive force and inversely proportional to the resistance.

10. The chemical activity of a substance depends upon the number of electrons revolving around the nucleus of the atom.

11. Substances that dissolve in water will cause the resulting solutions to boil at a higher temperature and to freeze at a lower temperature than pure water.

12. If the same pressure is maintained, the volume of a gas is varied directly as the absolute temperature.

13. A reduction of air pressure accompanies an increase in altitude.

14. Earth processes proceed in endless and recurring cycles, and change is one absolute function of the universe.

15. Strata of rock occur in the earth's surface in the order in which they were deposited, except in the case of overthrust faults.

16. When elevations and depressions are created, the elevations are attacked by agents of erosion and materials are carried to the depressions where sedimentary rocks are formed.

CONCEPTS

The following concepts were selected from a larger list used in the course.

Atom	Magnetism	Solutions
Diastrophism	Matter	Sound
Electricity	Motion	Space
Energy	Radiation	Time
Heat	Sedimentation	Vulcanism
Light	Solar System	Weathering

COURSE CONTENT

Not all of the course content listed is given in any one semester but varies with the interest and training of the instructor.

Unit I. Introduction

Definition of science. Division of the field of science. Organization of the course. Material dealt with in the course. Relation to other fields. Reasons for studying physical science.

Unit II. Scientific Method

Science as a method. Historical development of the methods of science. Inductive and deductive reasoning. Use of scientific method on other fields. Scientific attitudes.

Unit III. Structure of Matter

Modern concept of the structure of matter. Definitions of compounds, molecules, elements, atoms, protons, electrons, and neutrons. Early Greek concepts. Concepts of the alchemists. Seventeenth-nineteenth century concepts. Development of modern concepts in the twentieth century. Atomic energy. Radioactivity. Isotopes. Atomic energy tools. New elements. Atom splitting. Manufacturing of atomic bombs. Peacetime use of atomic energy.

Unit IV. Radiant Energy

Energy in the universe: importance, definition, classification, transformation and conservation, exhaustible and inexhaustible sources. Development of corpuscular and electromagnetic theories. Forms and uses of radiant energy. Light. Color. Spectroscope. Quantum theory and relativity.

Unit V. Electricity

Static electricity. Early and modern concepts of magnetism. Generators. Transformers. Motors. Batteries. Uses of electricity.

Unit VI. Chemistry

Historical development of chemical knowledge. Electrolysis. Solutions. Crystallography. Steel and alloys. Organic chemistry. Synthesis and use of representative compounds. Chlorophyll. Propaganda in advertising chemical products.

Unit VII. Heat

Heat and molecular motion. Historical use and concepts of heat. State of matter. Measurement of heat. Transference of heat. Heat and the human body. Control of heat. Humidity. Fuels. Heat engines. Heat in the home.

Unit VIII. Sound

Wave motion. Production and transmission of sound. Musical sound. Resonance. Acoustics. Radio. Vacuum tubes.

Unit IX. Geology

Utilitarian values. Theories as to the origin of the earth. Formation of the earth. Inner layers. Crust. Diastrophism. Erosion. Periods of earth's history. Conservation of geologic resources.

Unit X.   Astronomy

> Man's place in the universe.   Astronomy in history.   Laws of motion.   Motion of the earth.   Solar system.   Stars. The sun.   The moon.   The planets.   Instruments of space travel.

Introduction to the Biological Sciences

This course has had an uninterrupted and progressive history. During its entire history it has been supervised by only two members of the biology staff who have had long experience in teaching freshmen and were cognizant of the biological needs of students at this level in the general education program.   Most of the teaching has been done by the supervisors.

Textbook used in the course is *Principles of Biology* by W. G. Whaley, O. P. Breland, *et. al.*   Additional assigned readings were in *The Challenge of Man's Future* by Harrison Brown, *American Natural Resources* by C. H. Callison, *Topsoil and Civilization* by Tom Dale and V. G. Carter, *This is Our World* by P. B. Sears, *The American Land* by W. R. Van Dersol, *Natural History* published by American Museum of Natural History.

PRINCIPAL AIMS

1. To acquire a fund of information about biology.
2. To acquire a knowledge of and the ability to use the important biological principles.
3. To develop an understanding of scientific methods and scientific attitudes.
4. To develop a range of interest in the science of biology.

SECONDARY AIMS

1. To develop an awareness and appreciation of the natural laws.
2. To know the sources of valuable reading materials in biology in relation to general education.
3. To know the economic aspects of biology.
4. To know the interrelationships of biology and other fields of learning.
5. To develop an increased appreciation for the beauty in nature.
6. To acquire, through knowledge of the history of the development of biology, a more intellectual appreciation of the contributions of biology.

PRINCIPLES

The following principles were selected at random from the large list used in developing the instructional materials in the course:

1. In a specific environment over a sufficient period there occurs a succession of organic forms which continues until a balance or climax is reached.
2. The distribution of organisms is conditioned by the use of favorable highways and the absence of barriers.
3. The plants and animals in a given environment are mutually interdependent.
4. Organisms undergo more or less orderly changes from the beginning to the end of life.
5. Variation is a universal phenomenon among living things.
6. All living organisms have been derived from pre-existing organisms and resemble their ancestral stock more closely than do other organisms.
7. Every expressed character in an individual is the product of the interaction of heredity and environment.
8. Coordination in higher animals is brought about through the agency of nervous tissue and chemical coordinators.
9. Organisms at the beginning of the food chain are smaller and more numerous than at the end.
10. Either directly or indirectly energy-containing foods come from green plants because of their ability to "carry on" photosynthesis.
11. Organisms are essentially energy mechanisms, and are designed for the reception, storage, and release of energy.
12. Protoplasm is the one essential constituent of every living thing, and upon its properties the life of the organisms depends.
13. Germ plasm passes in an unbroken, continuous stream from one generation to another, while somatic plasm, an expression of germinal characteristics, arises anew in each generation.
14. The cell is the unit of structure and function in all organisms.
15. There is a constant integration of the various structural and physiological components of an organism so it can function as an active unit.

16. From the lower to the higher forms of life, there is an increased complexity of structure and this is accompanied by a greater division of labor.

17. Organisms are classified according to their natural relationships, and those which are of a similar origin are grouped together.

CONCEPTS

The following concepts in botany and zoology were selected as important ones around which the course content is developed.

Cell	Energy conservation	Morphology
Classification	Evolution	Physiology
Ecology	Genetics	Protoplasm
Economic	Historical	Reproduction
Embryology	Interrelationships	

COURSE CONTENT

Not all the course content listed is given in any one semester. The selection varies with the interest and training of the instructor.

Unit I. Introduction

The definition of science. The scientific method. Biology as a science. The origin of biology. The subdivisions of biology. Relationships of the physical and biological sciences. The ultimate search of all sciences.

Unit II. Structure of Organisms

Cell structure of animals and plants. The essential characteristics of protoplasm. Physical agents and protoplasm. The cell theory. Cell division. Mitosis. Osmosis. Simple cellular organisms. Generalized and specialized organisms. Division of labor.

Unit III. Different Kinds of Organisms

Why organisms are classified. Origin of the system of naming organisms. The plan of classification. Brief classification of animals. Brief survey of the plant kingdom.

Unit IV. Energy and the Living Organism

Food requirements of living organisms. Energy and its sources. Needs for the conservation of energy. Carbon cycle. Nitrogen cycle. Plants and photosynthesis. Animals and photosynthesis. Plant structures and pigments used in the process of photosynthesis. Use of energy by animals and plants. Soils in relation to plant growth and human health.

Unit V. Conservation and Wise Use of Our Natural Resources

Meaning of conservation.   History of conservation and wise use of world resources.   Natural resources in the economic and cultural progress.   Non-renewable resources.   Renewable resources: soil, water, forests, grass lands, and wildlife.

Unit VI.   Structure and Function of the Animal Body (emphasis on the human body)

Living organism as a machine.   Activities of the animal body. Organ systems and their functions.   Division of labor.

Unit VII.   Structure and Function of the Circulatory Systems

Origin, structure and function of the blood.   Mechanics of circulation: heart, arteries, capillaries and veins.   Fetal circulation. Rh factor.   Malfunctions of the blood and circulatory system.

Unit VIII.   Control of Animal Activity by the Nervous and Endocrine Systems

Structure and function of the different parts of the nervous system.   Sense organs.   Position and structure of the endocrine glands.   Function of the endocrine glands.   Malfunctions of the nervous and endocrine systems.

Unit IX.   Plant Growth Regulators

Chemical nature of plant growth regulators.   Sources of growth regulators.   Parts of the plant influenced by growth regulators.

Unit X.   Excretory Systems

Waste products of the animal body.   Structure of the respiratory system.   Function of the lungs in the exchange of gases. Function of the blood in respiration.   Structure and function of the kidneys.   Physiology of urine formation.

Unit XI.   Reproduction in Living Organisms

Reproduction among animals.   Human reproduction.   Human embryology.   Reproduction in the flowering plant.

Unit XII.   Parasitism and Disease

Nature of parasitism and disease.   Effects of protozoan parasites in the human body.   Parasitic worms.   Bacteria and diseases produced by them.   Viruses and diseases caused by them.   Immunity and how it is acquired.

Unit XIII.   Inheritance

Mendel and his discoveries.   Chromosome theory of inheritance. Meiosis. Maturation. Inheritance of like characteristics. Inheritance of variations.   Factor inheritance.   Determination of sex. Cross breeding and inbreeding. Sex-linked characters. Inheritance of human characteristics. Practical applications of heredity to plant and animal improvements.

Unit XIV. Economic and Social Interrelationships of Organisms
Energy cycle in the organic field. Relationships of plants and animals. Ecological factors affecting organisms. Plant and animal communities. Succession. Geographic distribution of organisms.

Unit XV. Evolution
Variety and multipicity of living organisms. Meaning of evolution. Theories on the origin of life. History of evolutionary thought. Evidences of evolution. Man's place in the evolutionary system.

History and Philosophy of Science

With the inception of the general education program at the Junior College level and its favorable reception and progress, the faculty of the College of Arts and Sciences introduced on an experimental basis a limited number of divisional courses for general education in the Senior College. From these initial offerings with various changes and modifications has developed the present program, i.e., Periods of Cultural History (five three credit-hours courses of which one is required) and either Principles of Cultural History or Advancement of Culture (both three credit-hour courses) in the Humanities Division, Great Social Thinkers (two two-hour courses) in the Division of Social Sciences, and History and Philosophy of Science (one three-hour course) in the Division of Natural Sciences. These courses form the core of the general education requirements in the Senior College.

This course has been a pioneering one for our College because information and experience were lacking for its formation and direction. It was unlike the general education courses for science in the Junior College in which workshops and conferences were frequently held for the exchange of intracollege and intercollege experiences, and to encourage participation in the new approach to education. Also, publications were available which not only explained the philosophy of general education but also contained progressive reports on courses in different colleges. History and Philosophy of Science had none of these guideposts to chart its course, so its progress has been one of trial and change. In the beginning, staff meetings were frequently held for the exchange of ideas concerning procedure, but as the course developed the meetings grew less frequent.

Since no report on the course has been made since 1936 and major changes have been introduced, a brief progress report seems necessary to enable the reader to better understand what has been accomplished to bring the course to its present status and also as a possible aid to others who may be anticipating the establishment of such a course.[2]

The aim of this course as originally described in the College Bulletin was: "to co-ordinate views on the historical development of the various sciences and the effect of this development upon philosophic and religious thought."

The first course, History of Science, was an elective three semester-hour course open to seniors in the departments of biology, chemistry, mathematics, psychology and physics. It was conducted by the chairman of the division who invited science instructors to attend and to participate in the discussion. Extensive reading assignments formed the basis of the lectures and discussions. Enrollment was small because the science departments did not consider that it belonged to them and did not encourage their majors to elect it. As an elective, it did not appeal to science seniors who were crowded with course requirements.

To overcome the initial weaknesses the course was reorganized on a broader scope as a History and Philosophy of Science. Members of the science departments became the principal lecturers while the chairman of the division acted as the coordinator. This procedure brought drastic changes in the course which have become deeply incorporated and are now well established. The science staff began to feel that the course belonged to them and entered wholeheartedly into its development. They required their majors to enroll, and the students, understanding that it was part of the requirement for the degree, took an interest in it. A disadvantage resulting from the reorganization was that each instructor crowded too much history of his particular science into the short period allotted to him and this caused a distinct lack of interdepartmental tie-up of either history or philosophy.

---

[2]Ellis Freeman. "Divisional Courses" *Jour. Higher Education*, VII (1936), 308-312.

When reorganized, the course became a full year, six credit-hour course required for the A.B. degree in the department of biology, chemistry, home economics, mathematics, psychology, physics, and for the three-year pre-medical and pre-dental requirements. The reason for including the pre-medical and pre-dental students was based upon the premise that they would not obtain sufficient instruction of this type in the professional training and it would serve as a general course to increase their comprehension of science and philosophy.

The next striking change was a reduction in the scope and time allotted for the course. The Psychology Department transferred from the Division of Natural Science to the Division of Social Sciences and dropped this requirement for their majors. The Department of Mathematics lost interest in its participation and withdrew, while the Department of Home Economics, realizing that their students did not possess the interest or scientific background for successful participation, also withdrew. These withdrawals resulted in a reduction in scope and improved the offerings of the remaining departments. The withdrawals and the reduction of course content also allowed a reduction to three credit-hours and confinement to one semester. Later, the pre-medical and pre-dental students were dropped because they lacked interest in the course and were unwilling to do the broad reading required.

As the course now stands, it is a three-hour, one semester lecture course required for the A.B. and B.S. degrees in the Departments of Biology, Chemistry and Physics. Occasionally a major in mathematics and philosophy who has had sufficient scientific preparation is enrolled.

Although scientists have an excellent knowledge of the historical accomplishments in their particular field, they usually lack training in the philosophy and logic of the fundamentals which underlie their science. Therefore the presentation of the course is so arranged that each scientist discusses the history and interrelationships of his particular science and professional philosophers present the philosophy and logic developing from, or involved in, the different fields of the natural sciences. To make the course a more complete instrument of general education, a social scientist is employed to discuss the accomplishments of science as they affect man and society.

In the present structure of the course Dr. C. E. Adams of the Department of Physics discusses the rise and development of physics and astronomy. Dr. H. B. Lovell, Biology Department, relates biological history from ancient to modern times. Drs. H. B. Wiley, J. P. Phillips, F. J. Johnston and N. R. Smith, all from the Department of Chemistry, present the beginning and advancements of chemistry. The philosophy of science is presented by Dean R. L. Barber and Professor R. C. Smith of the Department of Philosophy, and Dr. R. A. Warner from the Division of Social Sciences discusses the impact of science on man and society.

AIMS

1. To obtain a fund of historical information about each division of the natural sciences.
2. To interrelate the histories of astronomy, physics, chemistry, and biology.
3. To understand the important scholarly achievements, both past and present, in the natural sciences and the lives and accomplishments of the scholars who have contributed to these achievements.
4. To obtain an insight into the trends of science and possible future discoveries.
5. To understand the use of the scientific method in solving problems in the different areas of the natural sciences.
6. To be able to evaluate the quality of scientific thought.
7. To understand the nature of philosophy in terms of the problems that arise in the natural sciences, primarily with respect to the logic of the scientific method and the problems involved in the interpretation of the language of science (mathematics, models, graphs, etc.)
8. To understand the impact of the natural sciences on man and society.

COURSE CONTENT

For presentation the course is divided into six sections. Except for the introduction, which is conducted by the divisional chairman, the department supplies the instructor or instructors for its respective section. The number in parenthesis following the topic represents the number of fifty-minute periods alloted to it.

I. Introduction (1)
Course content. Methods of instruction. Textbooks. Reference books. Methods of grading. Scope of the ancient world.

II. Rise and Development of Astronomy and Physics
Astronomy and physics in the ancient world (3)
Scientific revolution (2)
Rise of mechanical view (2)
Conservation of energy (1)
Revolution of physical thought (3)

III. Biology from Ancient to Modern Times
Biology in the Ancient World (1)
Biology during the Renaissance (1)
Eighteenth century biology (3)
Progress of biology during the nineteenth century (3)
Modern developments in biology (3)

IV. Beginning and Historical Advancements in Chemistry
Beginning of chemistry (1)
Chemical revolution (1)
Fundamental laws of chemistry (1)
Chemistry during the nineteenth century (3)
Twentieth century chemistry (2)
Conformational analysis (1)

V. Philosophy and Logic of Science
Classical, medieval and contemporary philosophy and logic of science (6)

VI. Impact of Science on Man and Society (3)

The following scientists were selected from a much larger group to illustrate the caliber of the scholars discussed in the course.

Aristotle	Galen	Michelson
Banting	Galileo	Newton
Bohr	Gibbs	Pasteur
Copernicus	Harvey	Priestly
Darwin	Lavoisier	Rumford
Einstein	Loeb	Rutherford
Faraday	Liebig	Spallanzani
Fischer	Maxwell	Versalius
Fleming	Mendel	Wöhler

TEXT AND REFERENCE BOOKS

Textbooks students are required to purchase and from which the main assignments are made:

Modern Science and Modern Man by J. B. Conant
World of Copernicus by Angus Armitage
Short History of Science by W. C. Dampier
Great Experiments in Biology by M. L. Gabriel and Seymour Fogel
Scientific Revolution by A. R. Hall
The Logic of the Sciences and the Humanities by F. S. C. Northrop.
The Universe and Dr. Einstein by Lincoln Barnett

Selected references from a large group from which additional assignments are made or from which students may do independent reading:

Readings in the Physical Sciences by Howard Shapley, Helen Wright and Samuel Rapport
The Rise of Modern Physics by Henry Crew
Main Currents of Scientific Thought by S. F. Mason
History of Chemistry by F. J. Moore
The Historical Background of Chemistry by H. M. Leicester
The Growth of Scientific Ideas by W. P. D. Wright
Readings in Biological Science by I. W. Knobloch
History of Biology by Erik Nordensklöld

Evaluation

When one analyzes, over the entire period since their inceptions, the science courses that are a part of our general education program, there is evidence that considerable overall progress has been made, both in understanding the varied and changing needs for science in the program and the continuous effort made to develop valid science courses to meet these needs. As the courses have varied so much in their development, personnel involved, aims, principles, concepts and course content, each must be evaluated separately.

Introduction to the Physical Sciences has been under the supervision of Dr. Carl E. Adams for the past two years. As he is in the process of making major changes, no reasonable evaluation of the course can be made at this time. Important changes that he is instituting are: more emphasis upon certain principles, a stress of depth rather than breadth of coverage, better understanding of the scientific method, and science as intellectual discipline and a way of life. To determine course progress and the rating of student accomplishments, a number of proved educational instruments are used: intersemester tests, comprehensive final examination, reports on assigned problems, term paper, laboratory attendance and field trips.

As the Introduction to the Biological Sciences has had a more favorable progress than the Introduction to the Physical Sciences it can be more readily evaluated. We have continuously wanted to know how well the course or any part of it was meeting the requirements selected. Experience has shown that in order to obtain this information, the instruments of evaluation must focus on broad objectives, important needs, principles, concepts, and the selection of instructional materials. Weekly or unit tests, a comprehensive final examination, reports on problems and assigned readings have aided in giving the information desired. At the end of the semester, students were asked to express their opinions on how well the course content and methods of procedure answered their scientific needs. Also it was necessary to know whether it increased or decreased their interest and appreciation of science. When the opportunity arose, valuable information was obtained through consultation with students who had previously taken the course. Through the different testing programs, from class participation and student opinions, we have an index as to the success of the course and data for improvement.

History and Philosophy of Science through its long service as a natural science divisional course has frequently been evaluated by both faculty and students. The instructional staff considers that it is well organized for the time allotted to it (three class periods a week for one semester) but they believe that a more comprehensive and meaningful coverage could be made if it were extended into a year's course. The faculty enjoy presenting the history of their particular science and associating with the more mature minds possessed by the advanced undergraduates. Students are more ardent in their evaluations. The majority state that they enjoy the lectures and receive a great deal of historical knowledge and its interrelationships in the different sciences along with its philosophical and social implications. They all agree that the time is too short to comprehend all of the vast amount of material given in the lectures or from the many assigned readings. Frequent tests, including both essay and short answer types, are given to determine the effectiveness of the course and for making final grades.

chapter 14

NATURAL SCIENCE AT
MICHIGAN STATE UNIVERSITY

*Chester A. Lawson**

The general education program in science at Michigan State University has never been static, fixed, and immutable. From its beginning in 1944 to the present, the program has changed as the faculty responsible for it has become more understanding in the philosophical foundations of science, in the history and methodology of the discipline, and in the relations of science to other aspects of man's cultural development.

During the first eight years of the Basic College, students were offered general education science in either of two separate courses: one in Biological Science and one in Physical Science. Each course extended through three quarters and gave nine credits. These courses were taught by staff members of autonomous departments under different department heads, and students had the option of selecting one of the two courses as part of their general education program. However, all students who enrolled in the university were required to take at least one of the courses during their freshman or sophomore year.

The Biological Science course was designed to help students interpret man in light of his biological nature, and to accomplish this, students studied man in relation to all other living things. Students were expected to know certain fundamental biological principals and to interpret man as an individual and as a member

---

*The Author is Head of Department of Natural Science, Basic College, Michigan State University.

of society in terms of these principles. Work was organized under six topics: (1) Kinds of Living Things, (2) Characteristics Common to All Living Things, (3) Maintenance of the Individual, (4) Maintenance of the Species, (5) Interrelationships, and (6) Biological Evolution. The laboratory program was developed with one primary objective — to teach the student to think scientifically. The expectation was that the method of thinking and the mental attitudes of science could be transferred by the student to daily life situations.

The Physical Science course integrated various facts of astronomy, chemistry, geology, and physics into a fabric with threads of philosophy and historical aspects of science. The course was concerned with three major areas: (1) The growth of man's ideas about the origin and structure of the universe and the solar system. The purpose was to help students perceive the functions of observation, classification, and generalization in the development of natural laws; (2) Man's observations of the atmosphere and the structure of the earth. From this the student was to understand the relationships among physical factors in man's environment; (3) An analysis of the structure of matter. Topics included the study of heat, molecular structure of matter, and various forms of energy.

In 1952 the two departments were combined. The combined faculty was directed to produce a single course called Natural Science. This removed the elective privilege of the former program so that since 1952 this one course has been compulsory for all students.

The reasons for the administrative act that created Natural Science to replace Physical Science and Biological Science were several and varied, and for our purposes need not be explored. The point of importance was that the Natural Science faculty, composed of the combined Physical and Biological Science staffs, as a consequence, had some unique problems to solve. What was Natural Science? What relation did it have to general education? What would one do with it in the class room? The old securities had vanished. One could no longer teach biology, physics, or chemistry and assume that general education objectives were attained through students' learning the facts, hypotheses, laws and theories of the various sciences. Instead science in its entirety had to be considered, analyzed, synthesized, and molded into an instructional sequence that would be suitable for freshmen college students.

When the combined faculties of the Physical and Biological Science Departments first considered the problems in 1952 there were almost as many different solutions as there were people involved. Space limitations prevent a detailed description of the proposals and counter-proposals. It must suffice to say that the first step in the solution of our problems was to select the best of the laboratory studies from each of the courses and to organize these in some rational manner as a nucleus for the new course. Where it was necessary new laboratory studies were to be written.

The guiding principles in this first effort were as follows. The emphasis of the Natural Science course would be on laboratory work, with the lectures functioning to explain and enlarge upon ideas first encountered in the laboratory experiences. The student was to solve problems by his own processes. Concepts presented were to be of major importance and the student was to develop an understanding of how discoveries are made. The major task of the course was to convey to students what science is, what science has done, and what the limitations of science are.

The table of contents of the *Guide for Laboratory Studies: Natural Science,* published in September, 1952, was as follows:

First Term Work:

    (1) The Cell
    (2) The Nature of Matter
    (3) Diffusion in Living Things
    (4) Cellular Respiration
    (5) Organ Systems
    (6) Foods and Digestion
    (7) Cells and Internal Environment
    (8) The Nervous System and Reflex Behavior
    (9) Sensory Perception
   (10) Measurement
   (11) Symbolization
   (12) The Relations of Symbols

Second Term Work:

   (13) Motion of a Freely Falling Body
   (14) Temperature and Quantity of Heat
   (15) Heat

(16) The Periodic Law
(17) Light and Color
(18) Photosynthesis
(19) Biological and Physical Cycles in Nature
(20) The Influence of Organisms on Their Environment
(21) Weather

Third Term Work:

(22) Populations and Heredity I
(23) Populations and Heredity II
(24) Populations and Heredity III
(25) Populations and Heredity IV
(26) Kinds of Living Things: Animal
(27) Kinds of Living Things: Plants
(28) Rocks and Fossils
(29) Skeletal Homology
(30) Some Evidence of Evolution
(31) Classification of Man

The new course carried three additional credit hours so the total for the academic year was 12 term hours. The student attended two one-hour lectures per week, one two-hour laboratory period, and one one-hour recitation-discussion section per week.

Textbooks for a course such as was outlined above were nonexistent, so a syllabus was prepared by cutting and pasting sections of the syllabi of the original Biological Science and Physical Science courses. This syllabus served as the textbook for the first year of Natural Science.

At the time that the new course was inaugurated no one was satisfied with it. It was put together out of pieces of the two prior courses simply because, due to the necessity to produce a course within a few weeks time, there was no other alternative. It gave us a course to teach and an opportunity to search for a more satisfying solution. What we sought was a unifying idea that would organize and integrate the separate bits and pieces that we had put together for purposes of expediency.

So we set ourselves the task of finding some way of viewing science as a whole, of separating out from physics, chemistry, and biology that which was common to all of them. If a common element could be found conceivably it could serve as a theme around which we could build a meaningful course.

The task that had to be accomplished was to find some con-cept or system of concepts that would serve to organize and integrate all of the various sciences.   It became immediately apparent that such integration could not come directly through the medium of the theoretical concepts that operate in the various sciences.   The concepts of physical science differ from the concepts of biological science.   The biologist has borrowed some ideas from the physical sciences and has found them fruitful in the solution of some of his problems.   To the extent that this has been done, there is some overlapping of ideas; but biology has not yet become a subdivision of physics.   The biologist uses concepts of his own that resist interpretation in physical and chemical terms, and so long as this condition exists the physical and biological sciences will remain autonomous.

Finding no solution to our problem within the acknowledged disciplines of science we looked elsewhere.   The case history method proposed by Conant was considered and rejected as a total answer.   Case histories may be used as data to discover the unity of science, but they are not the unity itself.   And it was the unity that we sought, the integrating concept under which all of science could be explicated.   Something more abstract than a series of historical accounts was required.

We finally found the concept that we needed, but it took us some time.   During the 1952-53 academic year a new course was evolved which was quite different from the survey type course with which we started.   The assumptions that guided us in the development of this course were: (1) that it is more important in a basic science course to explore thoroughly a few areas than to atttempt to survey the entire field; (2) that an understanding of the means of arriving at solutions to problems is as important as the solution itself; and (3) that an understanding of the im-pact of this knowledge and method on mankind is also very important.

On the basis of the above assumptions we chose the cell theory, reproduction, and heredity for intensive study during the first quarter; geology and evolution for the second quarter, and the gas laws, kinetic theory, atomic theory, and electricity for the third quarter.

As no single textbook was available for this type of course, we selected one of the then current textbooks in general biology, another designed for a physical science course, and in addition *Science and Common Sense* by James B. Conant.

Conant's emphasis on conceptual schemes gave us our first clue to follow in the search for an integrating idea for Natural Science.   Conant's statement concerning conceptual schemes was "Science is an interconnected series of concepts and conceptual schemes that have developed as a result of experimentation and observation and are fruitful of further experimentation and observations."[1]   This definition may be interpreted as identifying science with a structure and a process.   The units of the structure are concepts, which are interconnected to form conceptual schemes, which in turn are interconnected to form the total structure of science.   The process of experimentation and observation lead to the development of concepts and conceptual schemes that in turn lead to further experimentation and observation.

If Conant's definition would hold for all of the different sciences we would have the unifying concept around which we could build a Natural Science program.   We could search out in each of the sciences the common pattern of conceptual schemes and the operations involved in experimentation and observation. We would expect to find different concepts and different conceptual schemes in the various sciences and probably the methods of experiment and observation would differ from one science to another, but basic to all should be the interaction of conceptual schemes to the perceptual experiences of experimentation and observation.

But what was a concept and a conceptual scheme? What relation did they have to the more familiar terms "fact," "hypothesis," "law," "theory" used so frequently in literature about science?   If conceptual schemes constituted the structure of science, what sort of structure was it?

It was at this point that we received help from the logicians. Some of us had been doing some extra-curricular reading in modern symbolic logic and as a result came across statements to the effect that scientific theories were deductive systems.   The logic texts described the nature of deductive systems in detail, and they suggested

---

[1]Conant, J. B., *Science and Common Sense*, Yale University Press, New Haven, 1951, p. 25.

the relation of such systems to theories, but in no case did they develop this supposed relationship. We pursued the idea.

Formal deductive systems are conceptual structures having identifiable parts related in a precise manner. Furthermore, deductive systems are operating systems in the sense that beginning from one set of statements one can move according to prescribed rules to another set of statements. Perhaps Conant's conceptual schemes, the theories of science, and the logician's deductive systems were one and the same. If this turned out to be the case we were a step further in our search for a subject matter that would be fundamental to all of the sciences.

Our first step was to familiarize ourselves with the deductive systems described by logicians. The second step was to discover whether such systems had any relevance to scientific theories.

A deductive system as described by one logician is as follows:

> In general, a deductive system may be described as consisting of a set of postulates, together with theorems derived from them in accordance with definite stated rules of procedure. Ideally, it is required that such a system include an explicit listing of all materials entering into its construction, both ideas and assumptions, and that rules for deducing theorems from the postulates and from other theorems already proved to be explicity stated. If every step in a proof is to be definitely accounted for, there must be no surreptitious use of ideas not defined or not announced as primitive. The same care has to be exercised with regard to assumptions. As a guarantee against invalid steps in making derivations, all the rules of deduction should be expressly set down.[2]

The essential parts or elements of a deductive system are (1) primitive terms or primitive ideas, (2) defined terms, (3) postulates, (4) theorems and (5) rules of procedure.

Primitive terms are those terms that remain undefined within the system itself. This does not mean that such terms have no meanings but that their meanings must be sought in some other system. As Werkmeister stated:

> Following the terminology of *Principia Mathematica*, we shall regard any idea which remains undefined

―――――――
[2]Ambrose, A., and M. Lazerowitz, *Fundamentals of Symbolic Logic*, Rinehart & Co., Inc., New York, 1948, p. 142.

with the system itself as a *primitive idea*. This does not mean that the idea cannot be defined at all; it merely means that if it is defined, its definition cannot be given in the terminology or the symbolism of the deductive system for the construction of which it is indispensable. Primitive ideas must be given in ordinary language and are employed only in order to clarify the meaning of the symbols that will be used throughout the system.[3]

Defined terms of a deductive system are primarily a convenience. Ambrose and Lazerowitz stated in their description of a deductive system:

> [The primitive ideas] provide the minimum apparatus of ideas necessary for setting out the postulates of the deductive system of truth-functions. It would, however, be inconvenient to be confined to this minimum apparatus . . . . The introduction of another symbol . . . defined in terms of the primitive ideas . . . would serve to express functions in a much more familiar form and thereby would greatly facilitate proof of theorems. For this reason the system to be set out includes an initial definition . . . .[4]

Postulates are statements that assert something to be true. They are meaningful propositions composed of the primitive and defined terms. The postulates of any system must be consistent, i.e., no set of postulates can contain contradictory statements. In addition the set of postulates must be complete. "A set is complete if its deductive power is adequate for yielding the totality of truths about its elements, i.e., if *all* the truths about the elements are deductible from the set."[5] Another desirable, though not essential, property of a set of postulates is independence. An independent set is such that no one of the postulates can be deduced from any combination of the other postulates.

Theorems are statements that may be derived from the postulates by following the rules of procedure stipulated for the system. Such rules for the deductive systems of logic are usually (1)

[3]Werkmeister, W. H., *An Introduction to Critical Thinking*, Johnson Publishing Co., Lincoln, Nebraska, 1949, p. 141.

[4]Ambrose, A., and M. Lazerowitz, *op. cit.*, p. 144.

[5]*Ibid.*, p. 146.

variable substitution, (2) definitional substitution, and (3) inference.

Having identified what logicians meant by a deductive system our next task was to find out if scientific theories would fit the pattern of deductive systems.   We discovered that the theories we analyzed did fit and, furthermore, we found that the application of the idea of deductive systems gave us a new and better insight into the structure and operations of science.   Northrop's book *The Logic of the Sciences and the Humanities* was very helpful, though we gained some additional insights by our own investigation of theories.

From Northrop we gained an understanding of the concepts that are used in science, and a useful classification of theories.

Northrop's discussion of concepts is more elaborate and involved than is necessary for our purpose.   Hence, I will select for description two major classes and three subclasses of one of the major classes.   The two major classes are concepts by intuition and concepts by postulation.   There are three kinds of concepts by postulation.   They are concepts by perception, concepts by imagination, and concepts by intellection.

> According to Northrop
>
>   A concept by intuition is one which denotes, and the complete meaning of which is given by, something which is immediately apprehended.
>   "Blue" in the sense of the sensed color is a concept by intuition.
>
>   . . . . .
>
>   A concept by postulation is one the meaning of which in whole or in part is designated by the postulates of the deductive theory in which it occurs.   Any concept which can be defined in terms of such concepts we shall call a concept by postulation.   "Blue" in the sense of the number of a wave-length in electromagnetic theory is a concept by postulation.[6]

Concepts by intuition are the concepts that are immediately given in sense perception.   They are the sounds, colors, tastes, etc., that serve as the raw data for the construction of the objects and events in our universe.   However, as soon as we interpret a given

---

[6]Northrop, F. S. C., *The Logic of the Sciences and the Humanities*, The Macmillan Co., New York, 1949, pp. 82-83.

association of such raw data as a kind of object or event we have entered the realm of concepts by postulation.

Presumably the essential difference between these two kinds of concepts is related to the origin of the concepts. Concepts by intuition are available to anyone with operating sense organs. On the other hand, concepts by postulation must be learned or invented. It is easy to see that such concepts by postulation as the gene or the atom were invented or created by the mind, but it is more difficult to see the everyday objects of our world in this category. Nevertheless, the fact that we can make mistakes of identification supports this position.

The category "concepts by postulation" contains several subclasses including concepts by perception, concepts by imagination, and concepts by intellection.

The concepts by perception are the familiar concepts of the public space of daily life, plus the persons, tables, trees, animals, and other objects that occupy the space. These concepts according to Northrop are in part sensed and in part imagined.

Concepts by imagination are of entities or structures which we can imagine but cannot sense. The concept of genes as beads on a string is a concept by imagination as is the idea of the atom as a miniature solar system.

Concepts by intellection are those that we can neither sense nor imagine. The many-dimensional structures of mathematical physics in those cases in which the dimensions are greater in number than three, are examples of concepts by intellection.

The above are the major types of concepts that are used to construct the conceptual schemes or deductive theories of science, and the theories may be classified on the basis of the kinds of concepts that they employ. Probably no one theory limits itself to concepts of one kind only, but each theory can be characterized by the relative importance of one or another kind.

For example the postulates of the cell theory as given by Baker consist almost wholly of concepts by perception. The first three of Baker's postulates are

> I. Most organisms contain or consist of a large number of microscopical bodies called 'cells,' which in the less differentiated tissues, tend to be polyhedral or nearly spherical.

II.　Cells have certain definable characters.　These characters show that cells (a) are all of essentially the same nature and (b) are *units* of structure.

III.　Cells always arise, directly or indirectly, from pre-existing cells, usually by binary fission.[7]

In contrast to the cell theory, the postulates of Mendel's theory of heredity as developed in his paper "Experiments in Plant-Hybridisation" contains at least one essential concept by imagination.　This is the concept of character (now called the gene).　Some of Mendel's postulates were (1) Constant characters unite by cross fertilization to produce the hybrid.　(2) These constant characters separate in the production of pollen and egg cells so that each gamete contains one of each pair of characters.　(3) Where more than one pair of characters is involved each pair separates independently of the others.

In addition to distinguishing theories on the basis of the kinds of concepts employed we sought to discover whether we could identify primitive and defined terms in theories.　The primitive terms in a logician's deductive system are those that are undefined within the system.　By applying the same criterion to scientific theories we found that each theory contained primitive terms, and that these terms play a unique and necessary role in the construction of a theory and in the relations of different theories.

For example Mendel's theory grew out of a combination of certain concepts used in the theory of reproduction, i.e., parents, offspring, fertilization, egg and pollen cells, and concepts from algebra, i.e., combination series.　Both sets of concepts were undefined in Mendel's theory hence were primitive ideas or terms.　In Kinetic theory the concepts of Newtonian mechanics are essential, but undefined, and are thus primitive ideas for this system.

Thus primitive terms or ideas in scientific theories are concepts borrowed from other systems of ideas.　The primitive terms plus the operations implied by them are used in the construction of a new theory.　The primitive terms serve to link theories or systems of knowledge to each other.

Defined terms, in the deductive systems of logicians, were used primarily as a convenience.　They were described as being

---

[7]Baker, J. R., "The Cell Theory:　A Restatement, History and Critique, Part I," *Quarterly Journal of Mic. Sci.* 89, 1948.

useful but not essential. They played a role in the operations of the system, but not one of fundamental importance. Northrop claimed that defined terms played a similar role in scientific theories. He stated, "Any scientific theory involves primitive and defined concepts. This follows necessarily because definition involves nothing more than the statement of certain concepts in terms of others."[8]

I may have misunderstood Northrop's discussion concerning defined terms and I may have quoted him out of context, but if not, my interpretation of both defined and primitive terms in scientific theories differs from Northrop's. Defined terms do occur in scientific theories but I believe that they have a function that is far more important than simple convenience.

The terms that are defined in scientific theories are the words that represent significant new concepts that are essential for the theory. For example Mendel created the concept of dominance and recessiveness in relation to the characters of his system. He defined them as follows, "Henceforth in this paper those characters which are transmitted entire, or almost unchanged in the hybridisation, and therefore in themselves constitute the characters of the hybrid, are termed the *dominant*, and those which become latent in the process *recessive*. The expression "recessive" has been chosen because the characters thereby designated withdraw or entirely disappear in the hybrids, but nevertheless reappear unchanged in their progeny . . ."[9]

The concepts "character," "dominant," and "recessive" are concepts by postulation and were conceived and used by Mendel in the construction of his theory. They were not just a matter of convenience but were essential, new ideas.

Northrop equated such essential ideas with the primitive terms of deductive systems and reserved the designation "defined terms," as indicated above, for the non-essential word substitutes. It may be argued, that this difference of opinion concerning the proper correlation of parts of a deductive system with parts of a theory is simply a minor disagreement over names. That this is not the case is indicated by the fact that Northrop's interpretation left unexpressed a significant relation among theories. His interpretation apparently omitted the entire class of ideas that serve as a link

[8]Northrop, F. S. C., *op. cit.*, p. 140.
[9]Mendel, Gregor, *Experiments in Plant-Hybridisation*, Harvard University Press, Cambridge, 1941, p. 8.

between different theories and that function significantly in the development of new theories.

Postulates are statements or propositions that are accepted as true, and in a general sense are assumptions. Werkmeister stated

> The postulates must be clear, specific, and "self-evident" that is to say, they must be such that they are readily accepted as "true" or as "necessary." The "truth" of a postulate can, of course, not be logically demonstrated, for it is the nature of a postulate that it is "postulated," i.e., that it is *stipulated as true* for the system which is to be derived from it.[10]

The demonstration of the existence of postulates in scientific theories was a simple matter. In many descriptions of theories the term postulate itself was used with reference to certain propositions. In theories where the word postulate did not occur, certain statements of these theories were identified as being postulational statements, i.e., they stipulated something to be true, and when taken as a group could be considered postulates of a deductive system.

On the basis of an examination of a number of historically significant theories we have arrived at some tentative ideas concerning the nature of postulates as they occur in scientific theories. In order to develop these ideas it is necessary to return to the discussion of concepts and conceptual schemes.

By viewing scientific theories as conceptual schemes having the form of deductive systems we, in effect, divided all of reality into two parts, the physical and the mental. The physical world is something existent "outside" that directly or indirectly causes the appearance or occurrence of concepts in the "mind." Concepts by intuition are directly caused. Concepts by perception are less directly caused and those by imagination and intellection still less directly. But whether caused directly or indirectly the consequence of the interaction of the "mind" with the physical world is the creation of conceptual schemes or patterns that are assumed to reflect the physical world. The concepts by perception reflect objects and the relations of objects that exist in the physical world. The concepts by imagination reflect objects and relations that can not be

---

[10]Werkmeister, W. H., *op. cit.*, p. 140.

observed but which might exist in the physical world, and the concepts by intellection reflect necessary but unimaginable physical conditions.

In terms of this dual view of the universe, the "mind" receives information of the physical universe via concepts by intuition and on the basis of this information invents concepts by perception, imagination, or intellection. Such concepts exist in the "mind" and are organized into conceptual schemes, but in addition the "mind" *postulates* that such concepts and relations of concepts reflect physical things and events in the physical universe.

Thus the cell theory with its concepts by perception postulated the existence of cells having particular relations to each other. The gene theory with its concepts by imagination postulated the existence of genes having certain relations to each other. The mathematical theories of physics with their concepts by intellection postulated the existence of unimaginable "things" having mathematical relations that were thinkable only through the conceptual systems of mathematics.

Scientific theories also stated a connection between the postulated world and the world of the senses. Unless a theory contained some statement concerning the relation of the postulated world to the world of direct experience the postulated world would be meaningless and useless. It would not be a functional scientific theory, but an idle dream or fantasy.

In summary then, postulates of theories state (1) the elements or units of the theory, (2) the properties of the units, (3) the relations and behavior of the units, and (4) the relations of the units to the sensed world.

The formal deductive systems of logicians contain rules of procedure, which state what procedures are permitted in making deductions from the postulates to theorems. The assumption is that if the postulates are accepted as true, and if the rules of procedure are followed without error, then the statements (theorems) that result from this operation will also be true. The operations usually permitted by the rules of procedure of logicians' deductive systems are (1) variable substitution (2) definitional substitution, and (3) inference.

These same operations occur in deduction from the postulates of scientific theories, particularly so if the theory is mathematical.

However, in theories that are not primarily mathematical the deductive operations seem to be of another sort. To understand this kind of deduction recall that some theories postulate entities or units that move or behave relative to each other and that this movement or behavior is correlated with visible phenomena. The postulates of such a theory state the nature of the units and their behavior. To make a deduction from such postulates one starts with the units in a given configuration and by symbolically moving them relative to each other according to the possibilities stated in the postulates one arrives at a new configuration. The operation of mentally manipulating the units constitutes the process of deduction and the statement of the new configuration constitutes the theorem deduced. The next step is to translate the stated new configuration into a statement concerning the visible phenonema that are actually observed. This latter statement constitutes a prediction.

In order to illustrate the above kind of deduction and prediction a quotation from Mendel's paper "Experiments in Plant-Hybridisation" is given below. In this quotation Mendel used the symbols A and B for the unseen dominant characters and the symbols a and b for the recessive characters. On the basis of the postulated behaviors of these characters Mendel deduced the recombinations to be expected from a cross of selected parents and then predicted what effect these recombinations would have on the appearance of the offspring. The quotation follows.

> In order to bring these assumptions to an experimental proof, the following experiments were designed. Two forms which were constantly different in the form of the seed and the color of the albumen were united by fertilization.
>
> If the differentiating characters are again indicated as A, B, a, b, we have:
>
> AB, seed parent; ab, pollen parent;
> A, form round; a, form wrinkled;
> B, albumen yellow. b, albumen green.
>
> The artificially fertilized seeds were sown together with several seeds of both original stocks, and the most vigorous examples were chosen for the reciprocal crossing.

There were fertilized:

1. The hybrids with the pollen of *AB*.
2. The hybrids   ”   ”   ” of *ab*.
3. *AB*   ”   ”   ” of the hybrids.
4. *ab*   ”   ”   ” of the hybrids.

For each of these four experiments the whole of the flowers on three plants were fertilized. If the above theory be correct, there must be developed on the hybrids egg and pollens cells of the forms *AB, Ab, aB, ab*, and there would be combined:

1. The egg cells *AB, Ab, aB, ab* with the pollen cells *AB*.
2. The egg cells *AB, Ab, aB, ab* with the pollen cells *ab*.
3. The egg cells *AB* with the pollen cells *AB, Ab, aB, ab*.
4. The egg cells *ab* with the pollen cells *AB, Ab, aB, ab*.

From each of these experiments there could then result only the following forms:

1. *AB, ABb, AaB, AaBb*.
2. *AaBb, Aab, aBb, ab*.
3. *AB, ABb, AaB, AaBb*.
4. *AaBb, Aab, aBb, ab*.

If, furthermore, the several forms of the egg and pollen cells of the hybrids were produced on an average in equal numbers, then in each experiment the said four combinations should stand in the same ratio to each other. A perfect agreement in the numerical relations was, however, not to be expected, since in each fertilization, even in normal cases, some egg cells remain undeveloped or subsequently die, and many even of the well-formed seeds fail to germinate when sown. The above assumption is also limited in so far that, while it demands the formation of an equal number of the various sorts of egg and pollen cells, it does not require that this should apply to each separate hybrid with mathematical exactness.

The first and second experiments had primarily the object of proving the composition of the hybrid egg cells, while the third and fourth experiments were to decide

that of the pollen cells.   As is shown by the above
demonstration the first and third experiments and the
second and fourth experiments should produce precisely
the same combinations, and even in the second year the
result should be partially visible in the form and color
of the artificially fertilized seed.   In the first and third
experiments the dominant characters of form and color,
A and B, appear in each union, and are also partly constant and partly in hybrid union with the recessive characters a and b, for which reason they must impress their
peculiarity upon the whole of the seeds.   All seeds should
therefore appear round and yellow, if the theory be justified   In the second and fourth experiments, on the other
hand, one union is hybrid in form and in color, and consequently the seeds are round and yellow; another is
hybrid in form, but constant in the recessive character of
color, whence the seeds are round and green; the third is
constant in the recessive character of form but hybrid in
color, consequently the seeds are wrinkled and yellow; the
fourth is constant in both recessive characters, so that the
seeds are wrinkled and green.   In both these experiments
there were consequently four sorts of seeds to be expected
— viz. round and yellow, round and green, wrinkled
and yellow, wrinkled and green.[11]

The deductions and predictions exemplified by Mendel's quotation supports part of Conant's statement that, "Science is an
interconnected series of concepts and conceptual schemes that have
developed as a result of experimentation and observation and are
fruitful of further experiment and observations."   Theories suggest experiments and observations to be made and predict what the
observations should be.   The observations actually made are compared with those predicted by the theory and if the actual and
predicted observations are the same then the postulates of the
theory are confirmed.   If, however, the actual observations differ
from the predictions, either an error has been made in the deductions, or in the experiments, or the postulates of the theory are
at fault.   If the latter is the case the postulates must be changed
or even discarded in toto and a new set of postulates invented.

This brings us to the problem of the invention or creation
of theory.   How do the postulates of a theory originate?   Conant

[11]Mendel, Gregor, op. cit., pp. 21-22.

says that they come out of experiment and observation; but in what manner do experiments and observations contribute? We have a tentative answer based on an analysis of Mendel's paper "Experiments in Plant-Hybridisation." In this paper Mendel described in detail the steps in the process by which he finally came to the conception of segregating and recombining characters and the formation of modern genetic theory.

The essential process in the creation of new concepts we have termed "retroduction" following the suggestion made by Hanson in *Patterns of Discovery*. The process begins when the scientist is confronted with data for which no organizing system is available. In other words data exist which do not fit any of the current conceptual schemes. In Mendel's case the known data concerning the phenomena of heredity could not be adequately explained by any known system of ideas.

The next step is simple in so far as what happens is concerned, but far from simple in so far as how it occurs. The step is for the scientist to recognize in the data certain relationships with some known but hitherto unrelated system. The process is essentially creative in which there appears an insight or revelation of likeness where none existed before. It is the act of bringing together ideas that no one had ever related before. Bronowski described this process as follows.

All science is the search for unity in hidden likenesses. The search may be on a grand scale, as in modern theories which try to link the fields of gravitation and electro-magnetism. But we do not need to be browbeaten by the scale of science. There are discoveries to be made by matching a small likeness from the air too, if it it is bold enough. In 1932 the Japanese physicist Yukawa wrote a paper which can still give heart to a young scientist. He took as his starting point the known fact that waves of light can sometimes behave as if they were separate pellets. From this he reasoned that the forces which hold the nucleus of an atom together might sometimes be observed as if they were solid pellets. A schoolboy can see how thin Yukawa's analogy is, and his teacher would be severe with it. Yet Yukawa without a blush calculated the mass of the pellet he expected to see, and waited. He was right; his meson was found, and a range of other mesons, neither the existence nor the nature of which had been suspected before. The likeness had borne fruit.[12]

The story of the development of Mendel's postulates is too long and detailed for complete exposition here. Only the main points can be given. The first of these is that Mendel somehow conceived that it would be fruitful to concentrate attention on hybrids and their offspring and attempt to equate the offsprings of hybrids with numerical ratios. Thus Mendel's initial creative act was to conceive of a relation between the unexplained data of heredity and numerical ratios. Mendel states.

> . . . among all the numerous experiments made, not one has been carried out to such an extent and in such a way as to make it possible to determine the number of different forms under which the offspring of hybrids appear, or to arrange these forms with certainty according to their separate generations, or definitely to ascertain their statistical relations.[13]

Experiments conducted under the guidance of his clue to statistical relations resulted first in the discovery of the 3 to 1 ratio of dominant recessive forms among the progeny of hybrids.

Further experiments led to the translation of the 3 to 1 ratio of visible characters to a 1:2:1 ratio of unseen and imagined characters. These latter characters correspond to what we now call the gene, though Mendel did not use this term. But the 1:2:1 ratio suggested to Mendel the algebraic relationship. $A + 2Aa + a$, where A represented the dominant character, a the recessive character and the entire expression $A + 2Aa + a$ represented the relations of these character among the offspring of the hybrids.

The expression $A + 2\,Aa + a$ led Mendel to the conception that the hereditary characters were related in a manner similar to that of mathematical combination series. This suggested further experiments, and further relating of the ideas of mathematics to the postulated characters until finally Mendel conceived the basic postulates upon which our knowledge of heredity is based.

The function of the mathematical system was primarily to serve as a guide in interpreting the data of heredity. Mendel's

---

[12]Bronowski, J., "Science and Human Values — I," Universities Quarterly, 10, May 1956, p. 247.
[13]Mendel, Gregor, op. cit., p. 142.

postulated characters were not in themselves numerical or algebraic units. They were supposedly real things that existed and influenced the development of organisms, but by assuming that during reproduction they behaved relative to each other as algebraic units behave in an algebraic calculation it was possible for Mendel to create relations among the characters that would satisfy the observed data.

This process of using a known system of ideas as a guide to construct a new system is what is meant by retroduction. It is also presumably the method by which new theories are created or by which unsatisfactory theories are modified.

An example of the modification of a theory was found in Morgan's work of about 1910. The then current postulates of genetic theory could not explain certain results Morgan found in some of his experiments. The results were not in error so something must be wrong with one or more of the postulates of the theory. Morgan made the corrections and thus discovered sex linkage, but he used a guiding system in the process. This guiding system was not mathematical. Instead it was cytological. The known history of chromosomes during gamete formation and fertilization gave Morgan the idea he needed to modify Mendel's postulates.

While any appropriate system of knowledge, i.e., any deductive system, may be used as a guide in the modification of an operating system or in the creation of a new system, mathematics has been particularly useful. The reason for this may be that the universe is mathematical as the Pythagoreans claimed, or it may be that mathematicians have proliferated so many systems that one can usually find an appropriate one. One advantage of using a mathematical system as a guide in creating a new theory lies in the fact that mathematical systems are already developed with units and operations of calculation or deduction carefully delineated. Thinking with such a system becomes mechanical and hence relatively easy.

Returning to our discussion of the relation of deductive systems to scientific theories, the concepts of mathematics and reproduction used by Mendel represented the primitive terms of Mendel's theory. The new concepts of character, dominance, recessiveness, segregation, and recombination were defined terms. The postulates were statements concerning the properties and behaviors of the characters and the relation of the characters to the appearance of the organisms.

We have finally arrived at he point where we can discuss the Natural Science course and can answer the questions raised initially concerning such a course. The questions were: what is Natural Science? What relation does it have to general education? What does one do with it in the classroom?

The answer to the first question has been given at length. Natural Science, as we conceive it, is the story of the development and growth of theories, conceptual schemes, or deductive systems as they operate in our continued search for explanations of natural phenomena. It is an exposition of how scientists operate mentally and experimentally to produce the interlocking systems of concepts and conceptual schemes that represent scientific knowledge today. Natural Science conceived in this way permits us to select certain areas for intensive study, while we cheerfully neglect others that for one reason or another are unsuitable.

Furthermore, Natural Science conceived as an interlocking system of ideas, in which one or more theories serve as primitive terms and guiding systems for another theory, permits us to teach science as an interlocking related whole rather than as an endless list of unrelated facts and terms to be memorized. An example of the interrelatedness of conceptual schemes which are primarily biological is given below.

Such an organization can serve as a guide for the development of a teaching program. The knowledge of primitive terms and postulates of the systems would give directions for the selection of the subject matter to be taught. Furthermore, by following this pattern it would be possible to impart some sense of the order and logic involved in scientific growth, and to present sciences to the students as a vital, growing, exciting experience.

The answer to the second question concerning the relation of Natural Science to general education depends on what is meant by general education. According to our interpretation general educational is a movement dedicated to conceiving and teaching a synthesis of man's knowledge of himself and his universe. It is a reaction against the fragmentation of specialism which neglects the fundamental relations that exist at the foundation of all knowledge.

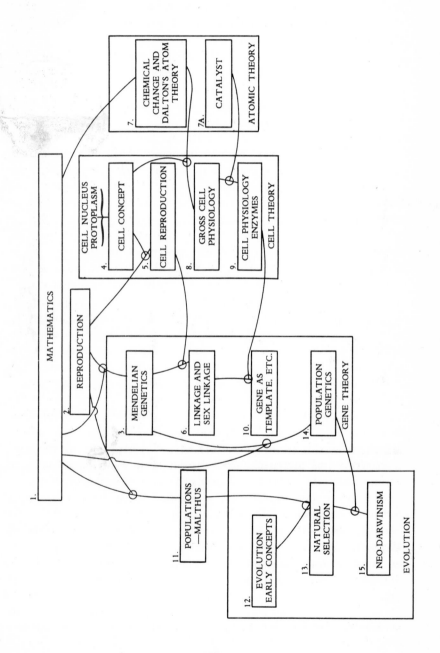

MATHEMATICS

1.

ATOMIC THEORY

7. CHEMICAL CHANGE AND DALTON'S ATOM THEORY

7A. CATALYST

CELL THEORY

CELL NUCLEUS PROTOPLASM

4. CELL CONCEPT

5. CELL REPRODUCTION

8. GROSS CELL PHYSIOLOGY

9. CELL PHYSIOLOGY ENZYMES

REPRODUCTION

2.

GENE THEORY

3. MENDELIAN GENETICS

6. LINKAGE AND SEX LINKAGE

10. GENE AS TEMPLATE, ETC.

14. POPULATION GENETICS

11. POPULATIONS —MALTHUS

EVOLUTION

12. EVOLUTION EARLY CONCEPTS

13. NATURAL SELECTION

15. NEO-DARWINISM

It is the task of the general educationist to uncover these relations and to spell them out in terms which are understandable to the average student.   If this definition of general education is accepted then Natural Science as depicted above is appropriate for general education purposes, because it offers the possibility of synthesizing and relating the whole of science.

The third question is related to classroom procedure, and for this question we have no new answers. A new subject matter concerning deductive systems, their relations and operations would be mandatory.   The logical and chronological sequence of material would be determined by the logical and historical relatedness of the concepts.   Some separation of the growth and development of physical and biological systems of ideas would be essential even though at the same time some interlocking would have to be shown.

At the present moment the first two terms of our course are concerned primarily with biological concepts with the addition of some geology in the second term as a part of the development of ideas concerning evolution.   The third term is reserved for mathematics and physical science concepts.   This arrangement permits us to deal with three major areas of the natural sciences, i.e., biological, physical, and mathematical, but at a cost.   We cannot go as deeply into certain areas as we think would be desirable.   Hence, we are discussing the possibility of inaugurating soon a program with two parallel parts.   One part would be concerned throughout one academic year with the development of biological concepts, while the other part would be restricted to the physical science concepts. Both of these proposed programs would have the same major objectives and have the same core subject matter of the relations of concepts and conceptual schemes, but these basic ideas would be exemplified with different materials in the two courses.

Another possible alternative would be to have a common term for all students and then to bifurcate the course into two parallel parts, one of which would be concerned with physical science concepts and the other with biological science concepts.

The present Natural Science sequence would be continued during the trial period and we hope that after several years of experience we will be in a position to decide whether the single course covering both biological and physical science concepts in tandem should be replaced by one or the other of the parallel programs.

chapter 15

GENERAL EDUCATION COURSES IN SCIENCE AT MILLS COLLEGE

*Richard Wistar**

Certain details of the graduation requirements of Mills College will serve to set the stage for this discussion of the courses in general biology and general physical science. Before graduating all students must take the six units of An Introduction to Literature and Writing, the four units of An Introduction to Values in American Life, the two units of Health Education, one of several courses in the Fine Arts, one foreign language through the second year college level, and one of six courses in Science.

The science courses available for selection are: the beginning courses in Botany, Chemistry, Physics, and Zoology, the General Biology, and the General Physical Science. The four beginning science courses are typical lecture and laboratory courses primarily designed to prepare the student for subsequent work in the field. The two general science courses consist of three lectures and a one-hour section meeting that will be described later.

During the last thirty years Mills has experimented with a combined life and physical science survey with several instructors handling various parts of the subject matter, and with the separated courses, each conducted by one instructor. We have found the latter alternative to be far more effective. The limitations that are inevitable with a single instructor trying to handle such a broad field are more than made up for by the unified approach that one person can bring to bear.

---

*The Author is Professor of Chemistry, Mills College.

201

One important factor in this situation is that class sizes are small enough to enable the same instructor to handle the lectures and most of the section meetings of his course. If this were not true we might have come to a different conclusion.

The Course in General Physical Science

1. A large part of this section is paraphrased from the preface of "Man and His Physical Universe" by R. Wistar, second edition, John Wiley and Sons, Inc., N.Y.C. 1953.

Courses in general physical science are planned and taught from many different points of view. The usual practice is to present a digested or condensed version of the four principal physical sciences; Astronomy, Geology, Physics, and Chemistry. The writer of this article has found that it is difficult enough to present in one full year the material that is usually considered the minimum basic background for further work in any one of the physical sciences. As a result of this experience, he has attempted an approach for non-science majors that differs from the usual one in several important aspects.

For one thing, a general physical science course presents a unique opportunity because it is a terminal course. There is no need to build up an elaborate vocabulary in any science. Such vocabulary is essential for further work in that subject but the student who does not continue to use it forgets it in a matter of days after the final examination. Time saved here can be spent profitably in generalizing about the scientific method and in pointing out the interdependence of science and contemporary society. These important points are usually crowded out of the standard introductory science course.

Few of the students who take courses in general physical science will earn their living as practising scientists, but all of them will be citizens in a world where scientific problems are constantly confronting the general public. The fluoridation of public drinking water and our national policy on atomic weapons testing are two current examples.

The central problems around which our physical science course is organized are not the only possible ones, but it seems to me that the basis on which they were chosen is essential for a successful course. The main topics are ones that are important in the field of physical science and are, at the same time, related to experiences of continuing interest to the students.   There is a two-fold purpose in this plan.   In the first place, the student's life after he leaves college will be richer for his having gained more under-standing of what goes on around him; in the second place, he will probably retain more of any subject that he learns around a framework of everyday experience.   The subjects are treated broad-ly.   There are many gaps in the field, but the teacher must remem-ber that if he does his job well the student will not stop learning when classes are over.   Those subjects that have been picked for treatment have been presented carefully and as rigorously as student preparation permits.

The usual order of treatment is to begin with facts of every-day experience, then to go on to facts that can be presented by demonstration, then to present additional factual material in lec-tures, and, from all this, to develop the models and theories that are currently accepted as the best representation of the nature of the physical world.   To the extent that it is possible, modern scientific developments are explained in terms of these models and theories.   Problems are put in their historical and cultural setting.

There has been no attempt to segregate the subject matter of the different branches of physical science.   Chemistry and physics are scattered throughout all the units.   Astronomy is mostly con-fined to the unit on the solar system, and geology to the unit on the geological history of the earth.   Photography starts a broad treatment that covers light and lenses, wave motion in general, sound, music, and color.   Forecasting the weather is the starting point for a discussion of gases and gas laws, kinetic theory, change of phase and the application of these to understanding weather and climate.   The unit on atomic structure presents the evidence for the atomic theory and then considers the evidence accumulated in the last hundred years leading to the Bohr atom, atomic energy, and the fusion reaction.

The class is broken up into sections of twelve students or less for a one hour laboratory period each week.   It has taken ingenuity to develop meaningful experiments for such a short period.   Even though they are simple, these experiments do give the students a rough feeling for the problems involved in accumulating data and in manipulating it so that it is stated in a useful fashion.   Some demonstrations are best presented to a small group and these are shown in the section meetings.

There is a program of outside reading of reports designed to expose the students to the best of scientific writing for the layman. During each semester thirty articles must be read from current issues of the Scientific American Magazine and from "A Treasury of Science" edited by Harlow Shapley. These are reported by title only. I am sure that parts of this assignment are done in a hurry, but with many students the exposure produces at "take," and they enjoy it. Finally, there are three book reports due each semester. The book list keeps growing at one end and is pruned at the other, and it includes anything I can find that has a reasonable physical science content and is interestingly written. The reports are carefully and constructively criticized for style, content, and critical analysis. One of these reports deals with the climate of the student's home town and is drawn from material supplied by the nearest weather bureau as well as reference texts. The part of the work described in this paragraph broadens the course and relates it to the student's life after leaving the campus.

First Semester

1. Experiments with light reflection and refraction
2. Focal length of lens
3. Speed of sound
4. Demonstration spark spectra, interference, diffraction
5. Demonstrations and experiments with polarized light, stereopticon
6. Scale model of solar system
7. Force table experiment
8. Exercises with solar system charts
9. Ditto
10. Exercise on use of geological survey map
11. Exercise on interpretation of geological sequence diagram

Second Semester

1. Experiment with Boyle's Law apparatus
2. Exercise on vapor pressure change of phase, and humidity
3. Exercise on isotherms
4. Exercise with weather maps
5. Experiments with static electricty
6. Experiments with Ohm's law and magnetism
7. Experiments with electric wiring and working problems
8. Experiment with assembling electric motors

9. Demonstration of automobile motor and ignition system
10. Demonstration and experiment with geiger counter, Wilson Cloud chamber and radiation
11. Experiment on plotting radiation field

Outside Reading and Reports

GENERAL SCIENCE
    Pasteur by Vallery Radot
    Logic of the Sciences by Northrup
    Search for Truth by Bell
    Evolution of Physics by Einstein
    Science and Method by Poincare
    Harvard Classics — Volume on Farady, Helmholtz, etc.
    Science and Common Understanding by Oppenheimer
    Design of the Universe by Kahn
    Science and Human Values by Wigner
    Main Currents of Scientific Thought by Mason
    Mathematics and Imagination by Kasner and Newman
    Philosophy of Physics by Planck
    Of Stars & Men by Shapley
    Flatland by Abbott
    The Sleepwalkers by Koestles

ASTRONOMY
    Mysterious Universe by Jeans
    Thru Time and Space by Jeans
    The Universe Around Us by Jeans
    Star Gazer by Harsanyi
    Star and Atoms by Eddington
    Exploring the Heavens by Fisher
    Stars and Men by Ionides
    Conquest of Space by Ley
    Nature of the Universe by Hoyle
    Copernicus and His World by Kesten
    The World We Live In by Barnett

GEOLOGY
    Sea Around Us by Carson
    Adventures in Scenery by Willard
    On the Trail of Ancient Man by Andrews
    Incomparable Valley by Matthes
    Early Man in the New World by K. Macgowan
    Volcanoes, Old & New by Coleman
    The Formation of the California Landscape by Bureau of Mines

LIGHT AND PHOTOGRAPHY
    Making a Photograph by Ansel Adams
    Visual Illusions by Luckiesh

MISCELLANEOUS
        Camera, Take the Stand by Herzog and Erickson
        In Search of Beauty in Music by Seashore
        Unfolding of Artistic Activity by Schaefer-Simmern
        Story of Color by Birren
        Music — A Science and an Art by J. Redfield
        Color Fundamentals by M. Graves
        Many Uses of the Atom by Kaempffert
        Sun, Sea, and Sky by Krick and Fleming
        Song of the Sky by Murchie
        Climate Changes by Shapley
        Birth of the Sun by Gamow
        Climate through the Ages by Brooks
        Ways of the Weather by Humphreys
        Climate and Civilization by Huntington
        Our American Weather by Kimble
        Mme. Curie by E. Curie
        New Pathways in Science by Eddington
        Science and the Human Temperment by Shroedinger*
        Mr. Tomkins in Wonderland by Gamow*
        Mr. Tomkins Explores the Atom by Gamow*
        Flights from Chaos by Shapley
        Fifty Years of Atomic Energy by Gamow
        Atoms and Energy by Massey
        Common Sense of Science by Bronowski
        The Universe and Dr. Einstein by Barnett*
        Search for Truth by E. T. Bell*
        Electrons, Waves and Messages by Pierce
        Rutherford by A. S. Eve
        Atoms in the Family by L. Fermi
        Copernicus to Einstein by Reichenbach
        Open Mind by Oppenheimer
        Atomic Physics & Human Knowledge by Bohr
        Climate & Energy of Nations by S. F. Markham
        How to Know & Predict the Weather by R. M. Fisher

General Biological Science at Mills College*

Since one of the roles of a liberal arts college like Mills is to
give to each student a sense of the interrelatedness of the world
around us, physical and cultural, we believe that each student should
at least be exposed to several of the areas of human knowledge
she might not otherwise choose to investigate.   There are, then,

*By D. Bowers, Professor General Biological Science, Mills College.

certain subect requirements leading to the Bachelor of Arts degree from Mills College. Among these requirements is a year of one science, physical or biological. In attempting to produce individuals with a well-rounded background, we strongly urge each student to study that science she has not encountered before. Many students have had experience with only biology, or only physical science in high school, and these students then are the ones we want to get into the area new to them. We offer several year-long courses in science, any one of which will fulfill the science requirement. However, we offer two general courses especially for students not intending to major in science, one in general physical science, the other in general biology. It might be possible in years to come to require students to study both these broad fields, but at the present, we must assume that one course will fulfill the ideals for a liberal arts training.

THE COURSE IN GENERAL BIQLOGY

There are four main approaches on which we base the course. We attempt to 1) acquaint students with man's physical structure and operation — as an example of the way in which a living machine functions; 2) discuss the hosts of other organisms with which we live; 3) present man's place in the biological world; and 4) explore the evolutionary processes by which present day organisms have come to be.

Our strategy in presenting the material to freshmen students not completely sold on the study of biology, is to begin where some interest usually already lies, that is, with man himself as a living entity. As in an automobile, there are certain things that must be present in order for a proper functioning of the machine, so also in a living system there are certain things which we describe and demonstrate that make it able to carry out the various activities ascribable to life. As we build the fund of basic facts concerning the structure and function of the human body, we try to point out correlations and interrelations so that with some important "trees" filled in, the "forest" itself begins to assume some form. It is the "forest" that will be remembered by the non-science student and it is thus important to present enough but not too many of the confusing individual "trees."

After a study of the human organism ending with reproduction, we move into the mechanics of heredity and finish the first half of the course with a discussion of human genetics.

The second semester begins with a presentation of the idea that we will be considering the process of evolution throughout the remainder of the course. This also finds a responsive note in students who, like most all of us, have wonderings about where or from what we have come. We begin by contrasting plant functions with the animal functions already studied and begin a survey of the plant kingdom with the simplest forms. The consideration of more complex plants follows. Our emphasis here in plants is on the development of modern, terrestrial kinds from ancestral aquatic plants and on the types of modifications of basic systems that have taken place in the course of this development.

We next move into the animal kingdom again at the simple level where plants and animals are oftentimes nearly indistinguishable and progress through more complex forms in a survey of the more important animal phyla. Here again, we point out the new characteristics that have led different animal types to successful survival in aquatic and terrestrial environments with an eye to making the "forest" stand out clearly while individual "trees" play a supporting role. Of course the relationships of other organisms to man are pointed out all along the way wherever pertinent to shedding light on man's position in the living world.

A section designed specifically to show the interrelations of plants and animals follows. Here, certain ecological principles are presented based on the factual information and interpretations of the foregoing material.

The final part of the course deals directly with evolution. With the background provided by the earlier work, this tends to tie together many different strands left dangling previously. Our discussion of the organic evolution of man brings us back to our starting point in the cycle.

We are not trying to make a man-centered presentation of biology, but rather we are attempting to show man's place in the world around us. This we summarize with a diagram like the following:

We claim that any well-rounded individual must have an acquaintance of some degree with this whole gamut and that our

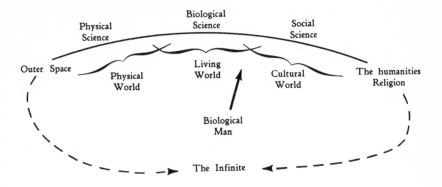

study of biology should have made a contribution for the individual student from this particular segment.

The format of this course is nothing new. It is composed of three fifty minute lectures and one fifty minute laboratory demonstration each week. The class is subdivided into several smaller sections for the demonstration period.

In these section meetings we demonstrate some simple experimental techniques and the results to be obtained with them, show the students at first hand some biological objects many of them have never seen, and engage in discussions concerning the topics presented in lecture. Periodic quizzing takes place here as a stimulus to the students to keep abreast of the course in private study.

There are three one-hour examinations and one three-hour examination in each semester. Since, as stated, our objective is the "forest" not just the "trees," most of our questions are of the short paragraph or sentence answer type which require of the student realignment of materials in some different way from that which was presented to them. Many questions partially destroy the gestalt of text and lecture by expecting some thought and cross cutting of our classroom presentation. Simple memorization of tables and lists of facts represent only basic activities for the student. Our goal is the practice in the use of facts to build bigger pictures.

There are some secondary objectives we hope to accomplish insofar as the course format will allow. We try to present some idea of the scientific method and science itself. We point out some of the contributions of biological science to our way of living.

Regarding the scientific method, it seems unrealistic to expect to get across to students this way of thinking in our short laboratory periods. Much more time must be expended by individual activity on the part of the student in a laboratory setting before such attitudes as those of a scientist will take root. Herein lies one of the main weaknesses of our course.

Whether there is any carry over from our approach to this particular subject into other areas, we are not prepared to say. In some students, we can see progress through the year in "getting the idea" of putting factual information to work in the production of larger concepts. This much, at least, is encouraging.

chapter 16

INSTRUCTION IN FUNDAMENTAL SCIENTIFIC CONCEPTS AT NORTHWESTERN UNIVERSITY

*Roderick L. Hines**

The generally recognized need for an introductory science course designed for non-science majors is met at Northwestern University by the Basic Science course in the liberal arts college. Basic Science is the direct descendent of the course, An Introduction to Science, discussed in the earlier edition of this series on general education.[1] As it is now organized, Basic Science consists of almost equal amounts of material from chemistry, mathematics, and physics. However, the topics are chosen and presented so that the pattern of the courses resembles the case history approach advocated by Conant in his book, "On Understanding Science." Relatively few topics are covered compared to the original course, and these are introduced with an historical approach so the students can appreciate the simplicity of some of the great scientific discoveries. Some aspects of the discoveries are carried through to our present day state of knowledge to illustrate the development of scientific concepts. Considerable emphasis is placed upon quantitative description of various experimental observations and their representation in formulas so that derived formulas can be used to predict other observations. Appropriate mathematical techniques are taught as the need for them arises. The philosophy of the present course is to give the student an understanding and appreciation of the

*The Author is Assistant Professor Department of Physics, Northwestern University.

[1]Earl J. McGrath, "Science in General Education," (1948), p. 230.

power and range of validity of the methods employed in mathematics, physics, and chemistry. These principles are stated in the university bulletin describing Basic Science as follows: "A year course dealing with some of the fundamental concepts and theories of the physical sciences and mathematics presented in lectures, demonstrations, and laboratory exercises. These basic concepts and theories will be developed through integrated problems from several of the physical sciences. The methods common to all sciences will be illustrated."

Basic Science is an elective course for undergraduates in the liberal arts college and other schools at Northwestern University. The bachelor of arts program requires two years of laboratory science which is met by selecting two of the following courses: Astronomy, Biology, Chemistry, Geology or Physical Geography, Mathematics, Physics, and Basic Science. Approximately 16% of the liberal arts students with non-science majors, graduating in 1955 and 1956 had taken Basic Science to fulfill part of their science requirement.

The original course, An Introduction to Science, differed considerably from the present Basic Science in that it contained two quarters of material from the physical, earth, and biological sciences, and required a related quarter of mathematics. As such, the number of topics covered was quite large and required a large number of lecturers to adequately present the different fields of knowledge. This created difficulty in maintaining continuity in the lectures and in suitable staffing of the discussion sections. It is almost impossible to find discussion-class instructors qualified in all three of the fields of earth, physical, and biological science.

The course material centers on topics which show the relation between the physical sciences and illustrate the scientific method. The course begins with a short discussion of the scientific method and then proceeds to investigate the nature of our solar system. Starting with observations by the students on the apparent motion of the sun, moon and stars, the geocentric theory of the universe is built up. Then the heliocentric theory of the universe as put forth by Copernicus is brought in and it is shown that both theories accounted equally well for the observed data until the invention of the telescope and the observations of Galileo tipped the scales in favor of the present heliocentric theory. Since accurate distances to various heavenly objects are required to differentiate between the two theories, the course digresses to cover the elements of trigonometry and graphical analysis.   Then a discussion of Kepler's laws leads into an introduction to mechanics which shows that the heavenly bodies move in accordance with laws which we can experimentally observe and verify on earth.

The next case history deals with Boyle's experiments with gases and it is shown that the same laws of mechanics which govern planetary motion also determine the behavior of gases.   In this manner the course proceeds from one case history to another and wherever possible shows the relationship between case histories.

The second quarter of the course begins with a study of number systems and the development of our present number system. The laws of exponents and the use of exponents in expressing the very large and very small numbers which appear in physical science are presented because of their subsequent use in discussing atomic theory.   Next the concepts of graphs and mathematical curves are presented and differential calculus is introduced in terms of the geometrical slope of a curve.   This knowledge is then used to solve maximum and minimum problems and is subsequently used in discussion of heat and thermodynamics.

Next the early work on investigation of elements is used to emphasize the importance of the concept of chemical elements. This leads naturally through studies of early combustion theories into the development of atomic theory as the foundation of modern chemistry.   A lecture demonstration at this point of the actual dimension of an oil molecule is very effective.   Chemical phenomena in terms of atoms, atomic and molecular weights, chemical molecular structure and isomerism are included.

Now that energy has been introduced in the vague form of heat involved in a chemical reaction, the course returns to physics to discuss the concept of work and energy in its various forms and to state the principle of conservation of mechanical energy.   Then the concepts of temperature and heat are presented and after demonstrations of several experiments with heat, the early caloric theory of heat is presented to explain the experiments.   Count Rumford's weight of heat and cannon boring experiments are used to prove the inadequacy of the caloric theory and it is replaced by the modern picture of heat as a form of kinetic energy of atoms.

The relation between heat and energy is clarified by the laws of thermodynamics and the consequences of these laws on engine efficiencies and our world-wide heat resources are discussed.

The third quarter begins with lectures on sound to bring out the subtle aspects of wave motion. Then a number of demonstrations with light are carried out to give experimental information on the nature of light. The early wave theory and particle theory are discussed and compared and the importance and technical difficulty of an experimental measurement of the velocity of light in a transparent substance as a test between the two theories is emphasized. Then, interference experiments are described to illustrate a case where only wave motion can satisfactorily account for the results. The photoelectric effect is mentioned to bring out the particle nature of light and the necessity of thinking in terms of both particles and waves. The need to understand the nature of light starts a brief presentation of electrical phenomena which ends with the problem of determining the work done when two charges are moved together.

The above problem requires integral calculus for its solution so more calculus is presented at this point and a number of related problems are worked out to show the scope of this new mathematical method. Then, as an interlude to show that there are fields of mathematics which are of interest in themselves and have little application, the topology of surfaces is discussed and among other things the theorm of the existence of only five regular polyhedra is proved.

Returning to electrical phenomena and the nature of matter, the modern atomic structure theory is built up after the periodic classification of the elements has shown that systematic order does exist. Radioactivity is discussed and Rutherford's bombardment experiment is used as the starting point for the modern theory. Some nuclear theory is presented and the course ends with a discussion of atomic bombs and other applications of atomic energy.

Lecture outlines of the course are handed out to the students at the beginning of each quarter. No completely satisfactory text has been found in view of the emphasis placed on case histories, the inclusion of mathematics, and quantitative calculations. Originally, "Fundamentals of Physical Science" by Krauskopf was used. Later, "Physical Science for Liberal Arts Students" by Swenson and Woods was used, and the present text is "Principles of Physical Science" by Bonner and Phillips. Some outside reading from books on reserve is assigned.

The entire class meets three times a week at one hour demonstration lectures. In addition each student attends discussion classes twice a week and a two hour laboratory period once every three weeks. Each quarter of the course carries four quarter hours of credit. Grades are given on the basis of the student's performance in weekly fifteen minute quizzes, a mid-term exam, a final exam and the laboratory. The discussion classes are limited to 25 students and are used to discuss assigned problems, lecture material, and reading assignments. Usually the discussion class instructor is one of the lecturers in the course, although if the course enrollment is large a postgraduate student may lead one or two classes.

The laboratory is an important part of the course and the experiments are chosen with the idea of giving the students experimental contact with the theories discussed in the course. During the laboratory period the students operate the equipment and record data under the supervision of a graduate student laboratory assistant. The students prepare their laboratory reports, which contain apparatus description and principles, outside of the laboratory. The laboratory equipment and facilities for the Basic Science course are separate from other laboratory facilities in the university and are supervised by the faculty members participating in the course. A list is given below of the laboratory experiments with a brief description of each.

Measurement of Fundamental Quantities — Measurements of length, mass and calculation of density of an unknown substance by direct and indirect methods.
Triangulation — Measurement of distances with trigonometry including measurement of the diameter of a clock on a university building using a simple transit.
Scientific Method — Measurement of distances and times involved in accelerated motion and in motion of a pendulum and graphical analysis of the data to obtain laws relating the measured quantities.
Gas Laws — Measurement of pressure of a given amount of gas under conditions of different temperature and pressure and comparison of results with known gas laws.
Identification of Unknown Substance — Identification

of a few selected substances by their reactions with typical chemical reagents.

Quantative Study of Chemical Reactions — Prediction and measurement of the quantity of material produced in a selected chemical reaction.

Properties of Heat — Measurements of specific heat and several calorimeter experiments.

Properties of Light — Measurements on reflection and refraction of light using ray tracing apparatus.

Radioactivity — Detection of radioactivity with Geiger counters and measurements of the absorption of different types of radioactivity in material.

The staff for the course consists of one member from each of the three regular departments of physics, chemistry, and mathematics. Each of the staff gives one third of the demonstration lectures and leads one or two discussion sections. The lecture material is arranged so that usually the lecturer changes only three times each quarter. During each lecturer's first year, he attends all of the lectures so that he becomes familiar with all of the course materal. One of the staff members is designated chairman to fix the responsibility for laboratory supervision and other matters in the course. Participation in the course is considered approximately one half of an individual's teaching load and the assignments to the course are usually of three or more years duration. Integration of the various lectures and maintainance of an even pace among the several discussion classes is important and is accomplished by weekly meetings of the staff. The weekly meetings occassionally turn into extremely useful discussions of the problems and philosophy of the course. The overall administration of the course is under the General Studies Program in the liberal arts college. The General Studies Program has several other interdepartmental courses which are staffed by members of different departments.

The course enrollment in the last few years has stayed close to 100 students divided about equally between both sexes. About 60% of the class are freshmen, 30% sophomores, and the rest juniors and seniors. The students are primarily from the liberal arts college (39%), and the business school (37%), with some from the schools of speech (12%), education (8%), and music (4%). The range of preparation of the students is very great and creates difficulty in setting the academic level of the course. Since it is specifically designed for non-science majors, no prior knowledge from high school science is assumed but students without some knowledge of science have difficulty with the course material. On the other hand, some students have had good high school courses in advanced mathematics, chemistry, and physics. These students cannot be prevented from enrolling in the course, yet an appreciable portion of the course will be repeated material and will lack the challenge that a good college course should have. Separation of the class into sections on the basis of preparation would be desirable but is not practical with the present size of the course. The discussion classes are small enough to permit discussion of related scientific topics as well as the course material. Also there is opportunity to discuss the political and philosophical effect of scientific discoveries in the past as well as in the present. Occasionally an unassigned topic such as evolution is discussed to show how it would fit within the framework of scientific method.

No changes are contemplated for the course in the immediate future. A certain amount of change comes with each change of lecturer for individuals have different ideas of what should be emphasized within the general framework of the course. It is possible that the adequate science preparation of the majority of the students will be recognized by spending less time on the earlier portions of the case histories and more time on some modern consequence of the earlier discoveries. On the whole, the approach of treating a restricted number of topics in a rigorous manner works very nicely in giving the student an understanding of science. The student will always get some knowledge of scientific works and thoughts from the newspapers and popular magazines, but an organized course of this type makes it possible for the student to grasp the real depth and universal validity of modern physical science.

chapter 17

NATURAL SCIENCES AND MATHEMATICS AT THE OREGON COLLEGE OF EDUCATION

*Anton Postl, Ph.D.**

Introduction

It would appear that in a volume devoted to "Science in General Education" it is not necessary to either define or defend the concept of General Education. Simply stated it is the modern equivalent of natural philosophy in liberal education. It can be science education for the non-scientist at its best once we have overcome the confusion of emphasis on quantity or coverage of the earlier survey type course in favor of quality of fewer select topics with the emphasis on fundamental background and with a historical perspective. In brief, such might be considered the basic philosophy for the natural science program in general education at the Oregon College of Education.

The history of the Oregon College of Education parallels in essence that of many other institutions of a similar nature in that it had its origin in a Normal School program which later developed into a successively more comprehensive program leading eventually to a regular four year collegiate degree program in elementary education. To this basic program were later added lower division pre-professional courses, a degree program in general studies, a broad secondary education program in the three areas of the Humanities, Science-Mathematics, and the Social Sciences. To these have now been added programs at the graduate level leading to the master's

*The Author is Professor of Science, Chairman of the Department of Science and Mathematics, Monmouth, Oregon.

degree both in elementary education and more recently also in the field of secondary education, both of which have received accredita tion by the appropriate national organizations.   Our most recei.. addition has been the authorization of a regular liberal arts program which is still in the planning stage and may be incorporated as an alternative for elementary teachers.

Currently, planning is in progress and is already partially approved to offer two alternate programs to students in elementary education.   One would consist of a double major wtih education as one and the other major in one of the three areas of the Humanities, Science-Mathematics, and the Social Sciences.   The second program would consist of the regular major in education with a regular minor in one of three aforementioned areas and a second teaching minor in the areas of Art, Music, Physical, or Special Education.

By enrollment, the greatest number of our students are in elementary education but it is our feeling that these teachers not only need a liberal background in the natural sciences as cultured and educated leaders in their communities, but need it even more strongly if they are to draw on it in part in their own teaching. We do maintain, however, a rather distinct separation of functions and that of the Science and Mathematics Department is to provide the necessary foundations upon which the professional education for teachers can subsequently be built.   The secondary education program, general studies, liberal arts, and the pre-professional programs of our college follow the more traditional lines of specialized single science courses, though students in general studies, in partic ular, frequently select general education courses.

Though our general education courses are thus in no way limited to students in elementary education, these students do, nevertheless, make up our largest single group and from the atten tion that science and mathematics education has recently received nationally, this group is in every way deserving of our best planning and thinking.   It is in the long-established elementary education program, then, that the greatest change, and we hope along with it progress, has been accomplished.   Some of these changes reflect merely the natural growth from the former briefer Normal School program to a three-year and now to a four-year degree program.   In such an expansion period it is only reasonable that the natural sciences and mathematics have a proportionate share of the expanded curriculum. Unfortunately, however, additional time is not in itself a criterion for increased accomplishment. If we have made any progress in our new program it must be stated that it is the result of the joint efforts and planning of the staffs of both the Education & Psychology and the Science & Mathematics Departments as well as of the mutual recognition of the importance of both aspects, academic background and professional competence, in the education of well prepared elementary teachers.

This coming school year will see us venture into what we hope will be a greatly increased and improved program. Our program in general biology has outwardly undergone the least change in that it has not increased in scope but simply has kept pace with the newer emphases in biology and an improved laboratory program stressing a little more the "bio" part of the course. One reason that we have not felt the need for an expansion in this phase of our program is that a very high percentage of our students have a background of one year of high school biology. On the other hand their high school background as well as our own offerings have been most limited in mathematics and it is for this reason that we are introducing a year sequence of general education background mathematics. For the time being, considering the weak background of many students we may not be able to do very much in the way of high college level preparation, but we plan to be alert and with the promising better high school preparation we hope to correspondingly raise the level of our course.

The high school background of most of our students in the physical sciences is also rather limited which caused us to increase our physical science course from a nine to a twelve term hour sequence. It is the latter course which has undergone the greatest change over the last decade and with which the writer has been most intimately associated and will therefore be expanded in more detail.

The Physical Sciences

A separate course in physical sciences was established over twenty years ago as a three credit hours-one term course in the three-year program which was later expanded to a full year in the four-year degree program. Both of these courses were at first attempted in the then prevalent survey course type organization and one can only shudder to reflect on the impossibility of "covering" the field of the physical sciences in one term! Both courses were without the benefit of individual laboratory work. Though this is not an altogether unusual practice, it is, nevertheless, difficult to see how one of the major branches of the natural sciences (biology) is carried on as a laboratory course while the other is simply a lecture course.

With the termination of the three-year certificate program and the accompanying single term course one of the first steps in reorganizing the course on a year basis was to establish the course on a laboratory basis as most any conscientious natural scientist in his particular field would likely want to do. The problem here, however, though the level of the work itself is quite elementary, is actually not so simple when one considers that few workers would claim a wide enough background in all of the branches of the physical sciences to set up laboratory exercises in each, nor were there, with one exception, any manuals available for such a course. Inasmuch as one of the major aims of the program was to acquaint the student with the physical aspects of his natural environment, it seemed best to illustrate wherever possible with local familiar examples or illustrations, and thus it was decided to establish a laboratory program of our own.

In devising such a laboratory program it soon became apparent that if the laboratory program was to be closely coordinated with the lecture program that the outline of the lecture work should serve as the principle guide of the laboratory work. Too frequently, however, the lectures are simply centered around a given adopted text and the task of working out an organization in line with the purposes and aims of the course are left to the author or authors. Many of the available texts of this period were still the multiple author compendiums of materials from the various branches of the physical sciences brought together for a survey type of approach. This approach frequently lacked in judicious selection and unity of philosophy. There are those who because of some of these problems would throw up their hands in disgust and offer nothing but the traditional single science course offerings in chemistry or physics but fail to see that a student devoting only one year to the physical sciences would in this manner have only the advantages of a possibly more intensive and rigorous course which as far as his total understanding of his physical environment is concerned, however, would, nevertheless be quite limited.   In a general education approach the answer then does not seem to lie with the traditional single-science pre-professional type courses nor is it to be found in the broad shallow surveys.   Another alternative was offered by those steeped in the cultural liberal arts type programs in an historical approach of a very few select topics thus getting away from the breadth of the surveys and substituting for intensiveness and rigorousness of a single science the thoroughness of the historical development of few select topics.   While this may acquaint the non-scientist better with the ways of science and scientists, it nevertheless, results again in a too-limited view and background.   The feeling of the writer, at least, was that somewhere between the two extremes of the pendulum of the survey and the case history approaches could be found a reasonable position that would satisfy the aims of a general education course.   To find it, at least for us, was the next task which led to the need for a concise statement of basic principles.

This search led first to the evolvement of a brief set of objectives, and secondly to an overview of topic organization and concordant relationships.[1]

I.   Objectives
    A.   General Objectives
        1.   To acquaint the students with the true aims of scientific endeavor.
        2.   To show the interrelations of the various branches of physical science which will enable students to obtain a unified picture of their physical environment.

    B.   Specific Objectives
        1.   To provide the fundamental background necessary to an understanding of the basic principles covered in the different branches of the physical sciences, an understanding which should lead to greater appreciation and enjoyment of their physical surroundings.
        2.   To provide an opportunity for students to work in an actual laboratory situation which will im-

---

[1]A General Education Course in the Foundations of Physical Science, The Science Teacher, XXI. 15-18, 1954.

press them with the need for objectivity, honesty, accuracy, and thoroughness, thus acquainting students first hand with the methods of the natural sciences.

3. To acquaint students with the literature sources appropriate to their level of understanding, enabling them to keep up with current developments.

The Fundamental Branches of Physical Science

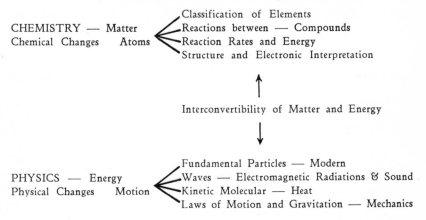

CHEMISTRY — Matter
Chemical Changes   Atoms

Classification of Elements
Reactions between — Compounds
Reaction Rates and Energy
Structure and Electronic Interpretation

Interconvertibility of Matter and Energy

PHYSICS — Energy
Physical Changes   Motion

Fundamental Particles — Modern
Waves — Electromagnetic Radiations & Sound
Kinetic Molecular — Heat
Laws of Motion and Gravitation — Mechanics

Having thus spelled out the objectives and overall organization, the next task was how to implement them in lecture room and laboratory. At the time it appeared to us that of the then existing texts the well-known book by Krauskopf[2] came in closest harmony to the aforementioned objectives and organization, and this text has been used rather successfully for a number of years.

The order of topics or major organization of the text, however, was adapted to have essentially an opening term with the major emphasis on the earth sciences, the second on chemistry, and the third on physics. The text has been supplemented for a number of years with a source book[3] for collateral reading to lend a historical perspective. The students also have frequent problem assignments and are expected to submit a paper each term. For the

[2]Krauskopf, K. B., *Fundamentals of Physical Science*, McGraw-Hill Book Company, Inc., New York, 1948.
[3]*A Treasury of Science*, Shapley, H. et al. Edit, Harper & Brothers.

first term a biography of a physical scientist of some brief contact during the term is chosen. For the second term, in order to acquaint the students with the contemporary literature a review of an article of their own choice from the current periodicals is assigned. For the third and final term an assignment of a little more comprehensive term paper on a special topic involving a literature search is made.

As part of our lecture programs we schedule each term the showing of a few well selected and coordinated films. We have found that some of our best films are from private industrial organizations.

Laboratory Program

The next major task was to organize a laboratory program which had for its inception only the conviction that students in a general education course in the natural sciences should not be denied the opportunity of individual laboratory work which, after all, is the most logical way to understand and appreciate the natural sciences. This required also the logistic support of a cooperative administration which was enthusiastically given.

The actual selection of experiments had to be made and it was hoped it would turn out to be more than just enough work to occupy the time of a requisite number of laboratory periods. There was to be not only variety of topical material but also variety in approach from experiments with liberal detail of instruction to begin with leading later to an increasing degree of independent thinking and planning; and it was hoped that a form of write-up most nearly like that of the experimental scientist would be more challenging and requiring of thoughtful participation on the part of the student than a mere routine fill-in type of write-up. Many of the experiments in the areas of physics and chemistry in particular are well-known and if any uniqueness can be claimed it is only in the incorporation of the local scene in the areas of geology and meteorology. Another novelty introduced was called a special experiment each term which permits the student to branch out according to his interests into an advanced experiment of his own choosing, a demonstration of a self-constructed model or exhibit, a piece of special equipment or apparatus, etc. Another aim through the years has been to have field trips in astronomy, geology, and to regionally important industrial plants. A more detailed description of these initial phases of establishment of the laboratory program has been reported elsewhere.[4] The experiments were initially mimeographed but as the number of experiments and participating students grew it was decided to have the material available in the form of a printed manual.[5] A list of the actual experiments follows:

ASTRONOMY
Location and Identification of Stars and Planets
The Solar System

CHEMISTRY
Physical and Chemical Changes
Chemical Equations and Calculations
Chemical Reactions
Acids, Bases, and Salts
Solubility Curves
Chemical Applications
Analytical Procedures
Some Special Tests

GEOLOGY
Identification of Rocks and Minerals
The Work of Running Water
The Work of the Sea
The Work of Glaciers
The Work of Volcanos
Historical Geology

METEOROLOGY
Weather
Climate

PHYSICS
The Metric System
Simple Machines
Concurrent Forces
The Pendulum
Temperature Scales and the Calibration of a Thermometer
Heat of Fusion
Wave Motion

---

[4] A Laboratory Program for a General Education Course in the Physical Sciences, Science Education 38: 304-7, 1954.

[5] Laboratory Experiments in the Physical Sciences. Burgess Publishing Company, Minneapolis. Minn.

Sound
Light
Magnetism and Electrostatics
Magnetism and Electricity
Electrical Power Consumption

Most of the experiment titles are indicative as to their content
but our guiding thought throughout all laboratory work is to keep
foremost in the minds of our students the trilogy of purpose, procedure, interpretation of results.

The experiments, as is evident, have been arranged alpha-
betically in order of the divisions of the physical sciences and not
in their chronological sequence. We usually begin with the experiment on the Metric System as we feel this introduces some of the
methods of scientific measurement, its instruments and units.

One of the exercises in chemistry entitled Chemical Equations
and Calculations does not involve actual laboratory work, but we
have found that having students do some of these basic operations
with the aid and presence of a laboratory instructor and an assistant has greatly helped to overcome this initial student consterna-
tion in chemistry. The scheduling of actual chemistry experiments
in the laboratory has not caused any insurmountable difficulties; in
fact, it has resulted in a more effective utilization of our available
laboratory facilities. The chemistry equipment is kept stored in
separate wooden boxes numbered with the same numbers as the
laboratory desk stations to make for a uniform distribution
throughout the laboratory. Each box has only the essential equipment with a check list so that students and storeroom attendant
may both have a ready check of the contents. The additional equipment and supplies necessary for this course were actually minimal
considering the available stock already on hand.

Four of the experiments in geology on the work of some of
the erosional and relief-building agents are largely based on work
with topographic maps supplemented with models and three-
dimensional plastic and shaded topographic maps to aid students
in their interpretations.

For the work in meteorology we keep a weekly weather log
from the appropriate instruments and also use regular Weather
Maps for elementary interpretation of weather records.

Evaluation and Conclusions

During the academic year of 1953-54 a joint study was undertaken at our school and two cooperating institutions, a parallel program at the Southern Oregon College and a "control" program at the Oregon State College in Corvallis. The main purpose of the study was to determine if individual laboratory work in a natural science course such as the one under discussion makes a measurable contribution to students in general education programs.

At the first two institutions the students were divided equally into lecture and laboratory sections. The lecture group had the usual three weekly lecture hours while the laboratory group had only two hour lecture periods but in addition a two hour laboratory period. The third student group at the Oregon State College were enrolled in about the same type of course using also the same text but under a different title and with a different number of hours per week. All of the student groups were pre- and post-tested with the same two tests to determine if any significant differences of performance among them could be found. The two test instruments chosen were:

1. A test of Science Reasoning and Understanding Physical Sciences Form A[6]
2. A test of General Proficiency in the Field of Natural Sciences Forms Y and Z[7]

The first of these two tests it was hoped would bring out any differences in accomplishment by the two methods of teaching towards the aim of General Education while the latter was more an index of differences in factual information background that was obtained by the different number of lecture periods per week.

The results of the study were inconclusive in that no significant differences in performance by the student groups under the two methods of teaching were evident. Though no attempt will be made to describe or defend the study[8] here in any further detail it might be of interest to mention the usual doubts as to the ability

---

[6]Cooperative Study of Evaluation in General Education of the American Council on Education, 1953.

[7]Cooperative General Achievement Tests, Educational Testing Service, 1948.

[8]The Value of Laboratory Work in the Natural Sciences for Students in Programs of General Education. Ph.D. Thesis, Oregon State College, 1955.

of the test or tests to measure or show what the actual contributions of individual laboratory work are beyond the obvious acquaintance with the ways and instruments with which scientists work which by itself must contribute greatly towards better appreciation and understanding of the natural sciences. The importance of individual laboratory in the training of prospective teachers who themselves will be expected to conduct laboratory experiments in their classrooms is so self-evident as to be hardly demanding any further defense except as with all other work that the laboratory if it is to be an important and valuable attribute must be well planned and organized and with an equal amount of preparation, even devotion, as goes into good lecture preparation and not as a subordinate time-consuming appendage. In the final analysis the success of any program rests on the planning, enthusiasms, and background of the participating staff which in turn is quickly reflected by the students who have on the whole accepted the laboratory program quite enthusiastically. During the period of special study when they were divided into individual laboratory and straight lecture groups, frequently the feeling of the latter group was that they wished they were in the laboratory program and reports from the laboratory school supervisors also indicate an increased willingness of the student teachers to experiment in the classroom which would appear to be only a natural corollary. In this connection it is only proper to state that our program has also had the enthusiastic support of the participating staff over the years. Too frequently it happens that programs of general education obtain only the grudging support of people assigned to this program in a purely service capacity whose real interests, however, lie elsewhere, i.e. with research or the pre-professional majors of their own special fields. At present we have several instructors teaching parallel lecture and laboratory sections and the students are free to select any one of these to fit their particular schedule. We thus approach the program on a cooperative basis with weekly conferences of the participating staff members which results in a coordinate program and a sharing of the basic load instead of overloading one staff member to the point of repetitious monotony. A common final examination covering both laboratory and lecture work is administered to all sections. These examinations are varied in character ranging from objective factual questions, to diagrams, problems, and analytical or synthesis type organization or essay questions.

Finally, our natural science program as part of general education has also been extended into the graduate program. With the inception of the Master's Degree program in Elementary Education at our college, a year sequence with a total of nine credit hours in General Education was added as a graduation requirement. It consisted of a series of three one-term courses entitled Contemporary Developments in the three areas of the Humanities, Science-Mathematics, and Social Sciences. Because of the feeling that while this is preferable to having all of the work in education it nevertheless represented insufficient time for any depth of consideration of any particular topic, this has now been changed to limiting the sequence to only two terms in the areas of minor interest, but lengthening one of the areas to a whole year sequence, thus allowing more time for one of the fields of greater interest. Coupled with the strengthening of the undergraduate preparation to permit a stronger background, this should permit much greater concentration in one of these fields for graduate level work even as part of a program in general education. Our present plan is that the year sequence if elected in the science-mathematics area would be arranged in consultation with our departmental staff and be based on the student's particular background preparation. The courses will likely be selected from the existing elective program though we have tentatively extended the Contemporary Developments course to a year sequence offering with somewhat narrower spectra for people with stronger backgrounds in either the biological or physical sciences. Our present one term broad spectrum course will be described in fuller detail elsewhere but includes elements of scientific organization, philosophy, literature with select topic material heavily based on the Scientific American books and magazine.[9]

Thus in essence is the program of general education in science and mathematics at the Oregon College of Education integrated with basic courses in each of the major areas of the biological sciences, physical sciences and mathematics, with elective offerings at the upper division level including such courses as Regional Natural History and History of Science and extending to the graduate level.

---

[9]A course in Contemporary Developments in the Sciences and Mathematics. Science Education. 43, 407-9, 1959.

chapter 18

THE GENERAL COURSE IN SCIENCE AT STEPHENS COLLEGE

D. Lee Howell*

For several years our basic science course, which is intended to be an introduction to natural science, has been in an experimental condition.   Each instructor has enjoyed the opportunity to explore, essentially unfettered, into those paths of science teaching that were opened up by his own imagination.   Reason, "intuition" and impulse have had free play, and ideas ranging from the conservative to the radical, have been exchanged.

The result is exciting!

An integrated science course with a sort of "hybrid vigor" is developing.   It stimulates the imagination and interest of our students by pointing up the personal and social implications of

---

*The Author is Professor of General Biology, Stephens College.

C. N. Rexroad, Head, Science Division, Stephens College

Mr. *Howell* is one of three persons teaching sections of General Biology which is the title for our broad introductory course.   As he indicates, each of the three, he, Miss M. M. Johnson, and Mr. Hutton use differing approaches and content.   The course carries three hours credit each of two semesters.   As taught by most instructors through the years it has resembled what is now offered in many programs of general education as Introduction to the Biological Sciences.   Presently the title will be changed to Introduction to the Natural Sciences to conform more closely to the course as now taught.

In line with the committment of Stephens College to general education the whole science program is dominated by the aims of general education.   Thus the introductory courses in the separate fields — Botany, Zoology, Chemistry, Physics, and Geology — are regarded as general rather than preprofessional courses. It is, however, in the development of a one year course serving as an introduction to both the biological and physical sciences that Stephens hopes to make a significant contribution to its own students and possibly to general education elsewhere.

the scientific endeavor, and at the same time provides each student with a broad and fundamental science experience.

The aim, however, is not to train scientists and techicians. Neither is it to inculcate a set of preconceptions nor to broadcast information.   It is rather, to educate — cultivate those elusive and priceless faculties of reasonableness and thoughtfulness.

The strategies and tactics of science and scientists are carefully examined; many of the conceptions and principles that have emerged from their assault on the unknown are thoroughly explored; and considerable quantities of verified information are studied.   But these are raw materials to be digested and assimilated.   They are food for thought.   They provide experience, against which other experiences must be weighed and assessed.

The beauty of an introductory course that embraces the whole of science is found in the inexhaustible variety from which consistently exciting and interesting materials can be selected.   The chief problem rests with the selection of an approach for the consideration of these materials which is integrating, consistent and logical, which has continuity, and which, at the same time, provides a sequence of experiences that can clearly be related, and applied to "everyday life."

A new scientific viewpoint has been developing during the past few decades which actually relates all of science and virtually all of the major human problems of modern times.   This approach — termed ecological — is concerned with the interrelationships between living things and their environments.   Ecological principles and concepts are emphasized and provide a basic structure in this approach to an Introduction to Natural Science.   A subject matter outline with brief explanatory remarks and rationale follows:

1. AN INTRODUCTION is a sort of overview in which the basic assumptions of science are examined and compared with those of other agencies that influence our thoughts and activities.   The "common denominators" of scientific methods and techniques are explored with emphasis on the importance of precision and accuracy in description, on repeatability and verification of observations and on the tentative nature of inferences and/or conclusions. This is followed by an elementary discussion of

2. THE NATURE OF MATTER AN ENERGY. An understanding of some elemental concepts of physics and chemistry is essential to any adequate treatment of natural phenomena; however, it does not seem desirable to introduce any but those which are immediately necessary this early in the course. These relatively abstract conceptions are gradually infiltrated when they can either be demonstrated with "concrete" examples or when they will provide a precise expression which will contribute to the understanding of an earth or life process. Those which are included here are prerequisite to a consideration of

3. EARTH PROCESSES AND THEIR RELATED FEATURES. Examination of the classical geological processes: vulcanism, gradation, diastrophism and metamorphism, provides students with the understanding necessary to place a reasonable interpretation on their surroundings, and at the same time, to describe the environment, which will serve as a frame in which living things can be set. The study of molten materials, and related earth features, followed by an analysis of chemical and mechanical weathering processes, introduces students to the "parent materials" from which the earth and its life have been derived and to some of the activities that effect the alteration of near surface materials. The gradational activities of wind, running surface water, ground water, "standing" water and glaciers together with massive earth movements are considered relative to their influence on the evolution of surface topography and to the development of conditions that are suitable for living things. The derivation of soils, sediments and the dissolved materials of fresh and salt water is also related to these earth processes. A view of

4. THE EARTH IN PERSPECTIVE rounds out the study of the earth as its space-time relationships are defined. Students typically have been entirely fascinated by this "new look" and later it serves as a springboard to some very interesting ideas. The place of the earth in the solar system and in the "total" universe is scaled down to comprehensive terms and some classical theories concerned with the origin and evolution of the solar system are examined. This is followed by a summary of the history of the earth and our time is viewed against the enormity of time past. At this point the emphasis begins to change from the earth to life as the fossil record is examined and interpreted. Having completed a description of earth structures and processes, its place in the cosmos, its history

and the development of its flora and fauna, attention is
turned to

5. THE NATURE OF LIFE. Characteristics, activities and
    especially the environmental relations of living things are
    described in a general way. These assume a broader and
    deeper meaning when related to the process of

6. ORGANIC EVOLUTION which is presented as an out-
    come of the interaction between heredity and variation
    with the environment. A consideration of phylogenetic
    relationships and taxonomic principles rounds out this
    overview of the nature of life. The overview paves the
    way for an expanded and refined view of actual selected
    "types" of organisms which are considered with the ac-
    cent on those principles which describe their ecological and
    alsu their evolutionary relationships. A variety of "type"
    oganisms is examined relative to each of

7. THE MAJOR EARTH HABITATS and the structures
    and activities of organisms are interpreted in terms of the
    conditions which surround them. The physical and
    chemical conditions of the marine, fresh water and ter-
    restrial habitats are examined and a representative "type"
    from each major taxonomic category occuring in the
    habitat is interpreted in terms of its adaptations to these
    conditions. Adaptations to the acquisition and utilization
    of food, to the maintenance of a favorable interaction
    with the biotic and abiotic factors of the environment and
    to the production and maintenance of offspring, are ex-
    amined in each type organism. Throughout these dis-
    cussions threads are woven into a fabric which covers the
    interrelationships of the earth and its life.

The preceding parts which constitute the larger portion of the
course are related to scientific method, to a description of the earth,
of life on the earth, and of earth and life processes and interrelationships. In the following

8. INTERPRETATIONS OF THE EARTH AND ITS
    LIFE, the development of this understanding is credited
    to science. Our current beliefs are compared and con-
    trasted with those of the ancients and of other cultures.

At this point the student is equipped with a related body of
facts and principles, a general understanding of easily recognized
processes and an appreciation for the reliability of this knowledge.

The foundation has been laid and the climax is built upon it.

> Interpretations of the earth and its life continue as accounts are presented of the "struggles" between the pioneers of science and the forces which resisted their "new ideas." Featured are such classical and important cases as those of Galileo and Darwin, in which scientists in their quest for knowledge found themselves at odds with the conventions of their times.
>
> Thus the first of a series of human social problems (Authoritarianism) with present day implications is suggested. Other

9. MAJOR ECOLOGICAL PROBLEMS FACING MODERN MAN, such as overpopulation, land use, water and air pollution, and hazards to the common human gene pool, are brought into focus and examined in terms of the facts, principles and processes developed in earlier portions of the course.

On these dynamic, sometimes controversial, but certainly timely and exciting issues the course is brought to a

10. CONCLUSION.

A wide variety of topics described above is supplemented either with special or with more or less standard laboratory exercises. Equally important, the sequence is such that illustrative field trips are synchronized with the geologic material in the autumn and with biologic material in the spring. Thus a full range of first-hand, practical experiences is developed for the students which is in harmony with the structure of the presentation.

chapter 19

THE PHYSICAL SCIENCE COURSE AT STOCKTON COLLEGE

Arthur T. Bawden*

The Physical Science course at Stockton College is an example of the impact of changes in an administrative environment on a program of general education. General education will thrive in the right kind of administrative environment and the reverse is to be expected. With changes in administration there will be an ebb and flow in emphasis on general education. An ebb in a given school should not be interpreted as a failure of general education. Even an ebb in a few schools, prominent or otherwise, should not be considered to represent a trend. Today there is evidence that general education courses in the physical sciences are more widespread than ever before.

As general education courses in Physical Science find their way into the upper two years of high schools the need for them at the college level may decrease, but for the present, vast numbers of young people enroll in public Junior Colleges, such as Stockton College, with little or no background in the physical sciences in the upper two years of high school. It is a waste of public funds and a waste of the time of many of these students to place them in technical science courses for which they are not prepared by training or aptitude. To do so dilutes the value of these courses for the technical students. Whenever California Junior College teachers of the physical sciences meet together the inevitable topic of discussion centers around the problem of maintaining standards for

*The Author is Professor of Chemistry, Stockton College.

admission to college Chemistry and Physics courses. The main emphasis in such discussions is that of keeping students of low ability and inadequate preparation out of these courses. Seldom is there a discussion by these teachers of the problem of meeting the needs of these marginal or less well prepared studnts in this age in which physical science influences their environment to such a great extent.

It is the counselling staff which is sensitive to the needs of the non-technical students. If such needs, when brought to the attention of administrators, meet with a sympathetic response a program of general education may come into being. Administrators have many problems, the most pressing of which command attention. Frequently these problems are those of finance, a building program, or maintaining good relations with the supervising board or the public. If the State University is not much concerned with general education there will be no pressure on the administrator from this source to encourage general education in the public Junior College which tends to pattern its offerings after the lower division program of the State University. In a few cases the administrator might provide the leadership for such a program, but usually the pressure must come from the counsellors or other teachers. The extent to which these teachers are given the responsibility for the educational program may be the determing factor. Even when the teachers are given the opportunity to plan, the form of organization may determine the result. For example, broad divisional courses might develop in a school which has a divisional form of organization, whereas a departmental organization might not provide a favorable environment. In the end, however, a general education program, regardless of the source of the pressure for it, will not develop and thrive unless it receives administrative backing.

Stockton College furnishes an illustration of the foregoing conditions. Stockton College is one of the tuition-free, public Junior Colleges of California which are supported by state and local taxes. Evolving originally from the lower division of a private college, the College of the Pacific, Stockton College developed an outstanding program of general education. This program was on an elective basis within a framework of a graduation requirement of a certain number of units in each of the Divisions.

For example, at least six units were required in both the biological and the physical sciences.

Stockton College eventually became a part of a highly centralized, unified school district which included elementary and high schools. Later, this district adopted the K-6-4-4 plan of organization and Stockton College became a four-year Junior College, having grades 11 through 14. These profound administrative changes inevitably led to the separation of the Junior College from the College of the Pacific, thus terminating this very interesting experiment. The faculty of Stockton College, an outstanding group of teachers who had been attracted by the excellent general education program, planned the program for the new four-year Junior College. They were influenced by a study of "Education for All American Youth," a publication of The Educational Policies Commission. The final program was patterned after this dream. It provided for a required pattern of general education, avocational education, and vocational education, and, in recognition of individual differences, a flexibility provision made it possible for counselors to adapt the pattern to each student's needs.

The new program had scarcely gotten underway when administrative changes resulted in taking educational planning out of the hands of the faculty. The whole required pattern of courses was thrown out and the College now had no courses or patterns of courses required for graduation except the small core of courses such as Physical Education, Hygiene, English, and Political Science, required by the California Educational Code, under which California public Junior Colleges operate.

The Physical Science course had been a "required" course at the eleventh and twelfth grade level for students who did not take Chemistry or Physics, but when all requirements were removed it enrolled fewer students. Because of this course at the eleventh and twelfth grade level the College level course was discontinued. Several years ago the K-6-4-4 plan was discontinued with the result that the new two-year Junior College had no course in Physical Science. A new course in Physical Science was reactivated within the framework of a free-elective system, under conditions in which there was very little money available for the purchase of equipment, and in which the pressure for large classes and a limited teaching load for the course did not provide time for developing demonstrations with what little equipment had survived the changes outlined above. This administrative desire for a general education course in the physical sciences, not implemented by providing an adequate teaching load or money for equipment, may not be peculiar to Stockton College. The rest of this account describes, the type of course which evolved under this administrative environment.

The Physical Science course, entitled "Man's Physical Universe," in the original pattern of general education was a six-unit course, three units each semester. It was a non-technical survey course specifically designed in terms of general education objectives. It stressed the scientific attitude and method, conservation, intelligent consumership, and the social implications which provided meaning for the subject matter. Individual laboratory work for non-technical students had already been proven to be almost useless in our experience with such students in sub-college level Chemistry courses. Such students do not appear to be interested in "learning by doing" and have very little scientific curiosity. They perform experiments in a perfunctory manner and, if possible, they will avoid doing the experiments. Our conclusion was that such students do not learn as much from individual experiments as the time devoted to them warrants. Furthermore, the experiments as performed did not seem to result in the development of the scientific attitude or a carry over of the scientific method to the solution of real life problems. Individual laboratory work might even then have been provided if by so doing the course could have received recognition by the State University as meeting the Physical Science requirement for graduation. However, since the University does not offer such a course it is not recognized as being equivalent to any course in its curriculum, and, in general, it is not considered to be equivalent in value to a technical course in Chemistry or Physics for non-technical students. So a lack of pressure from the University, and a very restricted budget and teaching load formed the basis for the decision not to provide individual laboratory work in our new course. Many studies have indicated that teaching can be done just as efficiently or even more so by lecture demonstrations in cases where there is no need to teach laboratory technics. However, lecture demonstrations, the substitute for individual laboratory work, were limited to a very few

because of the lack of equipment and teaching load time.   Fortunately, there are now available many very fine motion pictures
to take the place of lecture demonstrations*   These motion pictures have proven to be so successful that we would prefer them
to live demonstrations for large classes because they make it possible for all students to see the experiments even when performed
with small-size apparatus.   In many cases the motion pictures
employ equipment and an expenditure of time by experts in setting
up demonstrations which would not be available to any teacher.
In addition, motion pictures reach those students who are virtually
non-readers.

The opportunity to see such top-notch motion pictures as
"The Strange Case of the Cosmic Rays," or "The Unchained Goddess," produced in color by the American Telephone and Telegraph
Company, is one from which even our science majors could profit.
Through the medium of motion pictures our students hear many
great scientists, including some who have passed on.   The cost
of motion picture rentals averages about $100 per semester, a
cost which is offset many times over by the saving in teaching
load which large classes make possible.

Furthermore, the depth and breadth of our present course in
Physical Science, entitled "Matter and Energy" is very similar to
that represented by most of the motion pictures which we use.
The "Unchained Goddess," which requires about one and a half
hours for projection, represents a broad survey of meteorology.
It packs into this time a tremendous body of basic facts and principles and it is not harmed by making the presentation interesting
and even humorous.   This motion picture is a very fine illustration of the type of approach which we attempt throughout the
course.

Our present course, Matter and Energy, is a three-unit, one
semester course.   It is so difficult to teach the fundamentals of
Physical Science, together with their important applications and
their social implications, in a six-unit course that one might wonder what was behind the thinking that resulted in a three-unit
course.   Under a prescribed pattern of general education or under

---

*The author will gladly send a list of motion pictures used in his course,
Matter and Energy, to anyone who accompanies his request with an addressed,
stamped return envelope.

a general graduation requirement of six units in physical science, a six-unit course is reasonable, possible, and perhaps, preferable, but it is difficult to work such a course into the program of a student under the free-elective topsy turvy.   For many majors in such fields as art, music, dramatics, and education, the lower division requirements are such that it is difficult to fit into the student's program six units of Physical Science as well as six units of Biological Science.   Again, the pressure for the student's time in a vocational, semi-technical program leaves too little time for general education.   With the thought that "a half a loaf is better than no bread," the three-unit course was established.   The counselling staff has found it possible to "sell" this three-unit course to about one-tenth of the student body on a free elective basis each year. Furthermore it has been found that this course meets the physical science requirements of many of the teacher training colleges.

Once the three-unit course had been decided upon the question then arose as to the best approach for such a course.   The sampling or "block and gap" approach, preferred by many teachers, would seem to be the best approach for such a short course.   As we understand it such an approach emphasizes a few basic principles in sufficient detail to provide an understanding of the way in which scientific knowledge evolves.   This approach is obviously directed toward the nebulous goal entitled "the appreciation" of Physical Science.   To be sure, such a goal, if attainable, would seem to be desirable for the future "bee-keepers" as Slosson so aptly termed the future leaders in government and business who would make decisions so vital to the busy bees, i.e. the scientists, and so important in determining the amount of "honey" produced. However such an approach results in vast gaps just as a general education course in Chemistry or Physics would leave large gaps. The sampling technic is definitely not a survey of the fundamentals of physical science.   It emphasizes one objective to the exclusion of many other objectives of a general education course.   In general, it stresses depth whereas breadth would seem to be more desirable. A general education course rightly omits technical details that may be important for science majors, the omission of which makes possible breadth not attainable in more specialized courses.

A second type of course, preferred by relatively few teachers, might be designated as a course "about" physical science.   Such a course, designed in terms of general education objectives, would emphasize the scientific attitude and method and would describe the important contributions of phyesical science, showing how they have caused vast changes in society, and pointing out the problems of the present and near future resulting from current scientific advances. Such a course, emphasizing the social implications of physical science, would provide meaning to the facts and principles taught, but the background of fundamentals would be quite limited. Such an approach is very tempting to the teacher who is confronted with students who have been carefully selected by the counselling staff in terms of a very inadequate background in mathematics and high school physical science courses. Perhaps such a course would be ideal for such students, but the majority of teachers, trained in the physical sciences, do not have the background for such a sociological approach.

A third approach, and probably the most widely used, is the "survey" which emphasizes the fundamentals of physical science. A study of the texts available for Physical Science courses at the College level indicated that the three most popular texts were of the "survey" type and that the most technical ones were the best sellers. Apparently, the majority of teachers of Physical Science courses consider that they should emphasize the fundamentals of Physical Science and leave it to the students to work out their social significance within the framework of their total educational program.

Our Physical Science course, Matter and Energy, was designed to teach the fundamentals of physical science. These fundamentals include an emphasis on the main theories, i.e. the atomic, kinetic-molecular, ionization, electron, and nuclear theories. It also emphasizes the important laws which describe the transformations of matter and energy. Such an emphasis leaves very little time for applications, but some of the most important ones such as synthetic rubber, plastics, and drugs, telephone, radio, television, weather, climate, aviation, and primary power sources are included. This emphasis on fundamental theories, laws, and the vocabulary of physical science leaves very little time for a consideration of the social implications of scientific developments. The wide-spread speculation in the electronic, transistor, atomic energy, jet fuel, and rocket common stocks and in the stocks of companies which invest heavily in research, such as the photographic, chemical, and drug companies, indicates that the public is quite aware of the implications of recent scientific advances.   In fact, a consistent reader of the *Wall Street Journal* would be able to keep up with the impact of Science on society.   It appears that if we lay the foundation of fundamentals and provide a working vocabulary of important terms, the average person will do some thinking himself. Teachers may do their students a disservice by trying to do their thinking for them, and, of course, no teacher can think ten or twenty years ahead for his students.

After a two-year trial of our three-unit course, Matter and Energy, we believe that we are on the right track but we have found that we have used more "railroad ties" than necessary. We are now revising the course so as to maintain its present framework but to omit many of the technical details, thus providing an opportunity to expand the treatment of the fundamental theories and laws.

After twenty-five years' experience with Physical Science courses, off and on, we believe that our present three-unit course is to be preferred to the previous six-unit course in meeting the needs of the type of students who come to us in a free elective environment.   In such an environment the course stands on its own feet.   It must meet the students' needs or it will not survive.

chapter 20

THE BIOLOGICAL SCIENCE COURSE AT STOCKTON COLLEGE

*Verna R. Johnston**

During the lifetime of Stockton College — the past twenty-five years — three general education courses in the biological sciences have been offered in an attempt to meet the needs of our students for an understanding and appreciation of the basic principles of living things.   Two of the three courses served nobly in their day and then followed the track of the dinosaur to extinction. The third has survived for fifteen years and is at present mushrooming.

The initial attempt of Stockton College to provide a thoughtful biological background for students majoring in non-science fields came under the forward-looking administration of the late 1930's, a pioneer group of educators in many fields.   Stimulated by the Physical Science survey course introduced by Dr. Arthur Bawden, our able Botanist-biologist produced a companion course entitled Man and the Living World, which presented over a year's sequence of three units per semester exactly what its title implied — a broad philosophical approach to man and his relationships to other organisms.   The course surveyed the fundamental theories, concepts and principles of the life sciences, laying strong emphasis on conservation of natural resources, heredity and evolution.   The instructor used a lecture-demonstration teaching method primarily, with reference reading assignments and daily quizzes flashed on the screen.   (Prepared by student photographic assistance available from ample science funds in those golden days).

---

*The Author is Professor of Biological Science, Stockton College.

An unusual feature was the optional laboratory, which offered students who desired it, or who needed the extra units, a chance to do their own observing and learning. The optional laboratory units also met the transfer requirement for junior standing at College of the Pacific, the mother school attended by most lower division graduates at that time. The state university did not accept them as a laboratory equivalent. The instructor published a text for this course, titled by the course name, and has revised the book through several successful editions right up to the present.

World War II brought the Navy V12 program to the campus and with it a year biology survey course, composed of separate lecture and laboratory. This second general education offering in the biological science field proved very workable.

When peacetime activities resumed, the teacher who had developed the Navy Biology program received a science division memorandum indicating that Biology would be dropped, as there was no longer any need for it. He protested vigorously that peacetime students would appreciate a Biology laboratory survey course just as much as the sailors had, and won a reluctant approval to offer one section. The new class was scheduled at a most unfavorable hour when it had strong competition from Zoology, but, surprisingly, the section filled, and Stockton College's third general education course in the biological sciences was born.

The new course, entitled General Biology, proved to be a blending arena for many varieties of teaching technics and methods from the beginning. The most applicable features of lecture, laboratory, demonstration, discussion and field trips were combined into an eight-unit year course. The sole dissatisfaction of Navy Biology, namely the remoteness of the separate laboratory from lecture content, was eliminated by scheduling classes for two consecutive hours per day four days a week. This provided both interwoven subject matter and an ideal psychological interval for student concentration on one subject.

Between 1944 and 1954, then, Stockton College non-science students could secure a biological science background in either of two general education courses: (1) Laboratory-centered General Biology, or (2) Lecture-centered Man and the Living World (which had now dropped its optional laboratory). The philosophy of the two courses was virtually identical — to afford a broad knowledge of man and his environment as inter-related.

An inexorable growth in General Biology enrollment developed during this ten year period (and the more recent years, as well), and brought, conversely, in 1954 the demise of Man and the Living World. Several reasons explain this trend. Certainly the increasing number of our students who transfer to state colleges, the state university, or private colleges where they must meet a *laboratory* science requirement swung the balance heavily in favor of General Biology. And since the Stockton College physical science department offered no *laboratory* survey course designed for general education students, General Biology enjoyed a monopoly in this field — and still does. The hours spent over coffee cups with counselors and the innovations brought to the course by an enthusiastic core of instructors exerted influences equally apparent.

At present, General Biology enrolls about sixteen percent of the student body each semester. The staff consists of one full time teacher (the author) and four who teach one or two sections of Biology in addition to other courses. The class size limit of twenty six makes possible personalized laboratory work. The experiments, dissections, Rh and blood testing, panel discussion on controversial subjects, campus field trips, and other class procedures are all directed toward a minimum of technic and quick transfer of emphasis to man and his environment. The two all-day field trips per year to the mountains and ocean are reinforced by four to six hours of class preparation and follow-through. Student enthusiasm for the field trips always runs high. Excellent films, filmstrips and kodachrome slides present many basic concepts in an unequaled manner. All of the staff use an accumulative point system in grading and find that students seem to enjoy the security of knowing where they stand, pointwise, at any time.

Among the current problems which the course faces, field trips and lack of funds predominate. Growth in Biology enrollment has turned field trips into mass migrations. The personal touch and the impact of the native scene diminish to a point of low return when three Greyhound busloads converge on a nature trail meant for quiet absorption. It is unfair to ask already overloaded teachers to make three excursions individually *instead* of one on precious Saturdays.   There is no substitute for a seashore tidepool in proclaiming the great variety of life, nor for a mountain meadow in understanding the need for conservation of natural resources.   But there is a size limit beyond which field groups become unworkable.   Years ago it became necessary to reduce our field trips from four to two annually, and once again critical field trip decisions lie ahead.

Due to local financial problems, funds for junior college science equipment have not been available for several years.   This means that during General Biology's recent expansion from full-time use of one laboratory to two and one-half laboratories, the funds to equip the new laboratories with models, skeleton, slides, etc. have been lacking.   The era prior to the K-6-4-4 plan provided us with excellent microscopes, wall charts and one well-equipped laboratory and which now stand as lamposts amid the harassments of borrowing and rotating basic models among classes meeting concurrently.   The equipment shortage forced us to choose our most recent text partly from the standpoint of one whose sequence would facilitate borrowing.

But in spite of these difficulties, General Biology proffers a forward look.   The course enjoys a campus reputation of long standing for high standards mingled with a student-centered approach.   The General Education Conference which was held in Bakersfield three years ago indicated clearly that Stockton College stood among the leading ten per cent of California junior colleges in offering an integrated laboratory and lecture course in Biology for non science majors.   The majority of the schools represented were scheduling Biology lecture courses or nature study or standard Zoology and Botany for general education students.   Some offered a separate laboratory and lecture program in Biology, but Stockton College stood virtually alone in the two hour interwoven laboratory-lecture idea which has proven extremely successful here for fifteen years.   It is interesting to note that our state university will be entering the general education field at long last in the fall of 1959 with a course entitled Introduction to the Science of Living Organisms, a six-unit year course utilizing lecture and laboratory.

Stockton College experimented briefly two years ago with a modified General Biology course for terminal students who were poor readers.   Course enrollment was insufficient for more than one semester trial, and at present a minimum English test score screens non-readers from acceptance in General Biology.

Philosophically General Biology has changed little over the years, except in the inevitable individual emphases of its instructors. The course aims at developing breadth on a high level of excellence.   It hopes to stimulate interest in man and all life about him, and to demonstrate the problem-solving approach to the unbiased search for scientific truth sufficiently clearly that our students will be able to follow with understanding and some participation the rapid biological advances of our time.

But the author, for one, feels equally bound to suggest to these same students that, as Max Lerner puts it, all reality is not subject to the mathematical laws of the natural sciences, and the problems which will make or break America are no longer technological but social and cultural.

James Killian of Massachusetts Institute of Technology said recently, "It is the greatest humanistic responsibility of our colleges and universities to stress the kinship, indeed the unity, of all knowledge."

A general education teacher is concerned with the broad meanings derived from the specialized workers of many fields and has an unrivaled opportunity to bring fresh interdisciplinary commentaries to his classes.   If his classroom can occassionally glow with the exhiliarating awakening of a "new" idea, students and teacher alike will reach as far as each can stretch into the essence of Being.

chapter 21

THE BASIC STUDIES SCIENCE COURSES AT WESTERN MICHIGAN UNIVERSITY

*W. C. Van Deventer**

The general education program at Western Michigan University consists of 8 semester hours in science, 8 in social studes, 8 in humanities and 6-8 in communication skills. In each area certain choices are offered among courses, all of which are specifically designed for general education goals. For example, in social studies students are permitted to earn their 8 hours either by taking either a two-semester sequence called *Foundations of Western Civilization,* which emphasizes the historical approach, or one called *Man and Society,* which emphasizes the growth of social issues. In the area of the humanities, even wider choices are permitted.

In the area of the sciences there are three courses, all designed to emphasize general education goals, which may be used in four different combinations to meet the 8 hour requirement:

1. Physical Science, 2 semesters, 8 hours
2. Physical Geography, 1 semester, 4 hours
3. Biological Science, 1 semester, 4 hours

Students may take *Physical Science* 4 hours and *Physical Geography* 4 hours; *Physical Science* 4 hours and *Biological Science* 4 hours: *Biological Science* 4 hours and *Physical Geography* 4 hours; or *Physical Science* for two semesters, 8 hours. Relatively few students earn all of their basic studies science credit in *Physical Science.* Usually they elect one of the other combinations. In certain

---

*The Author is Chairman Department of Biology, Western Michigan University.

curricula students are not given a choice, and are required to elect one or another of the courses. In elementary education students are required to take a total of 12 hours, with one course in each area. A major in a science field is excused from 4 hours of his basic studies science requirement, but is required to take the other 4 hours in an area other than that of his major. A student with a major in the physical science area and a minor in biology or earth science or vice versa is excused from the whole 8 hours of the requirement. In a few highly technical curricula, the requirement is waived altogether.

The *Physical Science* course is essentially a survey of the fields of physics and chemistry with the introduction of selected topics from the field of astronomy. In the introduction to the syllabus there is the following statement: "The main objective of this course is to acquaint the student with some facts, phenomena, principles, methods and apparatus of physical science. With this in view, a few representative topics have been selected from the sciences of astronomy, physics, and chemistry, with energy as the dominant unifying concept."[1] The course is designed such that the first semester constitutes a complete unit, while the second semester consists largely of further and more detailed work in selected areas. Most of the astronomy and much of the chemistry, however, are included in the second semester.

The *Physical Geography* course is a survey course in earth science, with an orientation toward human problems and economic and cultural relationships. This weighting is expressed in the following quotation from the mimeographed course outline prepared by the staff: "An examination of the syllabus shows a heavy emphasis on physical science. This is as it should be in a course designed to meet physical science requirements. At the same time much of the material studied takes on life and meaning when considered in relationship to man and his varied cultural patterns Therefore, emphasis is given to man and to the political and socioeconomic problems of man where appropriate. Geography is uniquely suited to this task of bridging the physical and social sciences, and plays an important role in the general education pro-

---

[1]Kruglak, H., Marburger, W. A. and Knowlton, L. A., *Experiences in Physical Science*, Part 1. *To Live in a Nuclear Age*. Western Michigan University, Kalamazoo. Michigan. 1957.

gram of Western Michigan University."[2]   The units in *Physical Geography* include study of the earth as a planet, measurement and mapping of the earth's surface, rocks and minerals, land forms and forces contributing to their development, the atmosphere, weather and climate, the oceans, inland waters, and the major climatic regions of the world.   Relationships to man and human problems are included in each unit, and a final unit is devoted to a consideration of world power relationships in the light of facts and concepts learned.

The *Biological Science* course is essentially a result of evolution from the course described by the writer in *Science in General Education*, in the chapter entitled, "The General Biology Course at Stephens College."[3]   This course has been a part of the basic studies science program at Western Michigan University since the fall of 1953, and has undergone changes necessary to adapt it to its new environment and the needs of the students who elect it.[4]

Biological Science is a "problem-area" course, utilizing the "block-and-gap" type of organization.   The following quotation from the teacher's handbook which is a part of the syllabus describes its viewpoint and basic philosophy:

"This course attempts to set forth a related series of areas and units, in which teachers and students may find problems which are sufficiently challenging to be worthy of exploration.   These are set forth with the idea that the laboratory experiences rather than the textual readings will constitute the heart of the course. The readings are related to the laboratory experiences rather than the opposite."

"With the tremendous growth of the biological sciences during the past half-century, it is obviously impossible to "cover the field" of biology in any single elementary course without falling into the danger of superficiality.   Therefore the present course does not make this attempt.   Instead, the areas, units and problems are frankly selected with the idea of going into them relatively deeply,

[2]*General Course Syllabus, Physical Geography 105*.   Western Michigan University, Kalamazoo, Michigan.

[3]W. C. Van Deventer, "The General Biology Course at Stephens College," a chapter in *Science in General Education*, E. J. McGrath, editor, pp. 110-123, Wm. C. Brown and Company, Dubuque, Iowa, 1948.

[4]W. C. Van Deventer, "Designing a Basic Science Course for a Specific College Situation," *School Science and Mathematics*, February, 1955.

while at the same time necessarily leaving out others for which perhaps an equally good case for inclusion could be made. This is the "block-and-gap" approach which is now so widely used in general education science courses at the college level."

"The materials which have been included have been chosen for this purpose because they have been found to be particularly productive of problem-situations which are meaningful to students, and because at the same time, they include nearly all of the generally accepted subject-matter principles which research workers in science education have identified as being included in beginning biology courses."[5]

The subject matter of the course is classifiable under four general areas: (1) the interrelationships of living organisms, (2) heredity, (3) evolution, and (4) man's body as a community of cells. There is wide variation in the treatment of these, however, by different instructors and even by the same instructor in different semesters. In the writer's sections the spring semester and the fall semester are unlike because of the necessarily changed placing of the field experiences. In the fall the course begins with consideration of the interrelationships of living organisms, and in the spring with heredity. This involves changed emphasis and approaches in these and other units.

The various instructors in the course are free to use a textbook in addition to the locally-produced syllabus or in place of it, if they wish. They are asked, however, to follow the general scheme of course content indicated above, rather than to "follow the textbook" if they adopt one. Most instructors, after trying a textbook alone for a semester or so, return to the use of a part or all of the syllabus, either with or without a textbook in addition. At the present time the syllabus is published in the form of sixteen separates, so that an instructor may use any part of it or all of it. This scheme has added greatly to the flexibility of the course and the usefulness of the syllabus materials.

The methodological framework of the course is also planned to achieve a maximum of flexibility. In scheduling, there is no arbitrary separation of lecture and laboratory periods. The course

[5]Van Deventer, W. C., and Staff, *"Basic Ideas, Generalizations and Subject Matter Principles Included in the Biological Science Course."* Western Michigan University, Kalamazoo, Michigan, 1959.

is scheduled either for three two-hour periods per week, or for two three-hour periods.   At the discretion of the instuctor, and depending on the material being studied, any portion of this time may be used for lecture, laboratory, discussion, field trips, motion pictures, demonstrations, testing or other activities.

As has been indicated in the quotation above from the teacher's handbook, laboratory work forms the basis of the course.   The concept of laboratory which is used, however, is much broader that the usual definition of laboratory work in a science course. As it is used in *Biological Science,* laboratory experience includes all problem-solving activities on the part of students.[6]   Thus the laboratory in this sense is not confined by the four walls of the room in which the course is being taught.   It is carried into the field and the library, and the study room of the student.

In the classroom itself this broadened concept of the meaning of laboratory includes much more than the traditional dissections, microscopic observations and other work-book exercises.   The laboratory manual used in the course is a part of the syllabus.   It contains outlines for more laboratory experiences than any single instructor uses.   It is written in such a manner as to avoid too detailed instructions for the carrying out of laboratory experiences, and contains questions in connection with each experience, some of which can be answered readily, some after consultation of other parts of the syllabus, some with the aid of other references that the student finds himself, and some not at all.

It is intended that the student should come to think of science as a process in which the knowledge gained is constantly being used to discover and solve new problems, in connection with which new knowledge will necessarily be obtained.   The facts learned, therefore become less important than the mastering of the scientific learning technique.   Of course facts will be learned, but the learning will occur naturally, within a meaningful framework, and will not be mere memorization.   In this way there is a considerably greater probability that the facts which are learned, and the knowledge of the process by which they are learned, will be retained and applied in a functional way in connection with the problems of actual living.

---

[6]Van Deventer. W. C. "Laboratory Teaching in College Basic Science Courses," *Science Education* Vol. 37, No. 3 pp. 159-172, April 1953.

The laboratory experiences which take place in the classroom tend to be group experiences rather than individual ones. Whether the materials being studied involve dissection, microscopic examination or some other technique, students are encouraged to share what they discover with the rest of the class, and to attempt to answer each other's questions. This makes for the very opposite of a quiet, studious-appearing laboratory of the traditional type, but it is highly effective from the standpoint of problem-solving, and student interest is maintained at a high level.

With the current greatly increased enrollments and crowded schedules, it has been necessary on occasion to teach some sections of the course in rooms which were inadequately equipped for laboratory work. In such cases the writer has carried on some experimentation with self-directed laboratory and field experiences which can be done by the student on his own time outside the classroom. The most successful of these have been the construction of a balanced aquarium and the collection of key or indicator items and materials in the field, to show that certain habitats have been observed. Another instructor has utilized a self-directed laboratory experience involving comparative studies on germinating seeds and growing seedlings. It is possible that this experimentation may indicate an important avenue in the further evolution of the course.

Other experimentation on the part of the writer has been in the direction of increased reliance in student reading, and a corresponding lessened amount of time spent in lecturing. The time formerly spent in lecturing is taken up with (1) briefly discussing basic ideas and relationships which are necessary for understanding the material to be read: (2) answering questions raised by students concerning the material that has been read, and (3) carrying on discussions arising from such questions. In general, this method makes it possible to cover more material than under a lecture system, and, while some very poor students may do less well, the general level of attainment of the class appears to be increased. This experiment has been carried on for only five semesters, however, and it is therefore too early to draw definite conclusions.

While the inductive approach, which is native to science, is emphasized by making laboratory experiences central in each unit, and building readings around them, the importance of basic ideas and principles is recognized as being particularly important from the standpoint of the general student. Such principles exist at different levels. The most deep-lying of them are common to all science, and are largely attitudinal in nature. These include the common elements which run through all scientific work, such as objectivity and tentativeness. Lying in a stratum somewhat above these are principles that are common to large subject-matter areas, as the idea of interrelationship is basic to the whole field of plant-animal community study. In a still shallower stratum are the commonly accepted subject-matter principles, such as that green plants are ultimately responsible for the production of the world's food supply. Finally at the "surface," or in the uppermost stratum of all are the "facts of science."[7]

Each of the four large areas in the course is built around a single, basic, integrating idea. These are stated in the course materials. Within each area, subsidiary ideas or generalizations are also given. Finally, the subject-matter principles included in each area are listed. At the discretion of the instructor, these statements and lists of ideas may be placed in the students' hands as a basis for discussion, or may be brought out less directly in connection with the study of the materials. The teaching of ideas and generalizations must be carried on in the same way as any other teaching. If we expect students to learn facts, we teach them facts. If we expect them to learn relationships, we teach them to look for relationships. If we expect them to learn ideas, we must teach these also. It is only by letting the student see, in their natural setting, example after example of the things that we want him to learn, that he may eventually be able to go on, on his own initiative, to new things.

---

[7]Van Deventer, W. C., "The Use of Subject Matter Principles and Generalizations in Teaching," *School Science and Mathematics*, Vol. 56. No. 6. pp. 466-472. June 1956.

chapter 22

SCIENCE IN THE GENERAL EDUCATION PROGRAM AT THE WESTERN WASHINGTON COLLEGE OF EDUCATION

*Leona M. Sundquist**

Western Washington College of Education continues to have as its primary function the preparation of teachers, administrators, and supervisors for the public schools of the state. Both the bachelor's and master's degrees in education are granted. The college is also authorized to grant the bachelor's degree in the arts and sciences. This function is growing in scope. In addition the college has been designated to perform a junior college function for students in the immediate vicinity.

In order to accomplish these functions the total college program provides planned experiences in the areas of:

General Education
Professional education of teachers
Subject matter specialization

The science program is intimately associated with the developments in each of the above areas. The nature of the growth of the student body, the addition of members to the rapidly growing faculty, the degree of leadership exercised by the administration and curriculum committee have influenced certain aspects of the development of the science program over the past decade.

---

*The Author is Chairman of the Science Department Western Washington College of Education.

During this period of rapid growth the faculty has re-affirmed its acceptance of a General Education program as a fundamental part of the experiences planned for students in Teacher Education and the Arts and Sciences. In the last five years the faculty has re-examined and re-stated the objectives of the college. They are as follows:

The Aims of General Education

The aims of the General Education program of the college are to:

1. Broaden and intensify the student's understanding of man's
   a. physical, psychological and social growth:
   b. need to recognize the interaction between the physical and biological environment and the necessity for adjustment to changing conditions;
   c. need for an awareness of his cultural heritage and for achieving perspective in time and place.

2. Develop an individual who
   a. thinks creatively and imaginatively and is aware of the need of the individual for freedom of thought and expression;
   b. works effectively with others within the framework of democracy because he respects differences in others and is willing to accept responsibility;
   c. demonstrates active concern for the welfare of others and participates in programs designed to promote good physical and mental health in his community;
   d. acts in a manner consistent with a personal philosophy and an examined code of ethics;
   e. expresses himself through participation in aesthetic, intellectual, and physical activities;
   f. thinks in terms of quantity, number and measurement;
   g. reads thoughtfully and critically and writes and speaks logically and effectively.

This past year a General Education Committee has been appointed from the faculty at large to act as a sub-committee of the Curriculum Committee to start from scratch to study the General Education program, to examine its objectives, to define problems, and to provide a framework for further study. At this moment the committee is in the formative stages of its work and its statements are most tentative and may be modified.   However, it might be interesting to note the nature of the thinking that has been committed to paper at this time.

The statement of aims of the General Education program as agreed to by the total committee are:

1. to broaden and intensify the students' understanding of the most significant aspects of man's cultural heritage;
2. to train the student in the methods and tools of thought and expression;
3. to assist the student in integrating his knowledge;
4. to assist the student in developing his powers of aesthetic enjoyment and creativity;
5. to stimulate the student in formulating a philosophy of life based upon knowledge and reflection.

In addition, three characteristics of courses in General Education were proposed and accepted by the committee to aid in differentiating such courses from all other courses in the curriculum. These three characteristics are:

1. Factual knowledge is not an end in itself.
2. The methods of thinking in each field are stressed.
3. There is an emphasis on the relationship of the field to other areas of knowledge.

Certain recommendations have been formally adopted by the entire committee at various points in its deliberation.   These include the following:

1. The committee shall concern itself only with the instructional aspects of General Education.
2. The required General Education program shall be the same for teacher education and the arts and science students.
3. A standing faculty committee on General Education should be appointed to continue consideration of these problems.

Science Objectives

The objectives of the Science Department are correlated with the above stated objectives of the College.

Although students are channeled through three programs, i.e., Teacher Education, Arts and Science, and Junior College, the department is first and foremost concerned with the fact that it is working with individuals in different stages of maturity and who are members of a democracy in a rapidly changing world.

General Objectives. The following objectives are considered to be pervasive through all of the Science program and especially so for the General Education courses:

1. to provide situations wherein the student is required to examine and organize facts and materials in order that principles may be discovered, and concepts found and used in developing further understanding.
2. to provide practice in the development of techniques and habits of critical thinking leading to more successful problem solving abilities;
3. to provide for an examination of the ways scientists work so that the student may understand the nature of the scientific processes, its aims, limitations and functions in developing a perspective of science as an activity of mankind;
4. to promote a physical and mental climate which invites and inspires free inquiry into any aspect of scientific discipline; thorough appraisal of known qualitative and quantitative facts about scientific phenomena; objective evaluation of the findings, conclusions, and concepts;
5. to provide for the discovery that man is an integral part of an interrelated, ever-changing physical and biological environment so that he may more effectively adjust himself to its many demands.

Type of Students

The Science General Education courses were originally designed for teacher education students. But the character of the institution is being rapidly changed by an expanding Arts and Science program. It is the considered judgment of the faculty that Science General Education courses be required in the Arts and Science program. The science majors in both curricula, however, are advised to take the introductory courses in the appropriate physical and biological areas. This is recommended in order to facilitate their progress through the sequence of courses needed for a major. In the senior year, the science majors are required to take one of the following courses:

General Science 405, Science and Civilization, 3 credits
General Science 406, The Development of Scientific Thought, 5 credits

The pre-professional and junior college student may or may not take the General Education courses, although they are urged to do so.

For the rank and file of students the Science General Education courses represent all the science they will ever have. It is therefore preferred that such students, irrespective of careers or curricula, select the General Education type of course.

Science General Education Courses

Changes in the Science and Civilization Courses 101, 103, 104 of ten years ago have been in the nature of subject matter distribution within courses rather than in the fundamental philosophy. A number of factors influenced the changes that were made.

One factor was the addition of new faculty personnel without previous experience or orientation to a General Education science program. Their specialized training, their individual attitudes, their personal philosophies of education, their particular abilities have contributed to the modifications which have taken place. However, it must be emphasized that the Science Objectives as listed above represent the position taken by the staff as a whole.

Another factor precipitating the change was the matter of student enrollment and faculty loads. A revised distribution of subject matter by the modification of credits in existing courses and the addition of a fourth course was made in hopes of attaining better teaching standards. Teachers with specialized training could thus be assigned segments of the General Education program which they are best equipped to teach.

The sacrifice that had to be made was that of reduction of laboratory periods from two per week to one. Lecture classes were doubled in size. Laboratory sections were increased in number but each section limited to twenty-four students. This change was

given a great deal of consideration as it became obvious that staff
growth would not keep pace with enrollment.   Also the staff was
convinced that laboratory experiences are of the utmost value and
should be maintained at all cost.   It has become necessary therefore
to scrutinize with great care the type of laboratory experiences to
select.

The science courses for the Teacher Education students are:

Physical Science 101, Matter and Energy, 4 credits
Physical Science 202, Earth and Universe, 3 credits
Health Science 103, Human Biology — Health and
Hygiene, 4 credits
Biology 204, Principles of General Biology, 4 credits

The Arts and Science students are required to take Physical
Science 101 and Health Science 103.   This discrepancy between
the two curricula, is not based on the belief that there should be
a difference between the two.   It is rather the unfortunate result
of an arbitrary decision passed under the pressure of cutting the
required credits to allow for greater flexibility for students to pursue their majors in their specialized fields.   There is at present the
drive to reduce the General Education requirements.   Any reduction
in these courses and credits may result in a General Education program identical for both curricula.

The details of the courses as they appear below are presented
more or less as the faculty of each area compiled them a year ago
for the Report to the Commission on Higher Schools of the North-
west Association of Secondary and Higher Schools.

PHYSICAL SCIENCE 101 — MATTER AND ENERGY

Description of Course
4 quarter credits.   Three lecture periods and one 2-hour
laboratory period per week.   Prerequisites: None.   This
course is designed to provide an understanding of selected
concepts drawn from the areas of matter and energy,
to develop scientific attitudes and provide experience in
the use of scientific methods, and to consider the role of
science in society.

Text
Krauskopf: *Fundamentals of Physical Science*, McGraw-
Hill, 1959

Lecture Topics (Note: Selection of topics and emphasis may vary from one instructor to another.)

The nature and methods of science.

Measurement. Mathematical tools and mathematical relationships.

Kinds and states of matter.

Matter in motion. Concepts of mass, motion, energy, force, acceleration, gravitation, etc.

Heat and temperature. Kinetic molecular theory of gases.

Dalton's atomic theory. Combining weights, atomic weights, molecular weights. Basic laws of chemical behavior.

Periodic classification of the elements.

Fundamental concepts of electricity and magnetism. Discovery of the electron.

Rutherford's concept of the atom.

Electronic configuration of atoms.

The nature of the chemical bond.

The chemistry of life. Photosynthesis, carbohydrates, oxidation, amino acids and proteins.

Nuclear structure. Nuclear transformations and nuclear reactions. Nuclear energy.

Radioactivity, radiosotopes, radiation.

Laboratory Topics (Note: Selection of topics and emphasis may vary from one instructor to another.)

Systems of measurement. Determination of length, volume, mass, density.

Weight-volume relationships.

Falling bodies, — inclined plane.

Freely falling bodies.

Heat and temperature, absolute zero.

Specific heat.

The law of definite proportions.

Gram-molecular volume.

Electrical phenomena and measurements: electrostatics, conductance, electric fields.

Spectroscopy.

Wave phenomena.

Radioactivity, — detection.

Evaluations

1. Written examination. Carefully prepared multiple-choice items require careful reading and evaluation of data. Numerical problems require analysis of data and the determination of relationships. Some data are plotted graphically and predictions are made. Some essay questions are used to measure the ability to express ideas accurately and concisely.

2. Laboratory reports provide the student with opportunities to record data, to express relationships, and to draw conclusions.

3. Reports of readings in the periodicals measure the breadth of reading and the ability to analyze information and report ideas.

4. Term papers measure the capacity to select a pertinent topic, to search the literature for suitable references, to analyze the topic effectively, and to express ideas in an acceptable fashion.

5. Articles from newspapers and periodicals brought to class indicate growth in interest.

Remarks

A problem arises due to the varied high school backgrounds of students taking Physical Science 101. Some have had no physical science except a smattering in junior high school while others may have had good chemistry and physics courses in the senior high school. More adequate consideration should be given to ability grouping in this course.

PHYSICAL SCIENCE 202 — EARTH AND UNIVERSE

Description of Course

3 quarter credits. Two lecture and one 2-hour laboratory period per week. Prerequisites: Physical Science 101, Health Science 103. This course is designed to give the student an insight into the problems involved in man's changing concepts of the earth and universe and the impact of these concepts upon man's attitudes and thinking. This involves materials drawn from the fields of astronomy, geology, and related sciences which have been most instrumental in demanding of man a constant redefinition of his place in the universe.

Text

Krauskopf: *Fundamentals of Physical Science*, McGraw-Hill, 1959

Course Content and Procedure

Since a number of different instructors teach this course, considerable variation exists in the use of content and in procedures.   However each attempts to strive for the objectives as stated above.

Lecture periods are spent in formal lecture, class discussion, and the examination of films, slides, models, maps, etc.   The laboratory periods are devoted to as much individualized activity as facilities and circumstances will allow.   Individual and group projects and experiments are demonstrated; field trips are taken; rocks, minerals and maps are studied and observations of stars, constellations and apparent movements of heavenly bodies are made and interpreted.

Since the course serves General Education functions and is required of all Teacher Education students, an endeavor is made to engage in those activities pertinent to the experiences of children and the development of those concepts of the earth and universe which have greatly influenced man's thinking.   In this connection the point of view and the learning elements as expressed in Craig, G. S., *Science for Elementary School Teacher,* Ginn & Co., are used as guiding principles in the selection and use of materials in this area.

Throughout the course advantage is taken of every opportunity to emphasize those elements that have been closely associated with the development of scientific attitudes.   The student should begin to realize that:

> Man's conception of truth changes."
>
> "It is desirable to have confidence in the scientific method."
>
> "Much knowledge remains to be discovered."
>
> "Man has become an important determining factor of the environment of many forms of life.   His continued existence and advancement are dependent upon his wise modification and control of the environment.

Evaluation

> Quizzes
> Subjective and objective examinations
> Book Reports and assigned readings and papers
> Class discussions and demonstrations

HEALTH SCIENCE 103 — HUMAN BIOLOGY — HEALTH AND HYGIENE

Description of the Course
4 quarter credits.   Three lectures and one 2-hour laboratory period per week.   Prerequisites: Physical Science 101
— Matter and Energy.   A course designed to give the
student insight into those concepts of the biological
sciences which contribute to an understanding of the distinctive nature and characteristics of life, its cellular,
physical, and chemical bases.   There is special emphasis
on the function of tissues, organs, and systems of the
human body, and on the problems involved in the maintenance of personal health and hygiene.

Text
Henzil, John S., *The Biology of Man*, McGraw-Hill, 1954
Course Content and Procedure
The lecture periods are devoted to discussion of the ideas,
concepts, principles, and problems which are associated
with human biology, and the maintenance of the human
organism in its optimum state of well-being.
It is worthwhile to note that throughout the course continued reference is made to current news items of interest
(e.g., "Oxygen Lack Responsible for Cancer," "Take
a Big Pill Before Atom Blast") as well as newspaper and
radio advertisements, (e.g. "Science Never Fails," "Laxa-
tives," "Regularizers") which have a bearing on human
health and hygiene and which the students are asked to
analyze.   A bulletin board is maintained.
The lecture and laboratory aspects of the course are kept
closely coordinated.   The 2-hour laboratory period each
week uses prepared and living materials.   The following
topics indicate the type of laboratory activities.   Each
instructor may modify these experiences, in terms of order
or sequence, as well as emphasis.

1. Types of cells — plants and animal.
2. Cell processes—student and instructor demonstrations

Osmosis	Solution
Diffusion	Catalysis
Dialysis	Brownian movement
Surface tension	

The purpose is to provide opportunity for students
to examine common physical and chemical phenomena and to indicate how these phenomena help to

explain phenomena associated with protoplasm and life.

3. Frog dissection
Frogs which have been electrocuted and pithed, and prepared for each pair of students. An intensive two hours is spent in orienting the student to the various systems found in vertebrates, as exemplified by the frog. Constant comparisons are drawn between the systems in the frog and their homologues in the human using manikins, models, and charts. The microprojector is used to show blood circulation and living sperm. Parasites are noted and examined.

4. Reproductive System
A study of the male and pregnant female cat.
A study of the developing organism with its consequent differentiation.

5. Muscles and Skeleton
A laboratory period is concerned with the framework of the body and its development. The cat is used for the examination of muscles. Slides of muscles and bone and the human skeleton are used for demonstration and discussion.

6. Circulation
The following procedures are used:

> Blood typing major
> Blood typing Rh-optional
> Blood smears — Cells
> Blood count — Optional
> Blood pressure
> Blood pulse
> Blood temperature regulation

7. Respiration and Excretion
The following exercises are performed:

> Urinanalysis
>> albumin
>> specific gravity
>> sugar test
> Respiration
>> control of respiration
>> rate of respiration
>> chest expansion

8. Microbiology
The students prepare slides from cultures which they have previously prepared, using sterile techniques. Observations of these slides are made using oil im-

mersion lens. Discussion of disease causing organisms is usually coupled with these labs.

9. Digestion

The process of digestion is simulated in test tube conditions and the entire process is equated with the chemical process. The cat is used along with models and charts.

BIOLOGY 204 — PRINCIPLES OF GENERAL BIOLOGY

Description of Course

4 quarter credits. Three lectures and one 2-hour laboratory period per week. Prerequisite: Physical Science 101 — Matter and Energy; Health Science 103 — Human Biology. The course is designed to give the student an understanding of the major concepts of the biological sciences and their contribution to man's thinking and to society.

The course is concerned with:

1. The role of biological sciences in the modern world.
2. The scientific attitudes and methods in thinking and investigating.
3. Man's concepts of the world of life:
   a. Principles of genetics; their application to the problems of heredity, development of organisms, and their evolution.
   b. Problems involved in dealing with the variety and development of organic forms.
   c. Problems involved in dealing with the interrelationships of organisms and their environments; principles of ecology, their application to problems of evolution, survival, conservation and man's future.

Text

Hardin, *Biology — Its Human Implications*, Freeman, 1954
Course Content and Procedure
Each faculty member is free to organize content and procedure that best fits his training, experience and point of view. The Science Objectives and the Aims of General Education as described above are accepted as the goals of instruction.
The major change that has occurred in the course has been due to the fortunate experience enjoyed by the department in its participation on the National Sciences Committee in the *Co-operative Study of Evaluation in General Edu-*

cation of the American Council on Education. Certain aspects of that study, such as the *"Guide for Construction of Evaluation Items,"* and the list of aims below, are used in an attempt to engage the student in becoming active, in his own education rather than merely engaged in absorbing knowledge.

The course expects the individual student to grow in his:

> ability to apply science knowledge to new problems and situations.
>
> ability to analyze scientific data summarized in maps, tables, curves, charts, graphs.
>
> ability to read and evaluate news articles on scientific developments.
>
> understanding of the role— importance and limitations — of science in the modern world.
>
> willingness to face facts, revise judgments and change behavior in the light of appropriate evidence.
>
> understanding the point of view with which a scientist approaches his problems, and the kinds of things he does.
>
> ability to recognize need for additional significant and relevant scientific knowledge in a new situation and then be able to get it and apply it.

The above mentioned *"Guide for the Construction of Evaluation Items"* is given the student. He is told that this "Guide" is used by the instructor in conjunction with each of the content areas below in the organization of the instructional aspects of the course as well as in the construction of examinations.

The content areas from which materials and problems are selected and organized are:

> Classification — its need and function in science
>
> Heredity and Environment — Introduction to problems involved
>
> Mitosis, Meiosis, and Sexual Reproduction — significance of each in Genetics
>
> Life cycles in plants and correlated significances in adaptation and evolution
>
> Developmental tendencies in the animal kingdom and correlated significance in adaptation and evolution
>
> Evolution as a theory and its function
>
> Ecological relationships as a resultant of the interplay the various factors involved in the development of organisms

The content or problem areas as listed above do not necessarily come in the sequence as they are recorded. However, the sequence indicates more or less the pattern as it has evolved over the years. Factors influencing decisions are those of: faculty training and experience, the season of the year with the availability of appropriate and pertinent materials from the local environment, feasibility of field work, the character and quality of the class membership, etc.

Evaluation

The evaluation of the students' attainment of the objectives of the course is a most difficult matter.

1. Objectives examinations
    They serve quite well in those areas requiring simple recall and application of facts and principles.

2. Discussion
    Conscious effort is made to elicit the expression of ideas on the part of the students and to note changes during the quarter in his manner of thinking and the degree of insight exercised in arriving at conclusions.

3. Analysis of written work
    Opportunities are provided at the beginning of the units of work for the student to record ideas and explanations of phenomena. These are used as material for evaluation items later in the quarter. Then the student is asked to examine his statements, analyze them for critical thought and to offer modifications.

4. Weekly written abstracts of outside reading
    After the student becomes aware that these short written reports are examined for the nature of subject matter selected, the conciseness of expression of thought, ideas, and analysis, they do in a measure assist in providing evidence of growth.

5. Subjective examination questions
    If subjective test items are rather rigidly constructed they have proved to be the most effective means of detecting the degree of success the instructor has achieved in attaining the purposes of the course.

At best there is need for more effective means of evaluating the attainment of objectives which in turn is merely the other side of the coin which is that of effective in-instruction.

General Considerations

The strengths and weaknesses as discussed in the 1948 edition of *Science in General Education,* edited by Earl J. McGrath, still maintain.   In the main these involved the role of the teacher:

> his insight and attitude toward the function of science courses for general educational purposes.
> his willingness, ability and capacity to effect creativeness in teaching.
> his capacity to adapt specialized training in subject matter fields to the purposes of general educational objectives.

To these may be added the following considerations.   Over the years the General Education courses of the college have been very loosely organized in their relationship to one another.   Whatever integration that may have taken place is the result of individual faculty member's attempts and efforts rather than that of a coherently planned program.   There is need to augment individual initiative with administrative support and direction.   This is becoming more and more apparent as the institution is growing in size.   Staffs of different departments, offering General Education courses, are more and more isolated in different buildings and see one another very seldom.   New faculty are added who frequently have had very little training or experience with General Education courses.

There is therefore need for the establishment of a continued program of faculty education in General Education.   This is not only needed for the new and inexperienced members constantly being added to the staff but also for the reeducation of the older members.   Faculty need to keep abreast of the rapid developments in the fields of science and the bearing that these have upon the problems of society.   The staff needs time to consider the developments in fields related to the sciences in order to better effect integration.   In other words, a broad and well-rounded education is needed by the faculty as well as by the student.

Evaluation in terms of General Education objectives is an important instrument of education not only for the student but also the faculty.   There has been an expression for the return to a program of comprehensive examinations which was in vogue some years ago.   At that time there occurred a good deal of education and reeducation of the educable faculty.   The results of the tests certainly point up the strengths and weaknesses in one's teaching.

A matter not to be ignored in discussing problems of General Education is that of faculty load and time.   As serious an attitude toward faculty loads, size of classes and time for preparation and evaluation must be given the General Education courses as is given courses in specialized subject matter areas.   The instructor of General Education courses must feel that his contribution to the field of education is just as important as that of the specialist. In the long run it may be more significant in terms of the eventual outcomes of the problems facing society.

chapter 23

THE SCIENCES IN WISCONSIN'S PROGRAM OF INTEGRATED LIBERAL STUDIES

Robert C. Pooley, Aaron Ihde, Arthur H. Robinson, and Lowell Noland*

Wisconsin's curriculum in Integrated Liberal Studies was inaugurated in 1948, as the outhgrowth of a careful curricular study which led to a reform of the distribution requirements in general studies and institution of the I.L.S. program as an alternative method of satisfying general requirements. The two-year integrated program is open to election by any entering freshman, with a limitation of three hundred students in any entering class. It is expected that students electing the program will take it in its entirety, although transfers out of the program into the B.A. or B.S. general course are permitted at the end of any semester. This entails no loss of credit since the I.L.S. courses which have been satisfactorily completed are accepted toward general degree requirements in other courses and schools within the University. Students who have started University work outside the I.L.S. program may not enter it, nor may they elect individual courses within the program.

Students electing the integrated program are mostly from the College of Letters and Science, the program satisfying all general requirements except for language and a semester of American history. Upon completion of the two-year sequence, students

---

*Robert C. Pooley is Professor of English and Chairman of the Department of Integrated Liberal Studies, Aaron Ihde, Professor of Chemistry and History of Science, Arthur H. Robinson, Professor of Geography, and Lowell Noland, Professor of Zoology.

are ready to move into their major or professional fields. In certain majors, I.L.S. courses contribute toward the major; in others they do not. For example, I.L.S. 31 — The Physical Universe — noes not count toward the major in either chemistry, physics, or astronomy. I.L.S. 32 — Earth Science — is accepted toward the geography major. I.L.S. 33 and 34 — Biological Science — satisfies the introductory course requirement for both botany and zoology majors.

The I.L.S. program is administered by a separate department within the College of Letters and Science, but none of the faculty members teaching I.L.S. courses devotes his full time to I.L.S. matters. Faculty have been recruited from traditional subject matter departments and each professor continues to carry teaching and research responsibilities in such a department.

In most cases, an I.L.S. course is the responsibility of a single faculty member; in no case do more than two persons share the responsibility. Although this means that the person in charge of a course is responsible for a broad understanding of the area covered, it has been considered more satisfactory than having a panel of specialists each teaching a small segment of the course and assures a level of integration which is difficult to achieve in courses taught by a panel.

The Program of Studies

Two important principles underlie this program of integrated studies. The first is that since the goal of general education is preparation for life the courses can be broad rather than concentrated, and can be concerned chiefly with values rather than with techniques. The second principle is that through the exchange of ideas with other students who are studying the same courses at the same time, the average student can profit more from a prescribed course of study for his general education than from elective choices. He is still free to choose an era of specialization for the latter years of his college life and to select and prepare for a vocation.

The studies of general education are recognized as falling into three large fields or areas. The *humanities* embrace such subjects as languages, literature, philosophy, religion, history, music, and the arts. The *sciences* are biology, chemistry, mathematics, physics, astronomy, geology, geography and their many subdivisions. The *social studies* include anthropology, economics, political science, and sociology. The integrated program is made up of a block of 14 courses totaling 46 semester credits. There are four-semester sequences in the humanities, social studies, and natural sciences, and there is a two-semester sequence in composition. The sequence of courses and their titles and credits follow:

FRESHMAN YEAR

FIRST SEMESTER
ILS 11 — Greek and Roman Culture, 4 credits
ILS 21 — Early Man and His Society, 3 credits
ILS 31 — The Physical Universe 4 credits
ILS 41 — Composition, 2 credits,
Electives — Up to 4 credits

SECOND SEMESTER
ILS 12 — Medieval and Renaissance Culture, 3 credits
ILS 22 — Transition to Industrial Society, 4 credits
ILS 32 — Earth Science, 3 credits
ILS 42 — Composition, 2 credits
Electives — Up to 5 credits

SOPHOMORE YEAR

ILS 13 — European Culture, 1750-1850, 4 credits
ILS 23 — Modern Industrial Society, U.S.A., 4 credits
ILS 33 — Biology, 3 credits
Electives — Up to 6 credits

ILS 14 — Recent American Culture, 3 credits
ILS 24 — The International Science, 3 credits
ILS 34 — Biology, 4 credits
Electives — Up to 7 credits

It will be observed that there is room for an elective course in each of the freshman semesters and two elective courses may be taken during each of the sophomore semesters. Thus, an I.L.S. student may concurrently carry work in languages, mathematics, basic science, or some other area which may be pertinent to his ultimate major or professional field.

A large proportion of the students electing I.L.S. have gone on to major work in such fields as languages, art, history, political science, sociology, education, journalism, commerce, and law. A smaller proportion have gone on to the medical sciences. A few have majored in chemistry, physics, mathematics, biology, agriculture, and engineering.

The program as shown above has not lent itself well to majors in the physical sciences because of the need to take courses in both science and mathematics during the freshman year. Two years ago a modified variant of the program was opened for the purpose of making it more convenient for a student to combine I.L.S. with a physical science major. In this variant curriculum, the student is excused from two I.L.S. science courses (31 and either 32 or 34) and he may postpone to the sophomore year the start of the social studies sequence (21-24). He must however, in his junior or senior year, take I.L.S. 35 — The Development of Scientific Thought. This course examines the growth of a number of important scientific concepts, thus providing an understanding in the history and impact of science which is customarily absent from traditional science courses and which the student will miss by not taking ILS 31 and 32.

At the present time (1959) a faculty committee is undertaking a study directed toward the possibility of developing a parallel general education program suitable for students majoring in professional fields such as engineering, pharmacy, nursing, home economics, and agriculture. While the outcome of this study will be in doubt for some time, it is possible that there may be created for those professional students who desire it, a program incorporating a certain amount of integrated work in the humanities and social studies around the more traditional requirements in science, mathematics, and professional courses.

Physical Science

FIRST SEMESTER — THE PHYSICAL UNIVERSE

The guiding principle that has been followed in the development of this course has been the objective of the entire program, namely, to integrate subject matter from closely related fields without having the course degenerate into a superficial survey. Consequently, there has been an effort to make an examination in depth of a few important concepts within the area of the course, even though this is accomplished at the expense of other subjects commonly included in traditional courses.

Since it is not the purpose of the course, which draws its material from the fields of chemistry, physics, and astronomy, to train scientists, the systematic and detailed treatment characteristic of the usual introductory course is avoided. Instead, there is an extensive examination of a few major developments. In this way it is possible to concentrate on such mastery of facts and concepts as will enable the student to gain an understanding of the manner in which scientific progress is made. It is also possible to study scientific activity in its historical context, to observe the acceptance of scientific discoveries by society, and to note the impact on man's thought and on his way of life.

Four principal problems are studied during the semester: 1) the search for a planetary system, 2) the correlation of physical properties with the kinetic-molecular concept, 3) the growth of the atomic concept, and 4) the use of the spectrum to study stellar composition and motion.

Approximately half of the semester is spent on item 3. There is first a careful examination of the Daltonian atom and the problem of the determination of reliable atomic weights and chemical formulas. Once this problem has been mastered there is an opportunity to show how chemical research stimulated the growth of the synthetic dye and drug industry on the basis of an indivisible atom. The need for a structural atom is then examined in connection with the discovery of radioactivity, which in turn leads to a consideration of nuclear energy.

There is no text book which is entirely suitable for the course as presented. Krauspkopf's *Fundamentals of Physical Science* was used until 1958 when a change was made to Bonner and Phillips, *Principles of Physical Science*. Both have been useful, but it has been necessary to supplement the text with mimeographed readings and problems.

There are three lectures per week for the whole student group. Since there is no laboratory for the course, extensive demonstrations are carried out during the lectures. Discussion sections of about twenty-five students meet twice weekly for fifty minutes.

Discussion sections are mostly taught by graduate assistants. Suitable staffing of discussion sections has been a problem of some magnitude, since few graduate students possess the breadth and depth of knowledge which are necessary in this type of course. During the eleven years that the course has been offered, the assistant staff has included students majoring in chemistry (6), astronomy (1), geography (4), philosophy (2), and history of science (3). Successful performance appears to be correlated with a deep interest in teaching and a broad interest, not only in physical science, but in learning as a whole. When it has been possible to find such graduate students a satisfactory teaching staff has been developed. Weekly meetings are held with the group to correlate instructional plans, warn of difficulties, and otherwise guide new staff members. Seven of the former teaching assistants in this course have moved on to other colleges where they are now teaching an integrated science course.

SECOND SEMESTER –– EARTH SCIENCE

The Earth Science course has evolved from the interests and aims of several disciplines, represented by successive teachers in charge of the course, viz., two physical geographers, one geologist, and one meteorologist. Partly as a result of this history no single sphere of interest in the general field of earth science has been selected as a coordinating element. Instead, the Earth Science course is built around three major aims:

1. To demonstrate (and develop in the student) the methods of observation and inference required to reach conclusions in the non-experimental earth sciences,
2. To develop an appreciation of the complexities of the interrelationships involved in the processes active on the earth, and
3. To introduce the basic patterns of landforms, climate, minerals, and soil.

There are, of course, many subsidiary aims, among which the following are given special attention: (a) How earth science differs from other kinds of science; (b) The nature and use of the scientific techniques and tools most widely used in the study of the earth, especially mapping; (c) The history of earth science; (d) The development of curiosity and appreciation for one's physical environment; (e) Man's use and modification of his physical environment.

The Earth Science course is conducted with two lectures and one two-hour section meeting per week. The students work systematically through a textbook (Strahler: *Physical Geography*, John Wiley and Sons) with additional reading assignments and exercises each week. The lectures are ordinarily supplementary rather than explanatory of the textbook material. The section meetings are devoted to explanation, discussion, and laboratory-in the textbook assignments. The normal weather of a Wisconsin winter and spring unfortunately precludes much organized field activity. Several types of field trips have been tried in recent years. The most successful seems to be that tried most recently. Each section was assigned a topographic map of a local area. Whenever the subject matter of a reading assignment allowed, the class considered its application in that area. Near the end of the semester a trip was made through the area to give the students the opportunity to observe in fact what they have learned about the area and have been inferring from the map.

The course begins with several weeks devoted to the study of the major planetary relationships, the consequences of the earth's form, the concepts of time and distance, and the development of facility in reading topographic maps. The first series of lectures is also introductory and deals with such matters as the history of earth science, the history of mapping, and the attempts to determine the role of time in earth history. The second major block of work involves the systematic consideration of geomorphological processes and their expression in the terrain. The lectures deal with such related topics as how the character of the earth's interior is inferred, the development of the theory of continental glaciation, the movements of the waters of the sea, and the physical occurrence and use of minerals and energy. The third major section deals with the atmosphere, beginning with a systematic study of atmospheric processes and leading into climatic analysis and the earth's pattern of climates. The lectures introduce corollary aspects such as the effects of weather on man, storm development, and climatic change during the past three thousand years. The last section utilizes the soil mantle as a medium to illustrate the interaction of climatic, geological and biologic factors. The lectures deal with such topics as the classification and mapping of soils, the relation of soils to human nutrition, and the causes and consequences of soil erosion.

It is evident from the foregoing general outline that the Earth Science course is primarily intended to be an introduction to and illustrative of the necessary integration of the several earth science disciplines. It attempts to provide a general liberal background for the student rather than provide him detailed study of any single item. From the student's point of view it is a better course "in retrospect" than when he is taking it! From previous work he is relatively familiar with the detailed descriptive and analytical processes characteristic of other scientific study.   He finds it difficult initially to apply the processes of inference in earth science, not only at a somewhat higher level of generalization, but also in situations involving a far greater number of variables than he is used to considering.

The major difficulties of the course are those related to prior preparation, size of sections, and staff.   The appalling poverty of earth science education in high school means that much time must be devoted to such elementary subjects as latitude and longitude, time, ordinary map reading, and even simple scale concepts. Sections containing twenty to twenty-five students with markedly different levels of preparation are far too large to carry on adequate discussion and demonstration, let alone make a "scientific analysis" of a problem with student participation.   Consequently, the "laboratory science" experience can only be accomplished by assignment of outside exercises, which is an unsatisfactory process at best, both for the students and the instructor.   Probably, the major problem in the course is the fact that integration of diverse materials at this level requires considerable maturity on the part of an instructor. This is difficult to obtain in graduate assistants, especially when the more mature and capable graduate student in earth science finds it easy to obtain more financial subsidy from fellowship grants than from a teaching assistantship.

Biological Science

THIRD AND FOURTH SEMESTERS

When the Program of Integrated Liberal Studies was set up in the University of Wisconsin, half of the time allotted to science was given to biology, and this has permitted a somewhat more intensive treatment of this field than is possible in the physical and earth sciences.   The biology course was set up to have two lectures per week in the first semester, and three in the second. In both semesters there are two hours of laboratory work and one hour of discussion per week.   Two professors, a zoologist and a botanist, cooperate in the offering of the course.

The physical facilities include a laboratory for the exclusive use of this course, provided with a compound microscope for each student, and five demonstration microscopes and five dissecting binoculars. There is room for 24 students in each laboratory section. There are eight sections at the present time.

In the presentation of subject matter each new topic is first introduced in lecture, followed by study of pertinent materials in laboratory, and reading of assigned material in text and other references. After this in the discussion section any points needing elucidation are discussed, the significance and implications of the material are developed and the students are given a chance to ask any pertinent questions about the work covered. About once a month a written examination is given to test the students on the material covered since the last examination.

Drawings and written notes are not required in the laboratory work. Comprehension of observations made and experiments performed is tested by individual conferences in the laboratory as well as by occasional oral discussions with the class as a whole. The professor in charge makes an effort to spend some time every week in each laboratory section, more to get acquainted personally with the students and to see that the assistant has the requisite materials and help than to check on the assistant's teaching ability. This personal contact of the professor with all the students helps in unifying the class, detecting places where improvements can be made, and encouraging informality and free change of ideas between teachers and students.

The sequence of topics taken up during the year is as follows: in the first semester: the cell and protoplasm; cell division; cell specialization; unicellular organisms; seed plant structure; plant physiology; life histories of mosses, ferns and seed plants compared; fossil plants and plant evolution; characteristics of the major plant groups; a brief survey of main animal phyla; comparison of the ways in which plants and animals have adapted themselves to land life; and in the second semester: structure and function of the vertebrate body for eight weeks, with a dissection of a full-term, doubly injected fetal pig and lectures and readings on the organ systems; embryology; gametogenesis; three weeks of genetics, with fruit fly crosses to illustrate Mendelian inheritance, sex-linkage and crossing-over; ecology, with field trips to study community structure, bird migration and ecological succession; and finally a consideration of organic evolution, the origin of life and philosophical implications of human evolution.

Every effort is made, as occasion offers, to relate the content of the course to the other disciplines, e.g., agriculture, conservation, psychology, philosophy, aesthetic appreciation, public health and public policy. The fact that all the students have had the same background courses in physical science and earth science makes possible continual back-reference to material already studied.

The course, as is evident from the above description, emphasizes the structure and physiology of the seed plant and vertebrate animal, with less attention to lower plants and invertebrates. More time and laboratory effort is devoted to genetics than in other elementary biological courses in this university. The emphasis on these aspects is based on the conviction that it is important for the well-educated person to understand the mechanisms of his own body, how the food that he needs is produced from the raw materials of the earth by plants, and how all living organisms pass along heritable characteristics to their descendants through genes and chromosomes, which are subject to multifarious recombinations and to occasional fundamental changes (mutations) which may be increasing in frequency somewhat due to radioactive fall-out from atomic explosions.

The considerable time given to ecology and field trips at the end of the course is aimed at bringing home the concept that man himself is a part of nature, and must learn to live as efficiently as possible within the bounds set by his relationships to other organims, — to those that produce his food, compete with him for natural resources, produce disease in him and in his domesticated animals, and furnish him with food, clothing, wood, and other products, as well as adding to his sport, recreation and esthetic enjoyment of his environment.

A desirable improvement that might be introduced into the course would be the inclusion of more work on individual projects that would allow greater opportunity for cultivating initiative, formulation of working hypotheses, ingenuity in devising experimental approaches, and facility in the use of the library to find out what work has already been done in the field of interest selected. This, however, would require much additional apparatus and equipment, more laboratory space set up the experiments, additional teachers to assist in supervising projects, — excellent ideas, but not practical within the present budget.

chapter 24

SCIENCE IN GENERAL EDUCATION FOR HIGH SCHOOLS

*Ervin H. Hoffart**

The need for talented individuals in various fields of science has caused considerable attention to be focused on the science programs in schools. Study groups are now at work to design new curriculums for biology, physics and chemistry, and, in an increasing number of schools, science is being offered in the elementary grades. National Science Foundation and some industrial foundation sponsored institutes have been designed for the training and retraining of teachers; and federal aid is available for the purchase of apparatus. Complete courses for students and teachers in biology, chemistry and physics have been or will be put on film; and the twenty-one inch television screen is being tried in the classroom as a way to teach science. This activity is indicative of the concern on the part of many people to strengthen science education.

Today science is a part of everyday life, even a part of our culture. Dr. Killian[1] has stated that no one can be liberally educated today without an understanding of science; that science (and mathematics) are basic cultural subjects and should be taught as cultural disciplines.

To understand and appreciate science, it is necessary that we become familiar with its language, its methods and its objectives. The illusion that science is narrow and vocational must give way

---

*The author is with the Physical Study Committee, Educatonal Services, Incorporated, Cambridge, Mass.

[1]Killian, James R.. Jr.. Chairman of the Corporation, Massachusetts Institute of Technology.

to the realization that the study of science is broadening and that scientific ideas are related to ideas in other fields. It is clear that the training of professional scientists (or specialists of any kind) should not be the aim of secondary school science courses; science programs, including those in general education, must be designed to help develop the student's ability for independent thinking and judgment. Too often science is presented as a dull body of facts to be memorized. It is little wonder then that so few people realize science is the product of people like themselves, and that it has a structure which they too can understand.

Today's Science Courses

The science courses most commonly offered in high schools (grades 9-12) are general science, biology, chemistry, and physics. General science was first offered about fifty years ago; now more students are enrolled than in any other course in science. General science is usually required in the ninth grade.

Biology was first offered in high schools about 1910, as a fused course in zoology and botany. Its enrollment today is second to general science. Biology is usually offered in the tenth grade, and, like general science, is required in a large number of schools. The rapid growth of the enrollment in biology has been at the expense of the more specialized courses, botany, zoology, and physiology.

Chemistry and physics have been offered in high schools for a much longer time than either general science or biology. They are commonly elective courses offered during the last two years of high school, with physics offered more frequently in the twelfth grade than in the eleventh grade. Although enrollments in both courses have increased since 1900, chemistry has consistently had larger enrollments than has physics since about 1930.

Among the other science courses offered in high schools are physical science (a general science course, offered in grade ten, eleven, or twelve and including parts of chemistry, physics, astronomy, earth science, etc.), earth science, electricity, electronics, physiology, and health. Of these, physical science tends to be most common. It was first offered in high schools about twenty-five years ago, and although it has had wide acceptance in some areas, its growth nationally has been slow. In schools where a physical science course is offered, it is usually an elective course for the student who does not plan to attend college or to pursue a career in science.

Changes in the High School Population

From 1880 to 1930, the high school enrollment doubled each decade; from 1930 to the present, it has more than doubled, again with the result that well over eight million students are enrolled in high school today. There are indications that the enrollment will continue to increase for some time to come.

This rapid growth has produced changes in the character of the high school population, which in turn has been one of several factors pointing up the need for changes in the high school curriculum. Until the early 1900's, the tendency was to stress preparation for college; today the concern is for a general education for all students. The students in a high school today are much more representative of the general population. They represent a wide variety of backgrounds and interests and different needs which must be met if the high school is to serve everyone.

From this period of rapid growth has emerged what is commonly called the comprehensive high school; a high school which attempts to serve the educational needs of all the students in the community.

The Enrollment in the Science Courses

A study made by the U. S. Office of Education[2] shows the percentage of students in four-year public high schools enrolled in certain science courses. From data gathered from the 1956-57 school year, it was found that of the total high school enrollment 21.8 per cent were enrolled in general science, 20.5 per cent in biology, 7.5 per cent in chemistry, 4.4 per cent in physics, and approximately 1.2 per cent in advanced general (physical) science. Enrollment in other sciences in high schools was about 2.7 per cent of the total.

The study further shows that in 1956-57, about 67 per cent of the students in the ninth grade were enrolled in general science

---

[2]Brown, K. E. and Obourn, E. S. "Offerings and Enrollments in Science and Mathematics in Public High Schools." U. S. Office of Education, Washington, D. C., Pamphlet 120.

and 75.7 per cent of the students in the tenth grade were enrolled in biology.

Science Survey Courses

The most prominent characteristic of the high school biology course during the past thirty years has been its degree of flexibility in response to trends in general education. During the 1930's when survey courses appeared to be successful in other subject matter areas, a survey course in physical science was introduced. Then, in the early 1940's special courses in aeronautics, electronics, navigation, and other science related areas were introduced in the high school curriculum in an attempt to meet the growing demand for technicians, and the physical science course, per se, disappeared almost completely. Since 1945, there has been a slight increase in enrollment in the physical science course, but numbers are still small. It has, however, gained acceptance in some of the small high schools where separate courses in chemistry and physics are not practical, and in some of the larger high schools for those students not taking chemistry or physics.

One unique quality of science survey courses in high schools is the variety of subject matter that one finds in them; not all of it is science. Even worse there is little consistency in the relationship of the laboratory work (if it exists at all) to the course content.

In discussing science survey courses, Dr. Rogers stated, "Many schools give a children's smorsgasbord course which makes science seem just a pile of wonderful fact-knowledge in which names have a strange ability to explain things. Such courses stimulate interest, increase knowledge, and decrease superstition, but they damage the student's picture of science. With more thought about aims, less material, more careful discussion by teachers who are competent scientists, these courses could become excellent parts of general education."[3]

In his book, *The American High School Today*, Dr. Conant recommends the following science courses for the comprehensive high school:

_____

[3]Rogers, Eric M. "Science Courses in General Education," *Science in General Education* (Earl J. McGrath, Editor; Wm. C. Brown Company, Dubuque, Iowa, 1948) pp. 19-20.

"All students should obtain some understanding
of the nature of science and the scientific approach by a
required course in physical science or biology. This course
should be given in at least three sections grouped by
ability . . . .

"To accommodate students who are interested in
science but who do not have the required mathematical
ability, two types of chemistry courses should be offered.
For entry into one, at least a C in algebra and tenth-
grade mathematics should be required. The other course
should be designed for pupils with less mathematical
ability. The standards even in this second course, however, should be such that those with less than average
ability (assuming a distribution of ability according to
the national norm) will have difficulty passing the course.

"In addition to the physics course given in the
twelfth grade with mathematics as a prerequisite . . . another course in physics should be offered with some such
designation as 'practical physics'. The standards in this
second course should be such that students with less than
average ability have difficulty passing the course."[4]

With curriculum revision programs underway in biology,
chemistry and physics, it is difficult to predict what the future of
the science survey courses will be. Attempts to present the
traditional courses in physics and chemistry to the general education student and to the college-bound student in the same class
have resulted in inadequate programs for both groups. However,
the use of ability-grouping with the science courses now being
developed may very well result in science programs adequately
serving the majority of high school students.

Changes in Science Course Sequence

There is some evidence that the grade placement of science
courses may be changed somewhat in the future. Some attempts
to do this are already underway. The following is an example
of one such change:

"General science is being removed from the high school
curriculum and the program in science in the grades is be-

---

[4]Conant, James B. *The American High School Today*, (New York,
McGraw-Hill Book Co.. Inc.. 1959), pp. 73.

ing strengthened accordingly. Biology is being offered to those students with the capability and interest necessary on the ninth grade level, and chemistry will be offered to this group — or others with equivalent aptitudes — at the tenth grade level. This makes physics available in the eleventh grade and advanced science for those meeting specifications, in the twelfth grade. A course in physical science is being added to the curriculum for those students who are most probably terminal in science."[5]

Another change in science course sequence began as early as 1948 and is similar to the previous program in that it also recognizes the elementary science program:

"Biology is now required of all ninth grade students and may be followed by a physical science course in the tenth grade. This two-year program is followed by physics, chemistry, or advanced biology for those with interests or needs for advanced work. . . . The (physical science) course is planned to be of practical value to the student as well as an introduction to the specialized courses. Student interest is increasing in this course and others. Chemistry enrollment has increased and we expect the same trend in physics next year."[6]

Some schools have established 'track' programs in science which may include a one-year physical science course for slow students and advanced placement courses in biology, chemistry, and physics for the talented students, the usual courses in biology, chemistry and physics are then offered for the average students.

In light of the various attempts to shuffle the science courses there is evident need for science programs in which both direction and continuity are provided from kindergarten through high school. We are probably nearer today to the realization of such programs but much work remains to be done.

---

[5]Schaefer, D. A. "Advanced Science for Gifted Students," *The Science Teacher*, xvx:6 (1958) pp. 269.

[6]Lowry, Nelson. "Physical Science Today," *The Science Teacher* XVII:6 (1958) pp. 14.

*Physical Science Study Committee, 164 Main Street, Watertown, Massachusetts.

Science Curriculum Studies

THE PHYSICAL SCIENCE STUDY COMMITTEE*

The Physical Science Study Committee, which consisting of university, college and industrial physicists and high school physics teachers was organized in 1956 with the following specific aims:

> "1.) to plan a course of study in which major developments of physics up to the present time are presented in a logical and integrated whole; 2.) to present physics as an intellectual and cultural pursuit which is part of present-day human activity and achievement; and 3.) to assist physics teachers, by means of various teaching aids, to carry out the proposed program."[7]

The Committee's objectives were shaped in part by the recognition that existing secondary school science curriculums usually fail to make science a meaningful part of general education, and that as a result, too few people develop an understanding and an appreciation of the impact of science and technology on contemporary life.

The physics course developed by the Physical Science Study Committee is designed to show students some of the structure of physics and how it was discovered and understood by human beings. The course concentrates on fewer facts than are usually included in an elementary physics course. Understanding of these facts is emphasized; memorization is not. Considerable time is spent on the stories running through physics which tie the facts with explanations. Reasoning and careful observation are required to understand the stories. By working with simple apparatus designed with this purpose in mind, students can see how they use their developing ideas to steer their experiments. In this way concepts are developed, not just asserted. The laboratory is an important tool in learning ideas of science and of how science is built. The laboratory work in this course is on an equal level with the textbook, class discussions, and films as a means of learning and teaching.

A new textbook has been written, laboratory experiments and simplified apparatus have been developed, films have been produced,

---

[7]Friedman, Frances L. "A Blueprint." *The Science Teacher* XXIV:8 (1957).

a set of achievement tests constructed, and supplementary reference books written. To aid the teacher, an extensive set of teacher's guides have been developed. With the materials, the students start from simple measurements of time and space and end with the study of the wave mechanical explanation of the internal structure of atoms. As the story develops there are two essential sub-stories. One is the picture of wave behavior built up through a great deal of laboratory experiments with visible waves and as a part of the study of light; the other sub-story is the development of Newtonian mechanics where the concepts are developed experimentally through the laboratory work and the ideas of momentum and energy are stressed far more than usual. Electricity is then treated in such a way as to lead to the identification of the particles of which atoms are made. The course ends with the synthesis of wave behavior and particle mechanics in describing the atom.

From the beginning, the PSSC physics course has been designed for approximately the same group of students who would normally take physics in the secondary school. This group not only includes the future scientists, but also a large number of other students as well. Early results indicate that the course is suited for an even larger group of students than originally intended.

The acceptance of the program has been significant; growing from 8 schools in 1957-58 to 580 schools in 1959-60. Test results and teachers reactions indicate that the committee's objectives are being realized. Some revisions are being made in the text and laboratory as a result of trials in schools throughout the country, but these will not alter the overall emphasis.

THE BIOLOGICAL SCIENCES CURRICULUM STUDY

The Biological Sciences Curriculum Study[8] was organized by the American Institute of Biological Sciences early in 1959. The primary concern of the BSCS at the moment is to determine what the average high school graduate should know about the biological sciences. When this has been determined, a number of small sub-

---

[8]BSCS Newsletter No. 1, September, 1959. Biological Sciences Curriculum Study, American Institute of Biological Sciences, University of Colorado, Boulder.

committees will be recruited to design a coordinated curriculum for both the primary and the secondary levels.   In addition to an attempt to coordinate the recommended curriculum with other subject matter areas in the high school, the BSCS will also determine what additional biology courses should be offered to students in special categories such as college preparatory students and gifted students.

During the summer of 1960, a number of writing conferences will be held.   Each conference will produce a unit, or units, on some phase of biological science.   The material will then be put together to make up a textbook to be tried in selected high schools in the 1960-61 school year.

The BSCS is concerned with biology education at all levels, elementary, secondary, collegiate, and outside the classroom as well. First attention will be given to the secondary level; later the study will be extended to the elementary and college levels.

The proposed curriculum will reduce technical terminology and emphasize concepts and principles.   Something of the historical approach will be included and observational evidence will be stressed.   Authoritarianism will be avoided.

THE CHEMICAL BOND APPROACH TO CHEMISTRY*

As its name implies, the CBAC uses the concept of chemical bonds as the central theme for the development of a high school course in chemistry.

This approach was selected by a group of college, university, and high school teachers as the one most suitable for immediate trial.   The drafts for the first five chapters of the text were prepared during the summer of 1959 at Reed College and are being tried in selected high schools in various parts of the country during the current school year.   Further development and testing will be necessary before widespread adoption can be contemplated.

(Another study group in chemistry using a different approach is expected to start in June, 1960 at the University of California with Dr. Glenn Seaborg in charge.)

---

*Chemical Bond Approach Committee, Earlham College, Richmond, Indiana.

Conclusion

The ingredients for a good, integrated science program have been recognized for quite some time; for example, a science program for all grades, kindergarten through grade twelve, was emphasized in the Thirty First Yearbook;[9] the content of the PSSC physics course reflects the direction that physics has taken in the last half century; and the need to train more scientists, and to increase knowledge of science among all people has been recognized by scientists and educators. The science program which will result from the current efforts to strengthen science education will be only as good as the people are willing to make it through their support. Interestingly enough, as the science program is strengthened, other parts of the high school curriculum will be strengthened as well.

The best, most-up-to-date science program is of little value without competent science teachers to carry it out. In spite of all that is going on today, we still need to discover how to keep the good teachers in the classroom, how to win back the good teachers who have left the profession, and how to encourage increasing numbers of capable young people to select science teaching as a career. When we can do this, the other things will not be so difficult.

---

[9]Thirty-First Yearbook, National Society for the Study of Education, *A Program for Teaching Science;* (Bloomington: Public School Publishing Company, 1932).